Farming Hinton Ampner
The ~~Brexit~~ Virus Year

CHARLIE FLINDT

Farming Hinton Ampner
The ~~Brexit~~ Virus Year

Text & images ©Charlie Flindt

ISBN 9781914615030
A CIP catalogue record for this book
is available from the British Library.
Published 2019 Tricorn Books
131 High Street, Portsmouth, PO1 2HW

Printed & bound in the UK

Farming Hinton Ampner
The ~~Brexit~~ Virus Year

Foreword

'If one meets a powerful person... ask them five questions: "What power have you got? Where did you get it from? In whose interests do you exercise it? To whom are you accountable? And how can we get rid of you?" If you cannot get rid of the people who govern you, you do not live in a democratic system.'

Tony Benn, House of Commons, 22nd March 2001

That's why, on 23rd June 2016, I voted 'leave'.

In the farmhouse

Charlie and Hazel Flindt.

Not in the farmhouse anymore.
Anthony (working in London), Diana (working in Cambridge) and Jonathan (Newcastle University)

Pets.
Sasha – Malinois/GSD cross.
Bella and Evie – Flatcoat retrievers.
Cain and Abel - cats

In the farmyard
2016 Skoda Octavia Scout 2.0 diesel
2007 Hyundai Terracan (aka Tigger)
2017 Hyundai i20
2006 Subaru Legacy H6 (The Colonel's)
1999 VW Lupo 1.4E

In the barn
2012 John Deere 6630 Premium (c/w Steinbauer chip)
2018 Massey Ferguson 5713S c/w front loader
2010 New Holland TC5070RS/SL
2105 Kubota 400ci RTV – aka Pig.

Main farm kit
2006 Horsch CO3 seed drill
2007 Horsch Sprinter ST4
2018 FarmGem Diamond 3000 litre, 24m boom
2006 Kverneland 5 furrow plough.

Secondary Farm Kit
8.3m Dalbo rollers
3m Terradisc
3m mounted discs
Assorted haymaking kit
Assorted harvest kit

Introduction

When we join Manor Farm, it's the beginning of February 2020 – and the first day of Brexit Britain. It has been another shocking autumn for arable work. Very few acres have been sown, the barns are full of seed, and there's certainly no sign of any fine weather on the way. Still, there's nothing we can do about it. At least we've got our health, and we can still enjoy a trip to the Jolly Flowerpots.

Dedication

Countless and immeasurable thanks are due to Hazel for all she endures by being Mrs Flindt.

Apologies

Apologies to any readers who don't like profanities. 2020 was the year that everyone started swearing. Apologies are also due to the National Trust, who seemed to be sworn at more than usual this year – although it made me feel better.

Disclaimer

After a bizarre year of ten thousand arbitrary rules, it may just be possible, during the reading of this diary, to think that some got broken. In which case, I would like to use the 'Lewis Stempel disclaimer' and claim that some parts of this book are fictional. They're not, of course, but they might be in these instances. Perhaps. Or not. That's cleared that up.

Contents

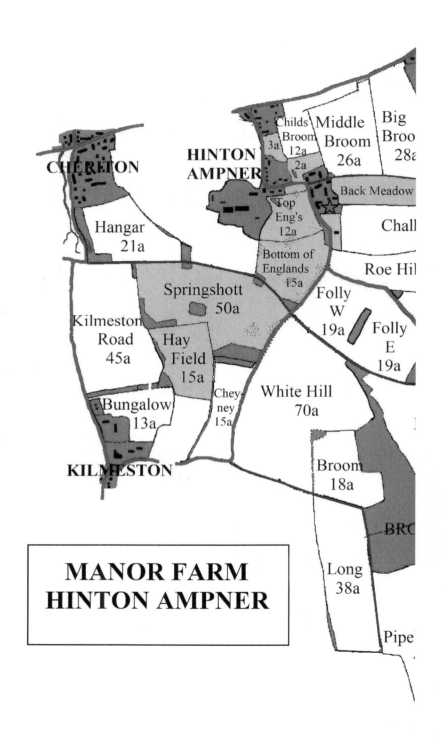

CHERITON

HINTON
AMPNER

Childs
Broom
3a 12a
2a

Middle
Broom
26a

Big
Broo
28a

Back Meadow

Top
Eng's
12a

Chall

Hangar
21a

Bottom of
Englands
15a

Roe Hil

Springshott
50a

Folly
W
19a

Folly
E
19a

Kilmeston
Road
45a

Hay
Field
15a

Chey-
ney
15a

White Hill
70a

Bungalow
13a

KILMESTON

Broom
18a

BRO

**MANOR FARM
HINTON AMPNER**

Long
38a

Pipe

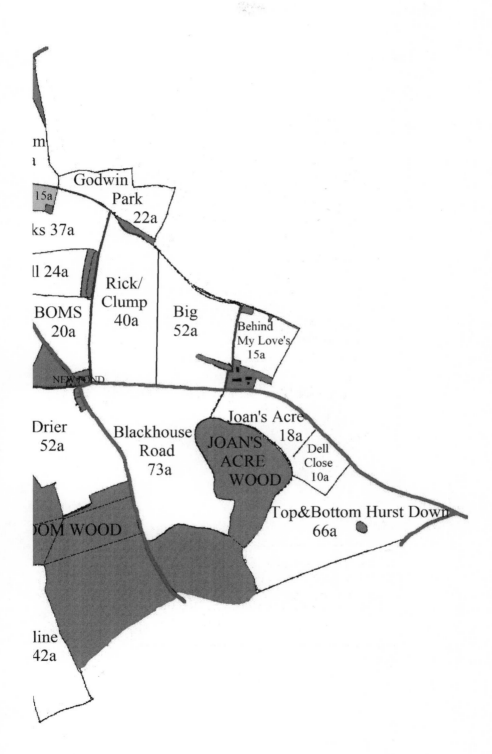

Field Names (sort of) explained

Back Meadow – The pasture at the back of the farm buildings. 'Horse meadow' in the old days, according to the old farm maps

Behind My Love's/BML's – I could explain it, but probably best not to.

Big – It's big. Probably the biggest at one time, although it isn't now.

Big Broom – the biggest of the three 'Broom' fields in the Godwin's block.

Blackhouse Road – The field next to the road to Blackhouse Farm

BOMS – Acronym for 'Behind Old Man Simpson', who used to live in New Pond Cottages just south of it.

Broom Field – Next to Broom woods, but unrelated to the Godwin's 'Brooms'.

Bungalow – There's a bungalow next to it, although the old boys called it 'dog kennel'.

Chalks – Mostly very chalky.

Cheyney – A Mr Cheyney farmed it in the 1950s.

Child's Broom – The smallest of the Godwin's 'Broom' fields.

Dell Close – The smallest field, with a dell in the middle.

Drier – Field next to the drier buildings. It was enlarged in the 80s, after we took on the meadows belonging to Joan Dutton. Many historic hedges were bulldozed out – but that's what you did. It was briefly two fields, with the old meadows area being named Violin Field, as Granny Flindt's violin teacher was Joan Meadows.

Englands (Top and Bottom) – Not a clue

Folly – Supposedly after the long narrow corpse in the middle of it.

Godwin's Park – Not sure why. It's part of Godwin's, but that's about it.

The Hangar – After the big Saxon boundary bank at the top of it

Hay Field – The best bit of grass for making hay.

Hurst Down (Top and Bottom) – No idea – apart from the usual query why we call high ground 'downs'.

Joan's Acre – Opposite, and once connected to, Joan's Acre House. It's not an acre, and it was never farmed by Joan Dutton. So I don't get it, either.

Kilmeston Road – The field next to the road to Kilmeston

Long – It's long.

Middle Broom – the middle of the three Godwin's 'Broom' fields.

Pipeline – It's got a pipeline in it. No idea what it was called pre-pipeline.

Rick/Clump – The lower bit was often where a straw rick was built, the upper bit was next to a clump of trees.

Roe Hill – 'Rough Hill' according to the old maps, but Grandpa Flindt pronounced 'trough' as 'troe', so probably Rough' as 'roe'. No idea where the original 'rough' came from.

Springshot – A big pasture where the springs rise at the end of the winter.

White Hill – Another chalky field.

Prologue

On January 7th, 2020, I drove up to the NEC in Birmingham to take my place on the *Farmers Weekly* stand at LAMMA, the huge farm machinery show. I was on a mission to flog a few copies of Book One while I was there, and maybe to persuade a few passers-by to take out magazine subscriptions at the same time. It was great day; I did indeed flog a few books and subscriptions, while exchanging good-natured insults with countless new best farming friends I'd never met before. I did feel sorry for one of the *FW* events team, who was nursing a shocking cold.

Two days later, as we were enjoying an armed walkabout round the farm, I started to feel decidedly odd, and rather spoilt the day by being grumpy and shouting at loose spaniels. (As if there's any other type of spaniel.) The next day, I was in bed – with, I assumed, man flu.

But it was a very odd man flu: the symptoms were unusual. It didn't go to my chest (thank goodness) and the sneezing was minimal. But I felt like I'd been hit by a bus, the bogies were full of blood, I had lumps and bumps around my joints, and the itching – my God, the itching! It went on for weeks, and my shirt spent most of its time untucked so that I could get to my torso for a heavenly but temporary bit of relief. A ruler had to kept handy to get round the back.

When a palm-sized red patch appeared just below my rib cage, Hazel and I decided it was actually nothing to do with the man flu, and blamed it on some sort of ringworm, probably picked up around the farm somewhere.

Either that, or some sort of virus.

Farming Hinton Ampner
the ~~Brexit~~ Virus Year

February 1st

That was not quite what I expected for the first day of an EU-free United Kingdom. I have never been in the 'wildly rejoicing Brexiteers' camp, and, with Hampshire Central being Remainer City, there were no local parties being organised. So I resigned myself to a quiet day, with a couple of games of rugby to watch, and that would be about it. I was sure I'd have a little smile to myself about the numerous pro-Brexit letters and articles I've written, and I'd perhaps relive the trip to Brighton for the Referendum Party Conference in 1996. And think that, after all that, it has actually happened. In theory, anyway.

In the end, it wasn't even as uneventful as that; it turned out to be a rather unsettling day. My fellow arch-Brexiteer Rufus and I had decided to head to the Thomas Lord for a small drink last night, to mark the impending political event in a sombre and non-gloating way, and the bowl of pretentious and expensive peanuts that went with our non-pretentious but still expensive pints were definitely curried. Not my thing. I didn't sleep well. Curiously, I could have sworn I heard fireworks at 11 o'clock; another party I wasn't invited to. I know Rufus had made plans to venture out into Bosham harbour at 11pm and set off a box of fireworks, but they can't have been his I heard – he's too far away. He did suggest that I join him out in the harbour to help film the little patriotic event, but I declined. The headlines in the papers didn't bear thinking about: "Two fat middle-aged men found dead in Bosham harbour; killed by explosion caused by lethal combination of fireworks and post-curried-peanut flatulence. Icelandic whaling fleet have dealt with the bodies. Blubber market saturated for at least a decade." Or something like that.

There was also the small matter of yesterday's *Flindt on Friday* article, which listed five things that didn't make sense about veganism – what with yet another Veganuary finally drawing to a close. One of the points I made was that it seemed odd for George Monbiot (cheerleader of the eco-movement, militant vegan, proud possessor of skeleton keys to the BBC and Channel 4) to use modern day chemicals to sort his prostate problems while demanding that agriculture is dragged back to the 14th century. I thought I had phrased it quite sympathetically, quoting Dad's problems, and wishing George a swift and successful return to health. Alas – something called a 'Twitter storm' had erupted, and there was mass outrage from Mr Monbiot and his dedicated followers. Fortunately, my Twitter account consists of nothing more than one 'tweet' plugging Book One, and another saying 'This is Twitter, eh? Can't see what all the fuss is about!'. But it was a slightly uneasy feeling all day, wondering what hate messages from eco-Baldricks were flying around the Twittersphere. Odd that they too are using 21st-century technology. Shouldn't they be sending their angry messages via parchment and quills?

Luckily, there were some mundane jobs to do to take the mind off all that nonsense. Bella is due to whelp in a week or so, so there were more preparations needed. All the dining room furniture had been shoved to one end, a fantastic 4'x4' box was scrounged from somewhere, assembled and filled with old blankets and rugs. Hazel decided we'd need a 'pig bar' in it – a rail running round the inside at just above puppy height, to avoid tiny ones being crushed by a reclining bitch. I'd never heard of it before, but spotted one on the internet, and mentally assembled one using 40 mm plastic piping, elbow and T-junctions. And then ordered all the bits – for the grand total of £20 –- from Wickes, for pick-up later.

While I was doing that, Hazel and her merry gang of Intense Dog Trainers were practising their hunt/drop/retrieves round the shooting strips in Chalks – even putting up a couple of hen birds who had survived the season. Once they'd done, she went off to Wickes, and Sasha and I walked the loop to Clump – Sasha dragging behind to smell-check every single strange scent.

Back indoors, I lit the fire, and enjoyed (some of) the start of the Six Nations. Wales vs Italy proved once again that it should be the Five Nations, and Ireland vs Scotland proved that hideous footballing habits are becoming part of rugby. (Hang your head in shame, Mr Hogg.)

And what of farming? The four-month sodden standstill continues. Eighty acres of wheat in the ground, 50 acres of OSR has survived – and that's it. The day was cruelly bright and breezy, but we need more than one day to even think about venturing into a field. Five or six days are needed. Desperately.

Mind you, on Brexit Day One, it was a relief to see the sun shine at all. I'm sure Osborne and Carney had said it wouldn't even rise.

February 2nd

It was somewhat inevitable, after a day's glorious sunshine and a brisk drying wind, that I'd be woken in the small hours by yet another deluge. We're getting used to it now – punch-drunk, if you like – after four months of rain. Funny to think that at the autumn equinox, we were all on a high after a second consecutive easy-peasy harvest (with yields to match) and were holding back on sowing anything to try and maximise blackgrass control.

I remember taking Jonathan up to start uni at Newcastle in a test Audi. We had a nostalgia fest, stayed in a fantastic hotel, and generally had an 'aren't we doing well?' moment. Then the weather broke.

Since then, I've had three days in the tractor, sowing about 80 acres of Crusoe to complement the 50 acres (out of 130 acres) of OSR that has survived the bugs. I've lost count of the number of days when I thought "Just one more dry day needed!" only to be woken by a downpour – just like last night. We've perfected the art of shrugging the shoulders and saying, "Oh well."

Another tractor-free day meant that we could get on and assemble the pig rail to go in the whelping box. A couple of hours with the jigsaw and a tape measure ("Measure twice, cut once!") and a slightly less-than-elegant rail lined the bottom of the box. Because it was all push-fit fittings, it was still a bit flexible, and we might yet replace it with solvent weld instead. Trouble is, Bella is looking more low-slung every day.

Before settling down for the England vs France game, Sasha and I did yet another yomp out to Clump. One day I'll get out there, kick the mud, find my boot stays dry, and rush home to find the tractor keys. Today was not that day. I went home and lit another fire instead.

England vs France was a great spectacle, but proof that the more belligerent the pre-match hype, the less impressive the performance. England seemed to have forgotten a lot of basics – although the front row won, and that's the only result that counts. And Jonny May was a legend. And if you assault the try-scorer once he's down, there should be a penalty in front of the posts after the conversion attempt.

Writing up the BMW X6 from last month's test proved awkward. How do you describe it in 520 words without using the word 'drug dealers'?

Hazel decided the time was right to move into the whelping room with Bella, so dragged the huge black La-Z-Boy chair in, and settled down to keep her company. Bella seemed very content with it, but we all went to sleep with the sadly plaintive mews of Evie seeping from the hall.

February 3rd

Everyone seems to have slept OK – but no pups.

After 12 years, Hazel is giving up her role as trade stand secretary of the Alresford Agricultural Show. Twelve long years of making sure that several hundred traders get the best site on the show ground, arrive on time, do what they're told, pay up, and generally enjoy themselves enough to want to come back for the next show. All in all, it has been a decade-and-a-bit without too much trauma; there was the year the rain got just too much – at 6am on show day – and it was cancelled. No one told me, of course, so I was fielding phone calls here, telling everyone it was still on, and at the show ground they were turning people back.

There was the year the hideous jobsworths from the fire service noticed that there was a show coming, rang a couple of days before demanding to know if everyone had the right paperwork (for a show that takes place in a lush green meadow), and, in an onanistic display of self-important power, threatened to shut the show.

Other lowlights include the gentleman from a certain caravan-based community, who was told his bouncy castle was no longer welcome. His answer was to drive to our yard and verbally assault Hazel. It was lucky I was in the area, and was able to suggest he make himself scarce. There are the professional marketeers, who ring up with all sorts of outrageous lines – claiming to have spoken to one of "your colleagues" and reserved a place ages ago. No, they didn't. Worst of all were the large military charities (no names, no pack drill) who genuinely felt that they were so important that they didn't have to pay for their pitch. Funny how the little old charities faithfully paid up, and got on with their great work, with a little less fanfare.

I'll miss some of the regulars who rang up year after year, and always ended up having a chat about life, the universe and everything. I'll even miss the optimistic calls with only days to go before the show, sure we could "squeeze us in somewhere" – cos that's what they'd been told at another show the week before. And the purveyors of organic yak handbags, a snip for the uber-wealthy of central Hampshire at £499.

Hazel has, of course, offered to help the new girl who has taken over the job, so she came round to get mugged by dogs and given a first session of 'this is what you do'. I moped round the farm, checking if last night's strong winds had done any worthwhile drying.

They hadn't, but it mattered not. Spots of rain at lunchtime turned to drizzle, which turned to a long afternoon of steady rain. Utterly unforecast rain. What is the point of the weather forecasters? A day, which, for a week, was promised as 'dry', turned out to be wet. Still, the good news is that they know exactly what the weather will be in a hundred years' time.

So I wasn't in the best of moods when *Farmers Weekly* emailed to say that Monbiot was still squealing like a stuck pig, and they were going to have to change the online edition of Friday's article; could I rewrite the bit with him in it, or should they pull the whole section? I told them the latter. Late in the evening, I fired off a furious email accusing them of gutlessness, and saying how sad it was that they'd caved in to the demands of one of the world's most famous eco-hypocrites. Probably unwise, but I pressed 'send'. I felt better for it.

February 4th

Dry, again. And feeling just that bit fresher. (The weather, not me.)
There were more terse emails between me and *Farmers Weekly* – the Monbiot affair is not done yet. Apparently (according to the Editor's message) I was well out of order; an apology is going in Friday's editorial, tempered with the message that *FW* will continue to fight for farming's future.

For some reason, this did little to make me feel better, so I set off for a long walk. I had no dogs to go with me – Sasha has some sort of trench foot, Evie is a git, and Bella continues to be on the verge of having her pups. So it was just me.

I went out across the stubbles of Godwin's, along the top of Clump (pausing to chat to a young mother with backpack and front baby sling – now that's keen!), and diagonally across Big Field. Suddenly, the mud was no longer sticking to my boots. Across the road into Blackhouse – same again: firm underfoot, and no sign of the blackgrass. Mind you, we've done three trips over it with Roundup, making the most of the four-month drilling pause to try and nobble the weed.

In the Drier Yard, an SSE linewalker was having a bit of a park-up. I interrupted his snooze and we chatted about field access, farming in general, and travellers in particular. Funny how when two complete strangers with even the slightest countryside connection meet, that topic is raised within five minutes.

The OSR in Drier Field seemed to be waking up and will need a first dose of fertiliser soon. Even Dark Lane has dried a bit in a couple of days, and it was encouraging that as soon I made it back into the farmyard, I didn't head for the sofa. I grabbed lots of keys – it was time to start thinking about drilling wheat again.

The first job was drive back down to the Drier Yard to check stocks. I've got 11 unopened bags of Crusoe, and a half bag of slightly manky stuff that had been sitting in the Horsch for three months before I opened up the bottom of the hopper and dumped it onto clean concrete, picked out the growy bits and shovelled in into a bag. Let's call it 5.65 t. What's left to drill? Well, there's the rest of Rick/Clump, and Big. About 10 acres, and 50 acres. Call it 60 acres, or 24 ha. 5.65 t with a thousand grain weight of 52 g over 24 ha would give a seed rate of 450 plants per square metre. I rang Tod to check if that was about right for this time of year – he was happy. If the really sticky stuff at the top of Clump is still undrillable, then it'll be put on a bit thicker. And the forecast is good for a few more days.

As the enthusiasm levels surged even more, I finished reassembling the Horsch, refitting assorted rotors and end plates that had come off for the big empty and hose-out a few weeks ago. I tested the rotor manually, and even spent five minutes rerouting some of the cables that now clutter up the tractor cab. Suddenly, farming feels like it's on again. Mind you, I'm away all day tomorrow, so that will act as a useful enthusiasm brake.

Hazel was utterly convinced that Bella would give birth overnight, and so the whole house went to bed in a state of excitement. Not Bella herself, of course; she waddled onto her bed blissfully unaware of anything.

February 5th

Bella continued with her campaign to not have any puppies by not having any puppies. She waddled and grinned and wagged her tail this morning as if she was just very fat. Perhaps that's all it is.

I made myself a sandwich, packed far too many copies of Book One into the back of the Skoda and drove to Stoneleigh for Dairy-Tech – the showcase for all that's modern and bang up to date in the world of dairy. Not my thing at all – and, I discovered, not Hazel's either; her early years on a dairy farm in Co Down were not as idyllic as I thought, and I was warned only half-jokingly not to come home with any ideas of returning our farm to dairy after a break of 60 years. I might end up being on the wrong end of a robot milker.

It was a lovely drive, but Stoneleigh itself looked very sad and forlorn. I suppose I remember it as the venue for the bustling mid-summer Royal Show, before that show crashed and burned. Now it's a curious grid of grassy squares interspersed with headquarters of assorted farming organisations, some of them in better nick than others.

We had to park carefully around the edges of the grass squares because they were still waterlogged, so it was a long walk carrying another box of Book Ones to the *Farmers Weekly* stand. It was worth the effort; we managed to sell another bunch, the compliments were kind, and I haven't lost my ability to provoke complete strangers to charge up and take the piss out of me. A rare talent indeed.

I had a break at one stage and wandered round the rest of the halls, and might as well have been on another planet; dairy technology is completely alien to me. Mind you, the busy crowd were enjoying it, and seemed upbeat despite the vegan onslaught that still grips the chattering classes. I was pleased to find the Kubota stand, and climb into a little tractor. Might it be suitable for replacing our only-18-month-old Massey – still in pieces down at the dealers with a dozen technical issues?

Back at the *FW* stand, we sold another couple of books, fielded even more insults, had a provisional booking for an after-dinner speech in St Albans and then, quite suddenly, the halls emptied. It was about 3.15. "Milking," explained Andy from *FW*. "We might as well all bugger off." So I did. I managed to avoid the rush hour pretty well, with only a broken-down car just south of Oxford holding up what would otherwise have been a fantastic clear run in the stunning sunset. Once again, some mysterious force took hold of my steering wheel and forced me into Winchester services for a McDonald's – well, it seemed apt to dine on as many beef and dairy products as possible as a reward for my day out. And that branch plays the most fantastic and previously unheard tracks you ever heard over the ceiling speakers. It's most odd; I feel an appreciative email coming on. I even brought a Big Mac home for Hazel.

But what she really wanted was a box full of flatcoat puppies, who just weren't playing ball. Suzi had been round for the afternoon, and made all the right noises, and I was convinced that Bella still looked reasonably content, but Hazel was beginning to get a tad concerned. She rang round some chums, and even made a trip to the vet's new megasurgery in Alresford for scans and blood tests; all were reasonably reassuring – but they said if nothing had happened by the morning, then they'd like to know, and things might get more serious.

The weather forecast was still good, though.

February 6th

I must have slept well – I missed all sorts of comings and goings during the small hours. Hazel was worried enough about Bella to ring Suzi for help. Suzi arrived at about 4 o'clock, and agreed that things weren't going perfectly, but suggested no panic yet. She woke me as she drove off at about six. For a couple of hours, we ummed and ahhed; Hazel got more and more worried; I gave my uninformed verdict that she was fine, it would all happen naturally, if we just gave her time. It all got a bit tense.

Gillian the ex-vet called in at eight, as she had promised during Hazel's batch of worried calls yesterday, had a brief wet-fingered prod, and announced with certainly that a C-section would be needed – sooner rather than later. Hazel rang Cedar Vet in Alresford, who were well briefed after yesterday's visit. So poor old Bella, waddling and puffing for Britain, was loaded once more into the Skoda and hauled to Alresford for a Caesarean. Never easy, never absolutely safe, never without complications. And just for once, Bella became slightly uncooperative. You couldn't blame her; 12 hours earlier she'd been prodded, poked and stabbed with needles. Hazel made her excuses and left them to it.

By this time, Suzi was back to lend moral support, and helpfully took the other dogs for a walk, and then settled down for tea and toast, and calming words for Hazel; by now, I was out in the yard, desperately trying to get ready for the first drilling spell in three months, pumping up tyres and putting the manky bag of seed back in the drill.

Moments later, Suzi was bouncing across the yard, grinning from ear to ear, with the news that Bella had conceded defeat just as the scalpels were being sharpened, and produced two puppies. The logjam had been broken. Huge relief all round. By lunchtime, she'd had seven, and Hazel could finally relax. There would be no stitches, no cuts, no medicines, just a simple (in the end) natural birth.

I felt it was now safe to head off to Rick/Clump, and start my drilling plan, which was to finish the landwork of Rick – the chalky bit – and then start in Big Field. I drove the Deere and the big Horsch carefully down the hill, through the gates into Roe Hill, into BOMS at the far corner, and unfolded. Within only a couple of yards I knew that ground conditions, while not perfect, would do nicely. I scrounged a lift home from Hazel, who was on her way to bring home the proud mum and her pups, had a cup of tea, jumped into the Massey and towed the seed trailer out into Rick. At last, I could get on with putting seed in the ground – the first bit of constructive arable farm work since those three days in the middle of October.

By dusk, I had done the odd little bit in Rick, and a good 15 acres in Big Field. And the forecast is still good. And Bella came home with eight puppies, not seven.

February 7th

A moderate frost, a lovely sunrise – what more could one want? Perfect for leaping into the tractor and doing a proper long shift sowing wheat. Just for a change, nothing like that happened. Hazel had been sitting with Bella and the pups all night, and needed a freshen up, so I sat in on the squeaking pile of mole-a-likes.

Then there were cattle to feed, papers to be got, assorted other jobs to do – and I was happy to keep my vigil going, so by the time I got the last bags of Crusoe on the old trailer, and trundled out to Big Field, it was past ten o'clock. I had a lovely couple of hours doing long turns, slowly relaxing into the job again. It's always a worry restarting after so many months off, with a drill you've only used for a couple of days, and tractor that was chipped – against the advice of the local Deere dealer. But everything seemed to work.

My only worry was how long seed continued to blow out of the pipes after I'd lifted the drill out of work. I hope it's just the dip in hydraulic fan speed when lifting the drill and operating the marker arms, rather than a big backlog in the pipes. I'll be cross if it comes up with huge gaps in it. The seed rate seemed spot on, consistently at the 250 kg/ha I'd plugged into the control box.

There will be a few gaps, up at the top of the field, where, thanks to some odd strata of soil, a line of springs sometimes emerges. This year, of course, running water could be seen. It reminded me of one of my first years here: two ploughs, a power harrow, and an old Massey 30 drill. I was on power harrow duty, keeping close up with the ploughs, and watched, fascinated, as a freshwater river ran down the furrows left by the last plough mouldboard.

Luckily, this year. I was running nearly empty when I hit them, and did a couple of loads with only one bag in at a time. At one stage, I contemplated only drilling downhill, but the time penalty, and the soil damage caused by all that extra driving, seemed daft. I just hoicked the drill up once or twice, and left gaps.

Over towards BML's the soil got better, and it was back to making a proper job. A couple of hours of really annoying short work above and below the trees, and it was time to hit the headland. Some of it was horrible, slippery and stiff, but I cracked on as it got dark and a burst of heavy drizzle came through.

The finished field measured 18.7 ha – that ST4 seems to consistently 'undermeasure' the area, which is odd, bearing in mind it's driven by radar, just like the CO3. It's no problem: it means I've got a bag and a half left over to go back to Rick/Clump with, and I think there's a bag of Panorama somewhere. Given a dry day tomorrow, I should finally nail those two fields. Given a dry day. We'll see.

February 8th

The light drizzle due to shoot through overnight turned out to be a couple of hours of heavy rain – we know this because Hazel was on dog duties, and Bella has now got the shits. Probably all that cleaning and licking of eight puppies. So there were a couple of trips out to the garden in the small hours, and both times it was very wet.

My early drilling plans were scuppered, so I did some seed shuffling and trailer parking up, and then headed home for assorted visitors – Julie with beautifully packaged parcels of old newspapers (perfect for puppy pee and poo), and the Editor on pigeon patrol and for a bit of cooing.

It dried nicely over lunchtime, so I popped out and did the rest of the headland of Rick, and then ventured into Clump again. Within yards, all the wheels were bunged up, the Deere was complaining, and I was making a right royal mess. Know when you're beaten, they say. So I abandoned it. At least I tried. Now we know why Dad kept Rick and Clump as separate fields.

I got home in time for a reasonably exciting Ireland vs Wales game, and a gritty, sodden, wind-blown but grimly entertaining Scotland vs England game. It isn't often you see endless high balls landing behind the kicker.

Bella is relaxing into her role as proud mother. She's getting used to an occasional short walk again, and landed on top of me on the sofa at one stage, daft as a brush. Thank God the Caesarean wasn't needed.

Big weather warnings for tomorrow – Storm Ciara in on its (her?) way.

February 9th

The Met Office called that one right – mind you, this storm is supposed to be about 1,500 miles across, so even they shouldn't have missed it. The house shook in the small hours, and heavy rain assaulted the windows.

A drive down to Cheriton shop revealed lots of branches down, and one mighty ash toppled over on the north side of Hinton Park, opposite the old rectory. Always a sad sight.

I joined niece Sarah in the Flowerpots for a lunchtime pint. She's had a great success with her first book, and is being hounded to come up with a second. The first one was about the legal trade, and she's dead keen to do anything but that for the second. Much of her childhood was spent here at the farmhouse, and so she has a huge soft spot for farming She has a plan to write a proper pro-farming book, but one written by someone who is an outsider. A dozen or so different farmers will be profiled, from all different types of agriculture, and she wants me to be one of them.

It seems a splendid idea, and I said I'd be delighted to help. I can't see it doing anything to change the general public's perception of farming; that will only happen when the food runs short.

A warm fire and a sofa beckoned for France vs Italy, and a beer-induced snooze meant I slept through a lot of it. Rather worryingly, the weather forecast is even more dramatic for tonight.

February 10th

Ye Gods, that did blow last night. A 2.36am, there was a terrifying roaring and howling, and it seemed to be coming from all different directions at once. Tucked under my space-rocket duvet, I wondered if it was a mini-tornado coming through. I also wondered if we were in for a repeat of the January 1990 storm, when the southernmost chimney toppled into the spare room, causing enormous damage. The repairs of the old farmhouse took months, and when they finally got round to the chimneys, the Trust took the lot down and rebuilt them – and filled the flues that weren't being used at the time with concrete, for added strength.

I remember arguing at the time that several fireplaces would be rendered useless by doing that, but was overruled. I have to say that at 2.27am, I was quite grateful for their added strength. Mind you, with all the extra firewood that should be available after Storm Ciara is done, we'll be longing for fireplaces.

'Storm Ciara' – once upon a time we had storms without names, or they were tagged by a significant date. Every one has to have a dramatic name these days – all part of the Met Office's sensationalisation of the weather. It goes with wind *gusts* being headlined in the forecast, rather than the old-fashioned average speed, and average temperatures being wrongly labelled as 'where they should be this time of year'. I've heard the local radio weather forecast talking of temperatures 'halving' from 10°C to 5°C, but even the Met Office aren't that scientifically illiterate. And when we're due for 'a week's rain' in a day, what week are we talking about? Still, it's integral to the average weather presenter's mission to get their ultimate prize; their own game show.

I tiptoed down to Cheriton shop to get the papers, and did a full drive round on the way home, spotting snapped off trees here, limbs down there, and more huge trees blocking the road at Brockwood Bottom. We were trouble-free, luckily. Dodgy shoulders rule out any waving of chainsaws at the moment.

We had our first band rehearsal of the year, and the first runout since the Alresford Show last year. Shed 3b was a bit damp and musty, and the temporary ceiling I'd installed in 2009 was beginning to look sorrier than ever. It may need some more DIY. Dan had agreed to come and play bass for us, and as the only one with any real talent in the room, forced us all to up our game a bit. Rumours abound of up to five gigs – great news after a year or two with next to none. There's talk of a couple of weddings, and the first of the 60th birthday parties, too.

After two hours of banging out a great selection of hits from the 60s right up to the present day, my bloody shoulders were killing me. Anyone would have thought I'd done an hour's chainsawing.

February 11th

Windy again, clear and very cold. Picker-up Nessa arrived to coo over puppies, and – far more importantly – brought cake. Most of the morning was spent gossiping. And eating.

I took the two younger dogs out for a decent yomp to Clump, which they loved. The clay is still saturated, and my attempts to finish it the other day look terrible. The big puddle in the old dell at the top of Roe Hill proved too tempting for the dogs who rushed in and played in it – Evie managing somehow to hang on to the tennis ball she'd carried all the way from home. A fantastic 'zoomies' session then following in the wheat stubble, with the pup just about staying out of Sasha's reach. It was a joy to watch in the winter sun – and they managed to run off some of the freezing water.

Neighbour Robert and I adjourned to the Flowerpots for our regular Tuesday moan – something that's particularly therapeutic as the months go by without any work being done. He'd managed 50 acres of something last week, too.

February 12th

The little loader tractor finally made it back from the repair shop. It has only been here for 18 months, but it has a list of faults as long as your arm. It was delivered with 4WD stuck on, the roof leaked horribly, the loader would only go 'up' while Hazel was stacking hay, and the brakes jammed on a few weeks ago. The dealers lent us a demo and took ours away for a proper dismantle and rebuild – luckily, still under warranty – and drove it back from Chichester this morning.

I've been mulling over the implications for a few weeks. It's obviously a Friday tractor (*tracteur de Vendredi?*), and our minimalist machinery policy means there's no room here for a machine that is constantly causing problems.

What to do? Persevere with it, and hope for the best? I said to the rep who was part of the delivery gang today that I want to meet someone from AGCO at some stage and discuss its future. I'll be angling for a warranty extension. Or do I chop it in now, and change to something more reliable? I sat in one of the Valtra 'A' series at Dairy-Tech and liked that one a lot. It would mean a huge depreciation hit, but I had to do it with the terrible Amazone sprayer five years ago when it was obvious that it wasn't up to the job, and just not dwell on it.

Not entirely coincidentally, the latest tractor sales figures – from 2018 – showed Massey's market share plummeting. I'll be surprised if they show an improvement in 2019.

There were more machinery maintenance matters this afternoon, when I took our 2016 Skoda Octavia Scout down to North's garage in Cheriton for a service. I had contemplated using the official Winchester Skoda dealer, with half an eye on its warranty, too, but the service manager was so rude and dismissive (and quoted me the best part of £500 for the work) that I thought we'd keep going with North's.

It's the curse of Skoda's success – there was a time when Skoda garages had to work hard, but now they're all sniffy and dismissive, thanks to how popular their cars are. It's just like the old days when that garage was VW only. Andy behind the desk at North's said that they'd recently invested in all the latest VAG diagnostic kit, so our timing was perfect. A slightly lower-tech job that was needed was a service of the magic Haldex coupling that is crucial in the Scout's brilliant on-demand 4WD system. Andy agreed they'd do that too.

I got a lift home (Hazel still housebound with puppies) in one of the many lovely old Saabs that North's keep on the road – many years ago they were Saab main dealers. Apparently, parts are still made and easily available for them. And there's a lovely 9-3 convertible sitting for sale outside North's reception. Hmmm.

In the evening, it was Growmore Quiz time – and not just any old Growmore Quiz. It was semi-final time, and we (Petersfield Wey) were just one step away from the final. All we had to do was beat the mighty Lymington Foresters at our new venue, the Angel. (It was once called the Pig and Whistle, but in those days a pint and a half didn't cost £7.50.)

It was the usual format, but with two important additions: an audience of thirty or so – and not just someone who wandered in by mistake – and a slight sense of seriousness. It was still good fun, and we won by just a couple of points. The fates fell our way occasionally: we were asked to name the Rolls-Royce off-roader, and guess who has been in a running battle with Rolls Royce to send one out to the farm for a road test for *The Field*, and failing miserably. It's called a Cullinan. And my debatable topic happened to be 'why we should all go back to imperial measurements' – something I've been ranting and raving about for years, and only half-jokingly. Bring on the final!

February 13th

A busy morning was spent trying to write up the next *FonF* and babysit puppies/ proud mum while Hazel came and went doing straw jobs and cattle. The problem is that we get Bella settled nicely, with all puppies firmly attached, and she leaps up and jumps out of the whelping box at the first sign of Hazel coming back though the door. The pups all scream for Britain, but seem to survive it.

The farm was still saturated, which, on a Thursday, is officially a good thing. It means I can grab a towel and my swimming trunks, and head down to the Nuffield hospital in Chandler's Ford and keep going with my post-hip replacement swim therapy. There's normally four or five of us in a boiling hot chest-deep pool, doing exercise routines to music, while being shouted at by Tracey the instructor. It was part of the deal when I had the hip done privately at that hospital, but within weeks I realised that it was the best therapy possible, and have paid to keep going after the initial few free weeks.

Mind you, the reason we get shouted at so much is that we all turn into a bunch of misbehaving schoolchildren – and I'm the youngest there by a good decade. There's a limitless supply of innuendos when you're lying on your back with a big pink woggle sticking up in the air.

An hour of that is fantastic (the exercise, not the innuendo), and just the job when there's no physical activity to be had on a waterlogged farm. And if you want to reduce all the hardbodies in the physio department to simpering wrecks, you show them a short video of puppies squealing.

February 14th

Big rain last night – really big rain. Water and debris came flowing round from the back of the barns, blocked the little drain outside the lawnmower shed, flowed into the mower shed, and then through the wall into the freezer room. Valentine's morning was spent mopping and squeezing towels. Who said romance was dead?

We were nearly out of logs, so despite the horrible mild conditions, I dug out my new electric chainsaw (checking it had dried out from its storage in the freezer room), and had a jolly hour cutting up firewood.

You're supposed to buy an electric chainsaw in some grand but impotent gesture to save the planet, but my reasons are slightly more mundane: first, you don't wreck an already fragile shoulder trying to pull start the two-stroke engine. Second, you can put it down while fetching another long limb off the heap, and it won't have burbled its way out of reach across the concrete. Third, it is a lot quieter, although the safety helmet is still as vital as ever for flying woodchips. Fourth, you can sharpen on the move by gently levering a shaped stone against the moving chain with your little finger. A hugely satisfying display of sparks ensues – something unthinkable with a petrol reservoir close by. Fifth, by the time the battery is done, so are you, and it's indoors for tea 'n' hobnobs.

I'm not sure of its longevity – the old Stihls just run and sun, and you have to remember to top up the chain oil reservoir, with, er, fossil-fuel sourced chain oil, and every time I plug it back in to recharge, you can be sure that the electrons are sourced from a fossil-fuel powered power station. I'm sure I'm saving the planet in some small way. Even logs are now falling foul of the eco-loons, but that's probably because we are able to heat our homes without the taxman knowing about it.

February 15th

Wet, windy and horrible.

Huge credit these days should go to the jolly teams of men who drive round the countryside during the quiet weather spells, clearing trees from the power lines. Sometimes it looks a bit drastic after they've chopped and shredded swathes of greenery away from the overhead cables, but two consecutive weekends of vicious wind have produced nothing more drastic than an occasional flickering of the lights. Bloody handy when we're all so utterly dependent on computers and televisions.

The storms of October 87 and January 90 knocked off the juice for days, but I suppose life was simpler then.

Thank goodness the power was still on; we could sit and watch the first hour of *Arrival*, my favourite first hour of science fiction. It started at 9pm, and Hazel and I, and a pile of dogs, settled down in front of the warm fire to enjoy it. And, as has happened every single time we've tried to watch 'the 9pm film' (whatever it might be), we're all sound asleep by ten. We have an enormous list of blockbusters we know off by heart until the 60-minute mark: *The Dressmaker, Oblivion, The Green Mile*, anything by Quentin Tarantino. We haven't the slightest idea how any of them finish.

There is, of course, a simple solution. The Freeview box has many channels that are '+1', i.e. they start an hour after scheduled time. Some years ago, there used to be a couple of '+24' channels, i.e. starting the same time, but a day later. I remember these in particular when Channel 5 had the Test Match coverage (the BBC couldn't afford it, of course: they had spent too much on inter-continental three-legged racing from Kurdistan, presented, of course, by Clare Balding.). It was a joy not to worry about missing the hour-long highlights package, because you could catch it 24 hours later, immediately followed by the +1 show you'd missed by watching the +24 show. You got a two-hour long feast of cricket.

So what's needed is for the movie channels to show a '+23' channel that starts, at 9pm, where the film left off (and we all fell asleep) at 10pm the previous day. It couldn't show the whole of the previous day's film, starting at 8pm, because of watershed issues (Tarantino?), and the way movies are getting longer and longer, we will soon be needing a '+46' channel, to show where we all fell asleep at ten the previous night where the film got to at 11 the night before. Too simple for words.

February 16th

Another hideous windy and wet night. More trees down, more flooding. Very little happened. Picker-up Ness came up again for a coffee and a puppy cuddle (not a euphemism), and I took two dogs out for a yomp to Clump and back. Chalks had a river running north–south in several places, luckily not strong enough to be washing anything away, but unnerving all the same.

Word of the puppies is spreading: the phone is ringing off the hook with people looking for quality flatcoats. I wish they could have seen Evie hooning around in the water in Roe Hill, skilfully evading Sasha while keeping hold of the manky tennis ball as if it were the most precious thing in Christendom. Which, to them, it is.

February 17th

Hazel had an early start dropping Sasha up at the vets to be spayed. Poor old Sasha – we'd tried terribly hard to breed from her, not least because she is the cleverest dog we've ever owned, and would have given anything to have pups from her to continue her line. Hazel found a suitable stud dog some months ago, drove halfway round London, twice, but the coupling just wouldn't happen. Some weeks later, a vet chum shoved a lubricated but still undignified finger up Sasha's lady parts and announced that it was never going to happen. She had some rare deformity in the tubes. She still gets very hormonal though, and has been unnecessarily aggressive in recent weeks with Bella's pups on the way (Tod got a full set of teeth in his arse) so we booked her in for spaying. And it gave Hazel an hour or two away from puppy-sitting.

I did a round trip to fill up the Skoda at the West Meon Hut petrol station (diesel nice and cheap at the moment), went on into Petersfield to pay in a couple more Book One cheques, and then headed north-west to the vets at Alton for a three o'clock pick-up.

Yet another storm came hurtling through as I negotiated the hideous potholes on the Selbourne road (it's amazing what modern tyres put up with), and I started to ponder the sowing situation. Another couple of days of this, and then a good ten days to dry out, and we really will be at the end of the winter wheat drilling window. Do we leave another 140 acres fallow to join the whole Stanmore block? And the winter beans aren't in yet either – that could be another 96 acres. It could be a quiet harvest, and empty barn, and a challenging cashflow year. And, of course, a quiet redefinition of 'public goods'.

Annoyingly a BMW X3 with French plates pulled out suddenly in front of me and proceeded to weave dangerously all over the road – enough for me to press 'save this bit' on the dashcam. He'd obviously had a good lunch, and I was quite relieved when we got to the A31 in one piece.

At the vets I was given a briefing on Sasha's aftercare (one that only just strayed the right side of patronising), and she was brought out, slightly unsteady on her feet, but pleased to see me. She had a skin-tight 'vest' on, which should protect the stitches without having to resort to the horrible 'cone of shame'.

Like all farm dogs, she gets very confused when urban vets go all squeaky when talking to them. Some years ago, we helped out the vets by letting a minibus full of students do a bit of work on calves – a bit of disbudding and the odd castration. We held back our pack of dogs until they were done, and then let them loose. But all three stopped dead in their tracks as the squeaky high-octave cries of "Oooh, hello doggy woggy!" started. I'll never forget Sasha looking back over her shoulder, as if to say "What do I do now?" I just hope the white van community don't learn this dog-stopping technique.

By evening, Sasha was well enough to be romping with Evie. Good job, squeaky vets.

February 18th

We decided that if we don't do some farming of some sort soon, we'd go mad. So Hazel came up with a plan to muck out the front of the back barn – where her cattle have been for months – to give them easier access to the troughs, and, perhaps more importantly, reduce the temptation to step out over the feeder gates.

We'd need the loader tractor fitted with a grab, of course, and the Deere towing our small but sturdy 4T monocoque trailer. It would all need a fairly lengthy logistical operation: nothing was where it needed to be.

First step was to walk down to New Pond and pick up the Deere and the drill, and bring them home to the yard. It was a dry and mild morning, so the stroll down the hill to the Folly was quite pleasant. A tumult of dogs running off leads in Dark Lane signalled that yet another professional dog walker was making use of my farm and the Trust's woods to earn a living, but they were relatively under control, so I just stood and watched them as they headed up into the woods. Funny how there's a shortage of ground-nesting birds.

The John Deere coughed and spluttered a bit after another long layoff, and I folded up the ST4 and headed home, via the top of BOMS, through Roe Hill, up the road and into the yard. I backed the Horsch into the corner and hitched off. We might get it going in some winter wheat before the end of the month – we might not.

I popped back down to the Drier Yard in the Massey, and had a big shuffle of assorted seed bags, discovering a bag and a half of spring beans stored in the little 4T trailer – which is a bonus. Spring beans are like gold dust this year, so I'll add them gratefully to the trailerful I held back at the end of harvest. At some stage I'll get the whole lot recleaned and bagged up. And then, after I've finished the winter wheat, the winter beans and the spring barley, get them sown. Blimey, that's quite a list.

I brought the now-empty trailer back home, switched it to the Deere, put the grab back on the loader, and we were all set and ready to go for a bit of muck cart. Trouble is, the evening was getting on, and rather than go down the pub wearing a faint smell of *Eau de Cattle Shit*, I knocked off a bit early.

The Editor briefly joined me and neighbour Robert for our Tuesday evening beer, making his apologies after a pint and a half and a packet of peanuts. It wasn't the liveliest of gatherings; Robert and I moped and moaned about the weather and the lack of work, and the Editor explained that he needed a clear head to go up to London to smooth-talk a key advertiser back into the magazine's pages. Once we had the bar to ourselves again, Robert and I agreed that the countryside is in a bit of a crisis – not just its farmers, but its magazines too.

February 19th

Agronomist Tod came round for another slightly forlorn discussion about the cropping plans. There's another ten days or so in the wheat cropping window, so we cut back the planned Zulu acreage by dropping Bungalow, and the very top and the very bottom of Kilmeston Road – one end because it will be sodden clay, the other because it is flooded. That should up the seed rate to some respectable level. We'll give the winter beans a bit more time yet, and everything else is 'carry on as normal'. Another week or two of this rain, and we'll no doubt be revising all these plans.

I puppy-sat while Hazel went back to her part-time job doing some accounts at a local racing stable – something that might be a very handy little earner if we don't get any seed in the ground.

February 20th

As I reached the car park today for another childish session in the hydrotherapy pool, I checked the phone and found a missed call and a message from Geoff at our buying group. He sounded, as usual, somewhat exasperated, so I thought I'd ring him back later – I may have worked out what I should or shouldn't have done by the time I get home.

In fact, it turned out that I had done nothing wrong. Far from it; he and I had made an excellent joint decision to only order enough fertiliser last autumn to top up the liquid fertiliser tank. The suppliers had done an enormous price hike for the spring deliveries, and Geoff had a hunch back then that the prices were too high and would come down.

He was ringing to say that prices had indeed plummeted, and although we should be considering ordering more now, we should actually only order half of our final requirement. He reckoned prices would come down further. Not sure exactly why prices are coming down so dramatically – probably a combination of oil prices being down and demand being non-existent (since so few crops have actually been sown) – but it was a very useful confirmation of a piece I wrote some time ago in *FW*, saying that, contrary to what Project Agrifear had said, input prices would drop to match demand and what we can pay. I got that right. I confess that I can't remember *not* ordering fertiliser back in the autumn, though. That bit came as the biggest surprise of all.

After a quick de-chlorinating shower, it was off to the Winchester NFU AGM at the Cart and Horses on the outskirts of Winchester. After the world's fastest meeting ("OK for Mike to keep on as chairman? Good. And Sam as vice-chairman? Super. Done.") we heard from Ally, the new star of *Mucky Boots*, a fly-on-the-wall documentary series about farming. It started on Channel 4 until they went vegan to support their investments in meat-free food companies, and now features on the excellent Quest. And as these things go, it's pretty good. It occasionally verges on the sensational – but you can't blame programme makers for that, and it's a fair 'warts and all snapshot' of farm life.

In fact, it's quite unnerving how familiar his farm and his situation is. He's on 500 acres, AHA from the Dutchy of Cornwall. I'm 900, National Trust. He came home rather earlier than planned to help out – me too. He wonders if time on other farms might have been handy. Ditto. He has no staff, but runs informal arrangements with neighbours, as we do. They have easy care sheep. And he's ginger and has played a bit of rugby. It was quite spooky. His face is perfect for TV, mine's only good for radio. Still, he spoke brilliantly, and won a lot of friends. It was a damned good pie at the Cart and Horses, too. And I sold four copies of Book One.

February 21st

Yesterday was the deadline for next week's *Flindt on Friday*, and for the first time in two years, I hadn't got a clue what to write about. I ummed and ahhed, started a dozen different ideas, and then came up with something which had only the slightest link to farming. I re-read it a few times, polished it up a bit, and sent it off. Luckily, it wasn't rejected.

Mind you, there's a lot of distraction going on at the moment, and the landlord's visit after lunch was enough to make one's mind drift off. But it turned out to be a very positive one: he was waving his huge compensation chequebook.

We're about to host a new pipeline through the farm, which will be carrying aviation fuel from Fawley up to storage facilities near Heathrow. It's not the first pipeline to come through the farm for this very purpose – there's one there now, but it takes a direct route through Pipeline Field (the clue's in the name), through the woods, then Drier Field, Blackhouse Road, Big Field and finally BML's. You'd think that a new pipeline taking the same stuff from the same source to the same destination would be laid on the same route. But no. The bit of the woods that was dug up 50 years ago is now classified (slightly mysteriously) as 'ancient' and therefore cannot be touched. So the new route is a huge semicircle to the east of the woods. Makes no sense to me, but there we go.

February 22nd

Our new state of 'empty nesting' was relieved for a couple of days as Diana decided to pop back for a short weekend. She's come a long way in five years, monstering Durham Uni and walking straight into a well-paid job in Bishop's Stortford. Mind you, she gave that up pretty quickly, and decided she'd rather have a fun but slightly less well-paid job, so now works at one of the computer gaming companies in Cambridge. It might as well be the Planet Zog, as far as I'm concerned, when she explains what they do, and what she does. It's certainly not Pac-Man.

She needed to see the puppies, of course, and a Churcher's College meet-up had been organised, so I popped into Winchester to meet her off the 12.30 train. The town was surprisingly empty for the middle of a Saturday. But the station was utter chaos. A derailment of a freight train further south at Eastleigh a few days ago is still causing problems with trains terminating (which conjures up visions of destructive explosions, for some reason) at Winchester, and passengers being ferried on in huge buses and coaches. It didn't do to pause and look slightly confused about which lane to be in – a cacophony of furious taxi horns ensued.

We hadn't had any Book One sales for a few days, so I casually clicked on its Amazon page. 'Currently Unavailable' it said. Ah. That explains it. My inventory page said it was still available, so there was no clue there. I emailed Amazon, and within moments got a reply that my book wasn't available because it hadn't been allocated a 'category', and that these were the steps necessary to sort that problem out. As is usual when dealing with global behemoths by email, their instructions proved useless, so I gave up and watched the rugby instead.

Italy were as usual useless, and Wales could be world beaters again if they stopped screaming at the ref and waving their arms like broken windmills in a storm. Dan Biggar, take note.

Diana was only slightly tiddly when I picked her up late from outside 'Spoons in Petersfield, and she'd had a very jolly meet up with four or five schoolfriends, one of whom was off to Italy for a four-year medical course, and another was now a science teacher. Where do the years go?

February 23rd

Luckily, the farm's still underwater, so I spent a long morning arguing with Amazon. They tried the 'you haven't given your book an allocation' line again, but then resorted to 'please send us all your financial details so you can start selling'. Luckily, because I only did this back in October, I had all the documents at hand, and uploaded them all again. Within minutes, Book One was once again available to buy. I'm still utterly baffled as to why it was withdrawn after five successful months, and I was being asked to effectively start all over again.

After a huge roast lamb Sunday lunch, Diana caught the train back to Cambridge. It was uncannily similar to 'leaveouts' from boarding school. I'd be picked up after Sunday chapel, get home for an enormous lunch (lemon meringue pie, of course), have a drive round the farm, maybe a spot of clay pigeon shooting or a rat hunt under the chicken house, and then back to school in the evening. And try not to blub through 'The Day Thou gavest, Lord, is ended'.

February 24th

Yet more howling wind and rain. Not a lot to be done. The good news was that a copy of Book One sold. The bad news was that was an eBay sale – so still no proof that the Amazon page is up and working properly.

The latest test car rolled up on time – a Jaguar F-Pace in hideous gleaming white. My mission is to get it as dirty as possible.

I parked down at New Pond and did a long looping walk over Rick/Clump and Big. The Crusoe I'd sown about three weeks ago is just about coming through – and the brow of Big Field was teeming with rooks who were delighted to have spotted it too. Was it worth getting gas bangers or even rope bangers organised? Not really. I only found a couple of slugs, and no sign of actual slug damage, and that's what I was really looking for.

February 25th

The next VAT deadline is imminent, so we need all the books back from the accountant, where they've been for a month or so. The office had been warned, so it was just a matter of flying down the A3 in the Jaguar, picking them up at reception, and flying back.

As usual, it didn't quite work out that way. The first problem was that it took ten minutes to shoehorn the massive Jag SUV into a parking space. Backwards, forwards, listen for the beeps and bongs, check the cameras, look over the shoulder, forwards, backwards. It felt a lot longer than ten minutes. I popped in to get the big plastic box full of files and ledgers, and then asked if I could leave the Jag in the car park and stroll into Havant for a bit of shopping. "Of course," said the girl at reception. "We won't clamp you." I only half believed her.

Havant on a wet and cold February day does little to lift the spirits. The short walk down North Street to the Meridian Centre meant passing lots of empty shops and some pretty sorry-looking pub sites – some demolished, some for rent, and others now converted to exotic restaurants. The Meridian Centre itself is slightly cheerier, but it is still a million miles away from frightfully well-to-do Alresford.

I was after some more TV aerial cable connectors. The join in the coax cable outside the old French windows separated in the wind last week, and turned out to be corroded and perished. In Argos, you could buy an extension kit, which included cable connectors, and a three-way splitter, for a tenner. I filled in one of the 'order cards' (which reminded me of being in the bookies) and presented it at the main desk.

"That's one TV cable extension kit, for ten pounds," said the man at the desk. "Do you have an email address at all?" I pointed out that I did, but it wasn't really relevant for this purchase. "Would you like an Argos Purchase Card?" he persevered brightly.

"No," I replied, somewhat less than brightly. "Look. I'll give you this ten-pound note, and you give me the cable. How about that for a plan?" He looked at me as if I were mad, pressed some more buttons on his till, and gave me my ticket with my order number. I couldn't blame the poor fellow; when Jonathan worked at Screwfix during his gap year, he was told that harvesting customer information is almost as important as getting money off them. I shuffled over to the waiting area (there's a lot of shuffling that seems to go on in Havant) and sat down. Luckily, they weren't too busy, and a couple of minutes later my precious cable arrived from central stores. I was shuffling out of the Meridian Centre and back up North Street like a local within minutes. And I hadn't been clamped.

I drove home through yet another deluge, and decided that I'd better try and get a few days hedge trimming in before the March 1st deadline. I hitched it onto the Deere and spent a reasonably successful hour down on the A272 edge of Godwin's trying to improve the Editor's view out of his kitchen window. Then everything went black, sleet started hammering down, and I couldn't see out of the tractor; the inside was misted up, the outside was a slurry of water and wood pulp. I went home.

The Tuesday Pots trip with neighbour Robert was much more cheerful. Emily behind the bar had just had her hair 'done', and, as is traditional in these circumstances, everyone in the bar is obliged to say how much their last haircut cost. And, as usual, our costs combined came to less that Emily's. A special mention to Emily's dad, sitting at the back of the bar, who pointed out that he'd done his nearly bald head himself only that morning. For nothing.

February 26th

A frost – excellent for vernalising the late-sown but just emerging Crusoe.
Once I'd done my puppy-sitting shift, I thought I'd clear some room for the pea seed, which is due late morning tomorrow. If I shifted the 8 t of winter bean seed down to the Drier Yard, that would give me room to unload the peas up at home, instead of asking a monster lorry to drive through the lanes and then get stuck in a soggy yard at New Pond. It took me a couple of trips, moving 4 t at a time (I don't trust the old 6 t bale trailer to take any more than that), and it was a delight to use the new-ish Massey Ferguson loader tractor now that it's back home and everything seems to be working properly on it – at last.

Finally, there was some Brexit-related news, as Defra reported their plans to shave lumps off our annual subsidy payments until they become nothing in seven years' time. The hysteria was somewhat confusing on 'social media'. The whole 'end of direct payments' thing has been widely forecast, and there will be other ways of getting the money – or some of it – by jumping through the 'public goods' hoops.

There is also the little matter of exactly the same process on the other side of the Channel – in fact, some of the figures I found online and then posted on the *FW* Facebook page suggested that over here we might be getting a better deal. Nope, little things like that weren't going to stop the anti-Brexit fury. We Brexit-voting farmers (despite instructions from the NFU, that's what most of us ended up as) were "turkeys voting for Christmas". How we laughed. Not.

Of course, if this season goes on as it is, and harvest is knocked back as much as some rumours are now – at last – suggesting, then wheat prices might make a lack of subsidy somewhat irrelevant.

We had a great post-lunch chat with the Trust's chief Estate Ranger, who wanted to talk through some of their plans for the future. Some years ago, such a meeting would have filled me with dread, but their thinking seems to have swung round to being perfectly in tune with ours. The public are welcome but on our terms. Dogs should be on leads – end of, as young people say. And if we wanted any trees sawn up, he'd be happy to come and deal with them. All in all, a very positive meeting – although I suspect he was only here to see the puppies.

Having said that, they weren't a particularly pretty sight today. Hazel has started them on puppy food – some sort of hideous-smelling mash, which gets splattered everywhere. I'm sure they'll get the hang of it after a few days. Bella is, of course, thrilled to pile in, lick the pups and finish the food off, all in the name of 'clearing up'.

I managed another hour's hedge trimming – interrupted by a handy confirmation of tomorrow's seed delivery – before more rain and wind sent me indoors.

February 27th

My early shift puppy-sitting was going well. The dining room was warm as toast, the pups were snoozing, and I'd found some cricket highlights to watch on Hazel's laptop. Unfortunately, the driver of the 'late morning' delivery had made good time and rang at about 8.30 to say he was half an hour away. Trouble is, the phone is on 'tractor' volume, so made me fall out of the chair, and woke up all the pups. I just about made it out of the dining room before they all started howling for food.

Having checked with Hazel that she wasn't far away from getting home with the other three dogs, I went out and opened up the gates and the barn for the seed delivery. I put the weights on the back of the Massey just as huge flobby flakes of snow started to join the rain that was coming down from the north-east.

The driver arrived as promised, and it only took a moment to unload the eight tonnes of pea seed and get them stacked in the barn. The barn's now officially full of unsown seed. There's all the winter bean seed in the left-hand lean-to, there's a trailer of still-to-be-cleaned spring beans in the right hand lean-to, and the tractor barn has a monster heap of Tower winter barley, Zulu winter wheat and the peas. How lucky that we don't put tractors in that barn anymore. Still, it was nice to be doing something constructive for a change. And what a good thing it was that I cleared some space yesterday.

Several more attempts to start a decent *Flindt on Friday* column failed, so I begged another day's grace, and headed off for hot pool swim hip boogie therapy. It did the trick, because by late evening, I finally had 600 reasonable words knocked together. I pressed 'send' and hoped it wouldn't be rejected by morning.

February 28th

On the way back from Cheriton Shop with the papers, my Guardian Angel whispered in my ear that a trip down to the grain store yard would be a good idea. I took his (her?) advice and arrived at New Pond to see the whole yard full of SSE vehicles: huge 4x4 vans, small vans and mini-diggers. The man in charge looked a bit sheepish – I obviously had the look of a farmer somewhat surprised to find one of his yards full to the brim with blue and yellow construction traffic.

It turned out that they were planning some repairs and maintenance down there. A tree leant heavily on the line to the barn a few years ago, and the posts were forced over at an angle. So they're doing some straightening and lopping, and doing some pole replacements over at New Pond Cottages.

"While you're here," I said, "what are the chances of moving the pole that means we can't widen the entrance to the yard? It was perfect for the lorries of 1960, but today's artics are less than happy when asked to reverse up in."

I steeled myself for a swift tooth-sucking refusal, with reference to forms in triplicate and planning issues and 'speak to my manager' and – "Yeah, we'll do that for you!" was the cheery reply. "About... here?" he asked, digging a sturdy heel in the grass about four feet south of where the present pole was.

"Perfect!" I said, and drove off, slightly shocked, but chuffed to bits at my good timing. Assuming it actually happens, of course.

Back indoors, there was a lovely email, forwarded from *FW* HQ, from some Lincolnshire farmers who had just read *FonF* – the one about how we all fall asleep an hour into the big 9pm film. Their comments were very kind. Funny – it was a column I bashed off in frustration at not being able to come up with anything proper farming-related, and it gets the quickest response I've ever had.

I replied, thanking them, and within an hour had flogged them a copy of Book One.

February 29th

The last day for legal hedge trimming. Tomorrow, the birds and bees pile into the leaves and branches, and must be left undisturbed. Unless it's a domestic hedge, in which case trimming can go on as normal. Nope, me neither. I only hope they remember that it's a leap year, and they aren't heading into the hedges today by mistake.

Mind you, very few field hedges have been touched, thanks to the ground being saturated. The nation's roadsides bushes are looking as neat as a pornstar's, and machines that have ventured out into the fields have made a terrible mess.

I made the most of the last 24 hours of legal trimming, attacking the shrubbery next to the garage (full of those shrubs that give off horrible dusts if you cut them by hand, with swollen eyes and itchy skin being the result), the low branches on the tracks going to the back barn and Godwin's barn, and ventured gingerly into the Top of Englands to lop a couple of oversized suckers that block the view from the house. Sure enough, it was saturated, and I, too, made a bit of a mess.

A short but spectacular snowstorm blew through at one stage, which should have been enough to persuade the fauna of Hinton Ampner to stay out the hedges for one more day. It also meant that I was less likely to be reported to the authorities by *Countryfile* viewers who think that because they watch *Countryfile* they are the ultimate arbiters on all farming activities. Ask neighbour Robert about his 'debates' with some of the good people of Tichborne.

The house was full of puppy visitors and potential buyers, and they all brought toddlers. Bella, bless her, was quite relaxed about small, noisy and over-excited humans, and Sasha (after a short period of inspection) simply added them to the pack that needed looking after, but Evie was a bit baffled. We realised she'd never come across them before – and apologies were needed as another three-year-old was sent sprawling. Luckily, they were proper crash bang wallop kinds, and after a short bawl, were up and running again.

March 1st

A splendid start to the new month: dry and windy. Just the sort of day to open up Tigger's doors and windows and leave them wide open in an effort to dry out a winter's collection of mud and water. Some of it comes off wellies, and some of it leaks into the driver's footwell from God knows where. A day with a March southerly blowing through it is just the job.

The Jaguar goes back tomorrow, so I thought I'd get a last few miles in it, and did my favourite test route. To Bramdean, across the Common to Ropley, and up the A31 past Alton, Bentley and through Farnham. Then it's north on the A331 through Aldershot and Farnborough, down the M3, a short bit of the A303 westbound, off at Micheldever Station, down the A33 for a bit, and then back through the lanes via Micheldever Wood, Swarraton, Alresford, Cheriton and home for tea and buns.

It's about sixty or seventy miles, takes a good hour and a half, and covers all sorts of terrain and roads – except for any off-road stuff. Then again, some cars, despite claiming to be SUVs, shouldn't be allowed out on the mud. No offence, Jaguar.

The A331 was particularly entertaining: all the hoons were out in their lowered GTis and 3-series BMWs. It was a deafening cacophony of chrome exhausts, over-tinted windows, extended wheel arches and phat bass. Driving skills seemed to have been forgotten in the race to impress. Just think, in not many years, such recreational driving using fossil fuels will be banned. I wonder if my 'road test' counts as recreational? It was certainly fun.

I felt sorry for a forlorn-looking Lancia Fulvia, parked up on the side of the M3 near Basingstoke, bonnet up. The driver was sitting up the bank, looking less than thrilled. Curiously, I was looking for one of those (a Fulvia, not a bank) in January, even getting as far as emailing a seller in Newbury. I noticed it had sold a couple of weeks later; a shame, because it was a bargain. I wonder if that was the one?

Back home, Sean and Dawn were round to cuddle puppies and take a million billion photos, and announce that they're moving on from Hinton after nearly ten years, and heading up to Beauworth. It's a shame, not just because they're great company, but also because Sean is a bloody handy link in the anti-poacher chain, always available for text reports and even jumping in the truck to act as moral and physical backup on occasions when I've been on patrol. And with news that next door's shoot are shutting their commercial side, and have laid off their full-time keeper, the whole SE corner of the farm will be pretty unsupervised when the lamping season starts again. If I do decide to go out and chase 'em, I'll be very much on my own. Not good news.

March 2nd

How could I ever have doubted the electricity board's pole gang? On the way out to check for slugs in Big Field, I spotted them hard at work in the Drier Yard, lorries and Transits and Hiabs and augers. Excellent news.

The Massey dealer rep arrived with some sort of Massey manager for the south of England, to chat about the problems with our loader tractor and where we go from here, if there are any more problems. It was all very good natured and relatively reassuring, and he explained that the recent huge job (take away, rear wheels off, huge brake rebuild) would all be covered by their 'just out of warranty' goodwill budget. I should effing-well hope so.

Three things were slightly disconcerting. First, some of the issues we've had were 'known about' by the factory – the brake problems and the leaking roof lining, for instance. Second, his proud announcement that every dealer now has a range of 'courtesy' tractors, available at a moment's notice to be shipped out to customers whose machines have let them down. I thought this spoke volumes about the problems that Massey are having at the moment. And third, he didn't have a business card, and wasn't keen to give out any contact information. For all I know, he was a bloke who was out the back washing buckets, and got roped in to pretend to be south of England area manager – but that's just me being cynical.

During lunch, the Jaguar driver arrived to take the F-Pace away. We walked around it slowly, checking for damage (I've managed to scrape a couple in the last two years), and, satisfied that there was nothing of concern, I 'signed' the silly tablet thing he presented, and off it went. No great sadness to see it leave.

With sales of Book One having completely stalled, I thought the time was right to try some paid-for advertising. I've milked as much freebie publicity as is humanly possible and am unlikely to be allowed to do any more blatant advertising pieces thinly disguised as 'Opinion'. I rang 'South East Farmer', and got through to their classified department – which sounded like little more than a charming fellow at a desk. I told him what I was up to, and that I had no idea where to start, and he was very patient. He said I should send him through a picture (landscape, 63 mm x 90 mm) and he'd slot it into the page opposite the crossword for a reasonable fee for two months.

Hazel and I nipped out to the gateway into the Top of Englands, took some moody shots of me leaning on the gate, book in hand, and over to the left of camera. I spent all of, ooh, ten minutes on 'Paint', adding some captions, and sent it off. Job done. Best of all, there's surplus in the Book One budget to pay for it. Let's see what happens.

After another very long tea/biscuit-filled afternoon with potential puppy buyers, I hitched off the hedge trimmer and onto the sprayer. I unfolded it in the yard, checked the electrics, and gave the booms a grease up, ready for a bit of proper farming tomorrow. And the evenings feel like they're getting properly longer.

March 3rd

Sometime over last Christmas, when some cold weather had been promised, I put some proper anti-freeze in the sprayer and flushed it down the booms. Normally, I use a couple hundred litres of liquid fertiliser to do the job, but thought I'd try a different approach this year. So my job this morning was to drain the blue stuff out and have a quick flush through with clean water.

That was the plan; unfortunately (or fortunately if you're trying to vernalise crops) it was a proper hard frost, and the lid of the sprayer was frozen shut. A hint of irony there. I left it for the rapidly rising sun to sort out, and had a quick drive round after getting the papers.

Not only had the electricity pole gang done a super job putting up a new pole just where I wanted it, but they had also left behind *two* old ones, and in these days of 24/7 battle against poachers and hare coursers, there's nothing better than a sturdy telegraph pole to lay across a gateway. I then drove out to the other end of the farm, and checked out Kilmeston Road, with a view to getting some very late Zulu wheat sown in the dry spell that was promised for this week – even though every 'dry' day is rapidly being replaced with 'deluge'.

Water was running across the bottom next to the source of the Itchen, and all the flat and low land was – to no one's surprise – too wet to walk on. But only a couple of topographical feet up the hill, the ground was dry and firm, and given another day with the lovely drying wind...

I was on puppy-sitting duties while Hazel went off and did another couple of hours of accountancy at the racing stables – although I did make use of the time to write up the Jaguar and get it sent off. It should have been simple, but it was somehow blooming awkward to find 520 interesting words about it.

Shortly after lunch, I was free to do some farm work – wonder of wonders. I grabbed the special key to the fertiliser tank, the Crop Advisors desk diary that I use every year to record all the fertiliser applications, rolled up the 2" flexible pipe that connects tanks to sprayer (I must order another so that both the water tank in the main yard and the fertiliser tank in the Drier Yard have got one) and set off.

As usual, it took a bit of time to remember how to get everything set up, but an hour later I was doing some field work. It was a bit of a struggle picking up the 24 m tramlines – I'd sown the OSR at an angle to the previous crop of barley back in August, and without laying down any new ones. And for the first couple of trips through (grassweed killer and insecticides) I'd used the still-visible barley tramlines. They had pretty well vanished by now, and, to make things more confusing, Team Tosdevine had used their sprayer out there in January set at 30 m. (I wasn't confident that the crop would survive, so an extra set of wheelings didn't matter.) It all turned out well in the end, thankfully, mainly due to my cheap'n'cheerful Teejet satnav kit – nothing more than a GPS guide to driving 24 m away from where you last drove. I did one whole tank, started a second tank, and headed home as it got dark.

In that short afternoon, the yard dried out, the topsoil dried, and the tractor wheels ran clean. I couldn't help thinking – and not for the first time in the last six months – that if only we could get a couple of days like that, we might get a day's drilling done. Neighbour Robert agreed with me furiously on that point in the Pots later on – mind you, we tend to agree furiously on most things after a couple of pints.

March 4th

There was much excitement in the farmhouse: the fencing gang were due in today. It has been many years since we overhauled the pasture fencing, and had it done back then with sheep netting to match the new cattle-free farm policy. These days, the rotted off posts (they don't last like they used to, of course – then again nothing ever does) dangle and droop, only being held in a vaguely vertical position by being stapled to the wire. Ninety per cent of them need replacing.

There's the small matter of having neither staff nor working shoulders any more, and a modern team with little crawlers and post knockers can revitalise a stretch of fencing ten, or even twenty times faster than we could now. Thirty years ago, an old trailer was kept in the cart barn, permanently loaded with a couple of dozen piles, three or four reels of barbed wire, a bucket of staples, and a selection of tools – all the wrong ones. The holemaker was actually an old pipe with a point welded into it, the hammer was a claw one, the sledgehammer was the type with the narrow rectangular head (a real post shatterer) and the staple remover was an old Claas combine finger. I caused a hell of a stir by working my way through the set, replacing them with the correct ones.

The trailer was always ready to go onto a tractor in the event of a broken fence, or when a whole stretch needed doing. Strainers were sourced from knackered telegraph poles, and they tended to rot before the posts. It has to be said that the whole farm was refenced by the estate carpenter in 1959 using oak, so it was a long time before they rotted. I could probably find one or two of those originals still out there.

Into the yard came the obligatory double cab, followed by an ancient Unimog towing a Kubota digger. There was a lot of chatting (the pick-up driver was, quite suitably, one of the pickers-up on the old grand shoot here), and Sasha had to be persuaded that legs did not need ripping off. Once that was done, she was best friends with all of them.

I did puppy-sitting until Hazel had gone through plans with them, and then, based on the optimistic forecast that tomorrow 'an area of rain would just touch the south coast, and then move away', thought I'd do a bit more seed shuffling. Back down the Drier Yard, I pulled the old bale trailer out, lifted off the 4 t of winter beans and popped then back in the left-hand lean-to, and brought the trailer home. I parked it at an angle outside the tractor barn, and almost popped a couple of bags of Zulu on it, ready for tomorrow's rush of drilling. But luckily, I resisted the temptation.

The new-ish vicar came in for a cup of tea and a 'get to know you' session, and stayed for far longer than we thought he would. We've had a few over the years – some real old-fashioned ones who would arrive at the farmhouse in Dad's time, five minutes before Five Nations kick-off ("Ooo, a sloe gin? Don't mind if I do!"), and give little nieces a ride round the yard on his Honda C70. We've had the trendy ones ("Call me 'Bob'"), the female ones (whose departure provoked enough gossip for five years of *The Archers* storylines), and uncontroversial ones – like the one Robert and I managed to get very drunk in the Pots. I seem to remember promising him a trailer ride round the farm for as many men of the cloth as he could muster. Never mind *The Archers* – it would be straight out of *Father Ted*.

Best of all, this latest one managed not to bring God into the conversation – which is always a bonus. I was a chorister as a boy, which meant eight church services a week, run by men who hit boys a lot, and Hazel – well, let's just say that she grew up in Co Down in the 1970s. As a result, neither she nor I have troubled the Good Lord with our churchly presence since leaving school. We've hatched, matched and despatched, of course, but after Anthony's christening was turned into a dour scolding of those who had turned up for not being on the pews every week, we didn't bother christening the others. This new vicar was clever, funny, and insisted that we should join him in the Fox for the Bramdean Friday evening pub gathering. That's a very good start.

I popped into Chalks to put a first dose of fertiliser on the Crusoe. All went well until I got up to the top bit. It was sticky to start with, and as rain came in again (which was odd) it got stickier still. I gave up for the day.

March 5th

It was time for a big meeting about the new oil pipeline going through the farm. When George the Land Agent emailed about all the interested parties getting together, I had replied that the forecast for today was quite good, and there was a fair chance that I'd be out in the tractor.

So when three land agents, one farmer, an archaeologist and an ecologist walked into the barn, the real joke was that that it was raining stair rods, and had been since about seven o'clock last night. Some of the massed ranks of compulsory Audis could only just make it through the New Pond puddle. So much for the rain briefly touching the south coast.

It wasn't a very long meeting. They needed to get out onto the route of the new pipeline, and do lots of exploratory digs, so we discussed numbers and size of trenches, where they could get into the fields, and where they could put a compound for all their kit (the white van community will be rubbing their hands). Two land agents and I left the rest to go yomping in the deluge, and went back to the farmhouse for tea and biscuits. It turned out to be the perfect way to pass the rest of a rain-soaked Thursday morning – even if it was supposed to be dry.

Still, if it's Thursday, and it's raining, that means yet another hour-long session of hip op therapy in the hot pool, giving it large in chest-deep hot water to assorted disco banging tunes. And if that doesn't take your mind off heavy farming issues, nothing will.

An old friend from cricketing days was launching a book – his second – at a famous independent bookshop in Petersfield, and had invited me to come along. It was the usual good-natured stuff: wine, nibbles, a few folk I hadn't seen for ages, some fresh faces – and, because it was a book about beekeeping, a rant from the author about agrochemicals and modern farming. I kept smiling sweetly, because it would have been unkind to piss on his parade with some agrifacts. Diplomacy is, after all, my middle name.

Mind you, I was so upset that, on the way home, I veered instinctively into McDonald's, and tucked into a Big Mac meal with a large strawberry milkshake – c/w as many yummy chemicals as possible. The eco-conscious paper straw, however, went completely floppy and was useless after only half a dozen sucks (oo err missis). But it's 'green', and that's what counts.

It had at last stopped raining, and I had the A272 all to myself in the little white Hyundai i20. Narrow wheels, underpowered engine, drifting slightly on damp roads – a complete hoot. Just like coming back from Petersfield in my Fiat 127 in 1980.

March 6th

The fencing gang had wisely abandoned their efforts in yesterdays' deluge, but were back today, in the slightly better weather. It was my job to tell them where we wanted the new kissing gate in the fence across England's. It would be a splendid chance to straighten the dogleg in the footpath that has existed since the stile first went in. I took Sasha and Evie, and a red feed bag, and strolled out in the warm March sunshine that was steaming off quite a hard frost. The dogs had a riot playing zoomies, with Evie just about keeping out of Sasha's reach, but being bundled unceremoniously whenever Sasha did catch up. In the meantime, I estimated a straight line from where the footpath enters the Bottom of Englands to where it leaves the Top, and attached the red bag to the fence where it met that line.

The new kissing gate will be about twenty yards east of the stile, and even if it is now strictly in the right place, there will no doubt be whining from the locals who know the land and the paths better than those of us who have been here for 60 years.

Meanwhile, another puppy buyer came and sat in the pen, and talked for about three hours – I think the buying decision was made within ten minutes, but we all love a good gossip while being gently mugged by flatcoat puppies.

I popped into Petersfield for a quick haircut ("Not too much off the top – it sticks up in the air these days if it's too short!") and paid in some more Book One cheques. I foolishly asked for a mini-statement, but had no ID. I still have the just-about-legal paper driving licence and offered that. No good. So we went through some security questions. I got date of birth right, but was unsure when the account was opened. Could be about 1912, when Grandfather Hamilton Flindt worked for the Westminster Bank. "He was in charge of the Bank's horticultural society" I pointed out. The man behind the till was less than impressed. It might be 1936, I mused, when Dad started work. Or perhaps 1991, when we took over the farm, and therefore the bank account. The man behind the till looked mighty relieved, pressed a few buttons, and hastily handed over the slip of paper – which still had a reasonably healthy balance on it. I thought I heard a sigh of relief from the lengthening queue behind, too. Just like when the man who claims he's got a UFO in his pocket finally gets off the bus.

Tod rang with some dramatic news: a supply of spring wheat seed had been found and was available if we wanted to abandon – at last – the idea of sowing winter wheat. It actually made things more complicated. I'd resigned myself to the remaining wheat fields (Blackhouse Road and Kilmeston Road) being Zulu or fallow, and as another rainy week crept by, fallow looked to be favourite – suddenly, there's another option on the table. Using it would leave a big pile of Zulu (as would 'fallow', of course), but if we sow Zulu and it doesn't come to ear, we'd feel mighty foolish. I told Tod we'd procrastinate for a couple of days and discuss it on Monday.

March 7th

Weird dreams about rally-prepared Fiat Cinquecentos doing high-speed manoeuvres in the yard got me out of bed far too early. God knows where they came from.

It was another dry-ish day, so I did yet another walk over Big/Rick/Clump. The earlier sown wheat is looking quite respectable, and the early Feb-sown stuff is coming through enough to be able to see the tramlines, as well as the 'extra' tramlines marked by a blocked spout on the Horsch. Little sensors that tell you if a spout is blocked always seem expensive, but surveying a slight barcoded field, you sometimes wonder if they'd be a valuable investment.

I lifted a huge flint from one of the tramlines and dropped it in the base of the hedge – a habit as old as farming itself on this sort of soil. Any cultivation job brings them to the surface (think of shaking your box of Alpen to get the raisins to the top), and we no longer have power harrows or stubble burning to shatter them. Mind you, our tyres last a heck of a lot longer without fields being strewn with one of the sharpest natural substances possible.

In days gone by, sets of gang rollers had a box on the back. As the acres passed underneath, the flints were collected, and unloaded into a heap in the hedge, then gathered up for building and track construction. I was doing this with Ernie on cold day in 1986, when one of the stones shattered as I threw it in the trailer, revealing the most perfect 'shepherd's crown' fossil you even saw. It came home with me, instead of heading into a gateway.

The 'box of Alpen' theory was roundly dismissed by one of the old boys working here; "They grow, you know." It was hard to argue with the logic. Big stones were taken away, leaving only small ones, and then big stones re-appeared in later years. No other explanation needed.

A few paces further on, I came across a horseshoe – another relic of farm work of old. They're still remarkably common, along with YL42 plough shares in assorted states of repair. I felt a pang of sympathy for the man working that horse, miles from the nearest smithy – in Kilmeston – who would have had to yomp all the way there to get his horse shod again. God knows the job was slow enough without losing half a day to visit the Kilmeston Kwik Fit of its day. It was a small shoe, most unusual. Maybe if I'd left it, it, too, would have grown. I wish the soil could talk to tell its tale.

Any ideas of popping out later today and giving all that wheat a good first dose of fertiliser were scotched by Heather and Keith arriving for coffee, and a natter, and a good play with the puppies. Later in the afternoon, I managed one tank on Rick/Clump, up to where I'd abandoned on the heaviest clay, and the area meter on the sprayer reckoned that I had eventually sown over three-quarters of it. Still not much, but still better than some souls have managed around the country.

Then it was home again for tea and honey sandwiches, a warm fire, and England vs Wales, in the company of the Editor, who, as usual, had all the dogs sitting on his head in delight. I'm not sure how much of the game he actually saw. We both spotted Jo Marler's sneaky cocktease, though, even if the ref didn't. Priceless. Instant Twitterstorm offendatron fury.

The house continues to fill with puppy admirers, and I couldn't help noticing the saintly Bella, sitting quietly, very happy for her pride and joy to be cuddled, manhandled, photographed, videoed, poked, prodded and generally adored. And even when Evie and Sasha leant into the cage – as they are now allowed to do – she was completely at ease as the pups were generally sniffed, licked and occasionally nibbled. Sasha's Malinois counting skills were as good as ever: one, one, one….

March 8th

On the way back from picking up the Saturday papers, I followed a dirty white van up Hinton Hill. There's a well-rehearsed set of questions that runs through your mind under these circumstances, which leads to the decision either to ignore it or ring the police. It was a white van, it was unfamiliar, and was doing the special speed that suggests it wasn't sure where it was going, but at the same time not completely lost – all points against it being benevolent. But, then again, it had poor man's personal plates, the thieving bastard types tend not to prowl the countryside at weekends (more people about), and it was in no hurry to get away once I arrived on its back bumper.

I followed it through the farm, right the way to the Drier Yard, where it did a U-turn. I wound down a window and asked if they were lost. "We're looking for Manor Farm!" was the reply, in a rather odd accent. Of course – they were Hazel's latest potential puppy buyers.

"Well then, follow me," I said, and led them all the way back to the farmyard. They were another lovely couple, and they'd driven all the way down from West Yorkshire. The fact that they were Dutch explained the curious accent. Even after three hours of cuddling, cooing and gossiping, it was still hard to pick up what was being said. Mind you, I'm getting deafer by the week these days.

The Scotland vs France game was a hoot – punches, red cards and a result that opens up the Six Nations table a bit. We're still waiting to see if this curious new virus that's causing international panic is going to bring the whole competition to a premature halt.

I picked up a slightly hungover Anthony from Winchester station in the early evening. He was taking a couple of weeks off, and thought he'd pop down to see the puppies and catch up on what looked like some well-needed sleep.

March 9th

It was yet another dry start ruined by rain. I popped into the doctors for some more pills, and generally moped about swearing at the rain. This new virus is bringing out all sorts of strange behaviour – panic-buying being the worst of it. I thought I'd join in and ordered an industrial pack of loo paper from APM, along with lots of other more traditional bits and pieces. They laughed and said we weren't the only ones draining the stock.

March 10th

There was something in the air – and not just the unshowered sweat from last night's majestic rehearsal. It was a genuine feeling that the weather is finally going to settle down, after almost exactly six months of incessant rain. It was enough to make me find the cropping plan from a couple of months ago, dig out a clean farm map, and have yet another reshuffle of what goes where. The supply of spring wheat changes everything. The Zulu will be shelved (although finding big enough rat-proof 'shelves' will be a major issue), and join the Tower winter barley in being saved for next autumn. We'll keep on with the winter beans, but simply scrunch them up onto a much smaller area. Most importantly, the pressure is relieved somewhat, if not 'off'.

Once the new cropping plan was sorted, I rang Crop Advisors to talk fertiliser orders, and we decided we'd wait one more week, and see if prices followed oil and gas down dramatically. Then it was the ring round of oil suppliers for both central heating oil and red diesel. Most of them had lopped a good 10p/litre off prices, although one said their price might change depending on the imminent budget. So I ignored their quote. Eveson's got both orders in the end and promised delivery within a couple of days. I popped up to the diesel barn, did some shuffling of UTV trailers and Pig, and drained the main diesel tank into the bowser, just in case they came early.

I was a month late with telling Hampshire Grain (or Trinity Grain, as they are now, but I'll never get used to it) how much of what type of crop I was planning to send up there this harvest. But how the hell can we estimate our harvest results this year? 140 acres of wheat of varying quality in the ground, and 50 acres of oilseed rape. And that, on March 10th, is it. There are promises of good weather coming, but time after time we've heard that, and the rain has just kept going. There are days when it seems that those 190 acres might be all that's there when we fire up the combine.

I optimistically did some sums, based on getting the beans, peas and spring barley in, and managed to round it off to the 1,000 tons that is my annual 'sell over the post-harvest 12 months' commitment. It left nothing to go into the 'off the combine' selling pool, but that's going to be the hit for this year. All you can hope is that the prices from last year's excellent harvest (which is being sold slowly at the moment) will surge as a result of no one getting anything in the ground, and it'll be swings and roundabouts. Bill at Trinity seemed relaxed about adding any spring wheat to my forms at a later date – if that does happen.

The enthusiasm continued when I casually emailed the company that does the best job of cleaning up and bagging our home-saved beans. I said I had a very full trailer of Fuego spring beans, and would they be available to process it? Moments later, they called to say they could be in tomorrow. Blimey, it's hard to keep up.

The spring beans would need to be all brought back from the Drier Yard, so that meant yet another game of 'seed bag Tetris'. It was off down the Drier Yard again with the loader, move the winter beans from the left-hand lean-to to the combine barn, move two old manky part-bags of winter wheat (one Panorama, one unrecognisable) from blocking in the trailers to the back of the left-hand lean-to, park the empty grain trailer (that had the winter beans in) also in the left-hand lean-to, and then hitch onto the very full trailer at the back of the right-hand lean-to, which....oh bugger... which had an utterly flat rear-left tyre.

Once upon a time, I would have sped home, grabbed the massive socket set, the jack, and the full size spare 12.5/80-15.3 that provides the rats in the tractor barn with something else to play on, rush back down and change the wheel. Not any more though. It was far more sensible to spend half an hour trying to get through to Micheldever Tyres to ask them to come out and do it. There was a certain amount of tooth-sucking (once I finally got through) and a half-hearted promise of getting out tonight – or first thing tomorrow. I said that would be fine – the seed cleaners won't be in till lunchtime.

I did a mental check of everything else we'd need for the visit of the seed-cleaning gang: I'd have to hitch off the sprayer and put the Deere on the bean trailer, open up the tractor barn to squeeze yet another batch of bags in – and we'd need the old general purpose front bucket for the tailings. Where on earth was that? There was much mental and physical searching until we remembered it had vanished – legally – on the back of a red pick-up belonging to the Winchester Welding Wizard late last year. It was rusting through in places, and a patch-up seemed more sensible than a whole new one. Some frantic phone calls managed to produce a promise that they'd drop it back later today.

The farmhouse descended into chaos as Tod arrived to talk through a bit of Godot agronomy (nothing to be done), confirm that a supply of spring wheat has been found (Saints be praised), and, of course, cuddle puppies. Two of Anthony's mates arrived to cuddle puppies, and two puppy buyers arrived to, er, cuddle puppies. Luckily, all of the dogs welcomed all of the visitors – these will be the best socialised puppies in England at this rate.

Once Tod had left, I unloaded the welded-up bucket, and did another yomp with Sasha across Big Field to see if it would travel for a late tank of fertiliser. It was borderline even before the heavy drizzle arrived to dampen farming spirits which had been lifted by the day's activities. As it turned to steady rain, I was cheered to see that Micheldever Tyres had indeed sneaked out sometime in the afternoon and sorted the flat tyre on the trailer. Bloomin' heroes.

And the day ended on a high with another great trip to the Pots with neighbour Robert. Although I didn't like the new doorknobs, and jolly well told them behind the bar. I think they were new. I asked what had been replaced, and everyone shouted "knob".

March 11th

Hazel had decided that the time was right to move out of the puppy room, and into her quarters in the west wing (the joys of having lots of spare rooms). This left Bella unable to summon her when a pee was needed, and so I was woken by whimpering at just after five. Thinking Hazel could actually do with a lie-in, I nipped downstairs and let Bella and the other two out, and then, quite inexplicably for that time of the morning, decided I'd get up too. I made the most of it, too, finishing the next *Flindt on Friday* and sending it off.

The bean-cleaning gang were due at lunchtime, so it was yet more seed shuffling. I dropped off the sprayer and used the Deere to haul the very full trailer of Fuego up the yard (very slowly, to avoid any more knackered tyres), picked up the bag-and-a-half of old stock and brought them up, too, and then just had time to take Anthony back to the station.

Dawn very kindly popped up from New Pond and sat down in the puppy pen for a couple of hours, so that Hazel could catch up on work up at the stables, and I could concentrate on the beans. By the time we'd finished, we had just over 9 tons bagged up and ready to go, and only a small heap of cleanings in the little blue trailer. I grabbed a bucketful and did a kitchen table TGW session – and reckoned we now had enough for about 90 acres.

It should have been a short job, but we were invaded big-time by the Hampshire Constabulary, all ostensibly on very important police matters, but mainly to cuddle puppies. Policeman Ian, of course, was only moderately soppy – he has a Hard Man of Hampshire image to protect; as for Policewoman Lynne – the less said the better.

March 12th

Another nice drying day wrecked by dramatic bands of heavy showers sweeping east. The bulk order of fuels arrived – the ones I'd ordered to make the most of the price drop. It was a cheery chatty driver, who seemed to know Hazel via the Alresford Show, and he was quite content to tell me I was wasting my money adding Topanol to the heating oil/Aga tank. I explained gently that as soon as I'd started using it as an additive, the Aga's service intervals had gone back up to six months, rather than eight weeks.

He popped 1,999 litres in (very important to keep it under 2,000 to ensure the VAT rate is 5% – no, I don't know why either), and then went round to the tractor tank and put 2,500 litres in that one. There was the most God Almighty crashing and banging as he finished; I was in the office at the time, so grabbed some wellies to see what the heck was going on. He was desperately trying to shut the access door, slamming it, barging it with his shoulder, but getting nowhere. Even from a distance, I could see that the bottom wouldn't shut properly, and the lower hinge had been broken by his considerable efforts. I opened the door fully, removed the large scalping stone that was in the way, and gently closed the door properly. Another repair job, but for another day.

Another trip down to the Chandlers Ford hot pool for an hour's swimming therapy couldn't have been more welcome.

March 13th

The forecast for next week suggested a decent session of flat-out sowing and spraying is due, so I thought I should crack on with the first dose of N on the wheats, and give the OSR a slightly premature second dose. The February-drilled Crusoe in Big Field was a mixed bag, good in parts, but completely rotted away up on the heavy ground. I might have to reduce my rather optimistic Trinity Grain predictions.

Behind My Love's looked lovely, having been drilled in mid-October, but was being hit hard by rabbits from our border hedge. And the OSR in Drier Field looked to about to kick off, with flower buds beginning to form on the most fertile areas.

I got back just in time to find a delivery van in the yard, and a driver wandering around the bits and pieces in the old calf pens in a way that would have normally had me reaching for Plod's number – if he hadn't been a delivery driver. He was trying to drop off the pallet of Roundup that Tod and I had decided would be needed for the big push next week.

The order had made it quite clear that we would need a phone call in advance if help was needed to unload the pallet, but we had had no such call. It turned out that the poor fellow had been driving round the village for some time, having used only the satnav to get to the Godwin's Farm corner, and then didn't know where to go next. I asked if he had a paper atlas. "Naaah," he replied, somewhat pathetically. All that technology to be used to help him along, and he couldn't be bothered. Funnily enough, only a couple of days ago an email arrived asking for the 'What3words' address for the spray store. Mind you, that will involve delivery drivers actually putting some effort into finding their destinations.

In a bit of a sulk, I left him to unload by hand, although I popped out for the last few, and then made a great song and dance about pointing out our mobile number on his ticket, and suggesting he used it in future. Not entirely sure the message got through.

Several farmers round here have commented, touching wood furiously, on the lack of poacher activity. But on my way out of my evening shower, I noticed lights on Roe Hill – not a searchlight, not driving around, just red static ones, and apparently on the road. With jimjams and dressing gown hastily put on, I grabbed Tigger's keys – Sasha was at my elbow within 0.32 seconds – and we drove down to inspect. Sitting in a car, looking thoroughly miserable, was a rally marshal, feeling a bit cold and wet, waiting for the first cars to come through on a 'navigation rally'. He initially mistook me for a fellow marshal. "What *are* you doing in pyjamas, Keith?" was his greeting.

I explained that I wasn't Keith, I was in jim-jams because it was nearly my bedtime, and, now that I'd established that he wasn't a poacher, might he know if cars would be roaring through till the small hours? He promised a short spell of rally cars coming through and then peace.

We then chatted for a bit, and he sympathised with us farmers when it came to poachers. He said that the night rally boys often came across very unpleasant gangs out in the countryside, often helping themselves to livestock. They learnt quickly to keep away from them, too, as weapons became obvious. It's the modern British countryside.

March 14th

Finally, the coronavirus is beginning to affect central Hampshire. The morning started with a flurry of texts from the usual suspects, with the latest virus-related jokes. "Doctor, Doctor, I think I'm Dean Martin." "You've got crooner virus." Or

"Doctor, Doctor, I'm obsessed with why people have died." "You've got coroner virus." Or news that there's a nasty strain of raccoon virus going round – but it only strikes dyslexics.

The Editor popped in for his Saturday morning cuppa, but the routine hugs/kisses with Hazel were off the menu. But we had a long technical discussion about the proposed ban on lead shot in game cartridges – big news in his world. Steel shot doesn't impart the same energy to the quarry, therefore it will need to be faster (more pressure in old guns), or there will need to be more pellets in the cartridge (longer cartridges in old guns), and they mustn't go through tightly choked guns (i.e. old guns). Basically, we established that old English side-by-sides are destined for the scrap skip. Bad news for the scores of farmers who still wave grandfather's trusty boxlock a couple of times a week from September to January.

Then it got worse: there was no rugby. It was so serious that I gathered up all the kit for cleaning out the nozzle filters on the sprayer (bucket of hot water, cocktail stick) and had a very jolly session working my way down the 48 nozzles. I had planned to replace all the nozzles themselves, but they hadn't been delivered.

The Editor, neighbour Robert and I then headed for the Pots, where the full, shocking impact of the virus became clear. We had all had our couple of pints, and thought we'd top up the last pint with a 'half'. This involves handing over the pint glass, which has about a third left in the bottom, and it will be refilled near as damn it to the brim. It's traditional to make approving and grateful noises ("Hmmm – a proper half!") about the generosity of our hosts.

Not this time. We asked for halves, and got exact halves, in half-pint glasses. The shock. The indignity. The outrage. The explanation: the glasses which we have been using might have our saliva on the rims, and, in the act of offering them up to the barrel for a refill, might touch the barrel, and the next glass might touch the same spot. The solution: clean glasses every time. We hadn't noticed that our first pints were in clean glasses. We were too busy discussing politically incorrect letters that the Editor had received over the years, and that even he couldn't publish.

It dawned on me, as three of Hampshire's roughest toughest country types sat in a pub sipping from dainty little glasses, that we are truly approaching the End of Days.

March 15th

Damp yesterday, damp again today – not as forecast. So we popped out to the Hay Field to put extra mesh and bars on the spanking new kissing gate on our border. It's 98% lamb proof, but now Murph's sheep are in, and starting to lamb soon, we thought the final 2% would be worth persevering with. There were only a couple of early Sunday morning walkers to chat with, although they all thought the new gate looked very smart.

I really had planned to pop out this afternoon and get a couple of tanks of Roundup on, but the southerly wind got stronger and stronger, and the rain continued on and off for most of the day. You couldn't turn on a radio or TV without hearing more concern about the virus, so that hardly made the day more cheerful.

News came through that the Growmore Quiz final has been postponed (like all great sporting events), although that should mean that our captain will be available. He would have missed this Friday's final because of skiing – although I couldn't see that happening now.

A long evening chat with Jonathan in Newcastle wasn't the most uplifting, either. He has bust a gut to get up there to study Politics and Economics, and his first year is in tatters. The lecturers started staging a series of walkouts and strikes, and now the course has ground to a virus-related stop. There's talk of the first year being abandoned, and – even worse for someone working fantastically hard at subjects he adores – everyone, including the abject slackers, will be nodded through on a 'pass'. He sounded very upset. Can't blame him, when he's paying £9,000/year for the privilege.

We had a long chat about his coming down to Hampshire again. He's got a good part-time job up there, but all his mates will have gone home soon. He could get another job down here, and live with us, but I'm becoming one of the high-risk public (bronchiectasis, blood pressure, ACE-inhibitor pills and all that), and if we went into voluntary lockdown, that would include him. We agreed to chat again in ten days.

Thank God for a hot fire and *Dragon's Den* to numb the mind on a grim Sunday night.

March 16th

A moderate frost, a brilliant sunrise and a blocked pipe leading to the cess pit; what more do you need to cheer things up on a Monday morning? We decided that sorting the pipe was important – bearing in mind more puppy visitors are coming, and both loos were out of action – and so started on the traditional game of 'hunt the drain rods'. To everyone's surprise, we found them within moments, stacked up against the old stable wall, and, even better, with all the fancy attachments in a bag.

It was then just a question of finding which manhole cover to lift, and assembling the right length of rod. I put the double spiral auger on one end, and the fantastically useful crank handle on the other, and within moments fished out a really satisfying chunk of puppy litter. It turned out that the bulk paper shavings Hazel had bought, and was merrily flushing down the downstairs loo, were somewhat less than soluble. It shouldn't have been that satisfying to clear it, watch the sludge flow though at last, and then run a couple of clean water flushes to finish the job off – but it was. The house was at last fit for puppy buyers.

"Get some paracetamol," said Hazel as I set off for the papers. Cheriton shop was sold out, so I went down the A272 to the West Meon Hut. They had piles of it. Piles of everything, actually. I told them off at the till – how are we expected to have a good old virus-induced panic-buying session if all the shelves are this well stocked? The girl laughed and said they were getting plentiful stocks of everything – several times a week. Let's hope it keeps going.

I came back from the Hut through the lanes, and walked out into TBHD. It was still soggy, but I reckon there going to be a whole bunch of stuff needing doing soon – and getting out there with some glyphosate is pretty well the first on the list of jobs, if I'm to head out there as soon as possible with some 'winter' beans.

First job was to pop down with the loader and move the telegraph pole in the west Joan's Acre gateway, and then get out there with the sprayer. The nozzle cleaning had done a perfect job, and with two 3,200-litre tanks of Roundup (2.5l/ha) and wetter (1l/ha) I did all of the Top and Bottom of Hurst Down, Joan's Acre and Dell Close, and then 99% of BOMS, with just a trickle coming out in the top corner. Very satisfying.

The virus is really kicking off: the Flowerpots has shut. It was news that took some time to sink in, and when Robert rang to discuss it, he sounded genuinely shocked. I think the children of the 1940s are struggling to comprehend the panic.

March 17th

After a brief puppy-sit, I was out spraying again. Hazel had moved the telegraph poles blocking the entrance to the Folly, so I did that one first, and included the shooting strips. I took a detour through Drier Field to check the OSR, and thought it looked quite respectable. It's easy to forget that at this time of year it can go crazy, racing off through the growth stages, and it's worth having enough N applied and ready. I've done two doses, so it should be fine for a bit.

From the Drier Field, I drove through BOMS and into Roe Hill, where I did the two game strips with the booms folded to 12 m, effectively double dosing them. I did the same again in Chalks for the long three sides of cover. The drift at the bottom worried me a bit, blowing onto one of the only good wheat crops we've got, but I pushed on anyway, finishing up at the dell. Then it was a quick hop into Big Broom, where I did the rest of the tank.

After a quick lunch, I went back out to finish Big Broom, and did Middle Broom as well.

By the time I'd finished those and headed home, it was too late to fill up and go out again. Honest it was. So I lit the fire and hit the sofa. Where's spring?

March 18th

Still dry, but a bit windy. But I needed to get the last of the spring barley ground Roundup-ed, so topped up the sprayer with enough for the Hangar and nipped out there. Luckily the breeze was south-westerly, so away from the many walkers and 'home workers' who were trying to escape the virus. There was one man in the middle of the field when I got there, exercising a large brown dog, but he beat a bit of a retreat when he saw me coming.

Then it was back to Child's Broom, which was a bit more sheltered from the breeze, and should have been a quick job if I hadn't been spotted from the vineyard the other side of the valley by neighbour Robert. My phone rang, and a half-hour chat about nothing ensued. While we were talking, the Grange Farm drill arrived and started work on one of the long, narrow fields right in the valley. I wasn't sure, but I thought I saw some dust. Nah – impossible.

After a rinse out in the field, I hitched off the sprayer and decided to crack on with my plan to convert my old Horsch CO3 to a bean-only drill. I didn't trade it in this time last year when I bought the ST4, and have been wondering exactly what to do with it. A couple of months ago I bought a big box of nearly new Horsch Solo coulters (specially designed for beans) and had been planning to switch the ST4 over when the time came. But then I thought: hold on, I'll be fitting 16 Solo coulters, then taking 16 back off again. A flipping nuisance. Why not convert the old CO3 and keep it as the Lean Mean Bean Machine? Right – that's decided.

I rang the Horsch dealers and asked them to order the spacer plates that let beans flow through better – quite pricey, but I thought it would be worth doing the conversion properly. I'll use a couple of washers as spacers until they arrive.

It was time for the difficult bit: taking off the heavyweight Duett coulters and fitting the Solos. You need a clean patch of yard to crawl on (ten minutes with the pressure washer sorted that), an old yoga mat, a wire brush for cleaning up old bolts, some threadlock fluid, a 7/8" socket and a 24 mm spanner – I've got an old Lemken plough spanner that's perfect. I hitched onto the CO3, lifted up as far as the rear wheels would push it (and fitted locking spacers), raised the tractor arms to the top of their travel, backed over the squeaky clean concrete, and set to work.

Three hours later it was all done. It wasn't easy, and I was feeling a bit sorry for myself by the end of it, but the weekly swim classes have definitely helped. Luckily, it gave me lots of time to think, and by late evening managed to come up with a *Flindt on Friday* that seemed the right balance of virus-related gravitas and humour.

March 19th

I asked Hazel if she fancied doing a major trailer shuffle in the hope of freeing up some space for the spring wheat seed that's imminent. She needed no second invitation, After yet another early morning handling some now quite chunky puppies, and their poo, a bit of 'outdoors' would be welcome. The blue trailer – with all the cleanings from the spring bean clean/bag session the other day – needed emptying down at the muck heap, but only after she'd waited for some idiot dog walker to get his car out of the gateway. He's a Bramdean local, too, with country connections, so you'd think he would know, but no. His explanation was that the gate was shut, so he thought no one would be using it.

Then she brought up the two empty grain trailers from the right-hand lean-to, and parked them in the empty Godwin's barn, and now the whole right-hand lean-to was empty. She reported large numbers of pigeons out on Drier Field – the only OSR that survived the beetle – so I nipped out in the latest test car – a Mitsubishi L200 – cut a couple of 'pea sticks' and set off some rope bangers. It was still pretty sticky out there, and the road tyres slipped and slid quite entertainingly. I was quite surprised not to be reported as hare coursers by the home-working New Pond residents.

I cleared the mud off the L200's tyres by fetching Jonathan from Winchester station; he'd decided home was the best option. He'd cheered up considerably from our phone call the other day, and seemed quite cheerfully fatalistic about life's twists and turns at the moment. The scrapping of a uni year and having to come home are trivial compared to some of what's going on. Nice that he recognised it.

March 20th

After hauling two more trailer-loads of seed from the tractor barn down to the Drier Yard, I'd finally cleared room for the spring barley seed. I even managed to just miss the bin lorry as it hurtled through. The seed had been promised for tomorrow morning (a Saturday, which is unusual, but everything is at the moment).

The last bits and pieces to get the old CO3 going were relatively easy. Swap over the control boxes, change the fan baffles to fully open (after sowing OSR in August), give the whole thing a grease up, and it was ready to go. Oliver's – the local Horsch dealers – rang to say the special bean spacer plate I'd ordered had arrived, so I did a few more miles in the test L200 to fetch it. It didn't fit, so I resorted to a couple of washers behind the old plate, and hoped that would solve the feeding issues that sometimes arise with beans.

Attention turned to the little white i20, which Jonathan was about to drive all the way up to his flat in Newcastle to get all his stuff, and drive back tomorrow. The academic year is abandoned, the tenancies on the brand-new flats have also been stopped early – everything is in chaos. Hazel filled the tank to the brim while getting the papers (and stocking up with whatever is available on the shelves at the moment), and Jonathan and I then did tyres.

Getting him back on the insurance was less easy. At least there was someone in the NFU office, but it took ages to do what I was convinced would be a simple bureaucratic job – adding a name on the list of drivers, especially as that name had only been removed last September. But there was another lengthy list of questions, with each reply being greeted with a cooing "lovely". And, no, it couldn't be done on the spot; he would have to be 'referred to the underwriters'. Luckily, the mighty underwriters approved, and after an hour's wait, the NFU rang back to say he was insured. When I was Jonathan's age, we all just jumped in the nearest car and drove off – I assume we were all covered by the farm's blanket policy, but I've never checked.

He refused my offer of a navigation guide, ungrateful so-and-so, but taping a bit of paper marked up with 'A34 Oxford – A423 to Banbury – A361 Daventry – M1 J18 to J32 – M18 to J2 – A1 North – A69 Gateshead' to the dashboard is probably a bit old hat, and some of the roads don't exist anymore. "Dad, I've got my satnav," he said wearily. I'll ignore him if I get a message saying he's lost – in Swansea. We waved him on his way – I was very jealous; very little beats my memories of setting off in my Alfasud to do the same trip in the early 1980s – even when there were more villages to be negotiated, and fewer motorways.

The seed lorry rang to say he'd be here today, and would late afternoon be OK? That suited me fine, and he made amazing progress on the now near-empty roads, and I had him unloaded and on his way by about four. I'd just finished the final tweaks to the little drill, so in a fit of enthusiasm, I set off all the way across the farm to Bottom of Hurst Down with one bag on board, and started in the shortest point work. It worked out pretty well exactly as calibrated, although it was still a bit sticky. Mind you, it has rained almost continuously for six months.

I rang Hazel for a lift home, and so ended the first week of constructive farm work since the September equinox. And the March one is tomorrow. Spooky.

Tod texted to cancel's Monday's rehearsal; Ian the Drummer is self-isolating, and Tod's attempts to persuade him that nothing could be worse than the moulds, fungi and general unhealthiness in Shed 3b had failed. Grim times.

March 21st

A significant farm moment: for the first time in exactly six months, choosing between wellie boots and dealer boots. The world is finally drying up. The pond at New Pond had no water in it. Two disgruntled ducks are down there looking utterly pissed off.

While this footwear debate was going on, Hazel came back from a foraging trip to the Co-op in Alresford having had a long chat with Policewoman Lynne in one of the aisles. The word on the constabulary street (Letsbe Avenue?) is that they're being primed for 'public order' duties. Nothing serious – yet – but plans are being quietly put in place. A slightly sobering thought. Apparently, they chatted for so long that a customer mistook them for staff, and asked where the pâté was. Could only be Alresford.

The Editor rang early, desperate for his Saturday morning coffee'n'gossip, not to mention the chance to cuddle puppies. I apologised profusely and said that we were indeed shutting up shop as much as possible – much as we'd love to have seen him, it was probably better that we kept our distance. Promises of imminent pigeon-shooting frenzies cheered him up a bit.

I had another good long day out in Hurst Down, finally getting out of the short work, and doing the flipping awkward bit around the old massive chalk dell. By the time I got to the level stuff on top, the ground really was beginning to dry up, and

I found I could get away with putting a tonne in at a time, rather than just one bag.

Just as I was relaxing and thinking how smoothly everything was going, bits started falling off. I lost another couple of following discs somewhere – God knows where, because I hadn't spotted them in the worked ground anywhere. Luckily, they don't seem too important behind the Solo coulters, and there's no point driving round Hampshire looking for replacements on a Saturday, even without 'lockdown'.

With the turns getting longer, I was pushing on a bit faster, and playing catch-up on the time lost faffing round in tight corners and around dells. But my plans to get the whole lot done in two long days and an afternoon are, as usual, in tatters.

Jonathan arrived safely back from Newcastle, with the little Hyundai fully loaded with all his stuff. He was raving about the drive, with empty roads, glorious spring weather, and his song selection blasting through the speakers. It was the 80s all over again, I told him. (Although the music was better back then, of course.) I also said that he should cherish his easy-peasy two-day, 660 mile round trip. He'll never see the like of it again.

March equinox means Diana's birthday, so we rang her up for a catch-up. She seemed in great spirits; yes, she's working from home, but her new house has a room for all her computers, she's stocked up nicely, and the world of online gaming is anticipating the best time it has ever had. Everyone's at home, stuck for things to do.

March equinox also means it's the 24th anniversary of BSE day. Curiously topical to think that wild-eyed predictions of human deaths (c 140,000) ended up being wide of the mark by rather a lot. (Present tally: 177.)

March 22nd

Another fine, cold and windy day. I spent most of it up at Hurst Down, finishing the landwork as it got dark. Hazel and Jonathan built a race for next week's TB testing – nice to have some muscle at home to help.

I was interrupted mid-afternoon by the Literary Agent, out walking his aged black lab. He's always good for a chat, so I pulled up and stopped the engine. We covered the virus, Richard Branson, my book, conspiracy theories, National Trust walkers, George Monbiot and who the hell had been cutting little walkways out of the woods into my fields – it turned out it was him. I nearly called him one of those bloody White Settlers, but didn't. He's far too charming to merit that label.

March 23rd

The fuel gauge on the Deere said 16%, and the Hurst Down headland is big, and (after all that turning on it) will be tougher than the rest. I need more fuel.

Two ways of doing it: one, drive the Deere all the way home from what is the most remote part of the farm, or, two, dig out the aged fuel bowser. Not even sure it's legal any more, but there we go. Option two won. So I had a very enjoyable half hour shuffling Pig, Pig's trailer, and the ride-on mower to get to the bowser. It had very soft tyres – made worse by the fact that it was about three parts full – so rolling it to the front of the barn was quite a challenge. Luckily, Hazel arrived just at the right moment, and we got it hitched on.

I drove it round to the yard to get to the compressor, then remembered that I'd had to disconnect the barn fuses in the wet weather – they kept blowing the trip switches. The recent dry weather meant that the aged wiring had dried out, and careful reinsertion of the old fuse was successful. With nicely pumped-up tyres (and Tigger's front left, again) I set off through the lanes.

It's always a slight worry towing the bowser through the sunken Hampshire lanes. If you're in a tractor and trailer, or tractor and sprayer, it's easy to persuade people to back up if you meet them. The bowser is small and invisible, so it's harder to win the argument. And reversing it isn't easy, being small and very sensitive on the steering. Luckily, the early Monday morning roads were deserted.

The art of maintenance is to write down stuff you think might cause trouble in the future. The on/off switch on the bowser pump failed last summer, and eBay produced a couple of cheap replacements. (Break one, buy two.) It was only when I saw smoke coming out of one of the newly connected switches that I realised why they were cheap. I then spent every harvest combine refill session spraying a cooling mist of water onto the switch – bearing in mind that the field floor was covered in tinder-dry straw. At the end of harvest, I put the bowser away, making a mental note to replace the switch with something a bit sturdier.

And then promptly forgot about it. I was two minutes into refilling the tractor when I could smell something very hot. Sure enough, the switch was beginning to cook again. Luckily, the field floor was mud, it was another cold morning, and I had a full bladder, so I let it run as long as I dared. There was plenty in the tank when I decided to give the pump a rest, and did the long drive home.

It was obvious that the cold wind was drying out the seedbed very fast, and – and here's a phrase I never thought I write after the last six months of rain – we'd need to roll it fairly quickly to save moisture. I put the Dalbo rollers on the Massey, gave both tyres a good pump up too, hauled them out to Hurst Down and gave them a good greasing. With Jonathan happy to puppy-sit, Hazel was offering to roll this afternoon, so I marked out a few of the hard-to-find tramlines to get her started.

In a long dusty afternoon, I finally got the headland done, finishing with an annoying bit of seed in the bottom of the drill – too much to run out on a headland – and Hazel rolled most of a slightly rough looking seedbed into a picture of smoothness. On the way home, I couldn't resist a full turn of Blackhouse Road, marking out the headland with the CO3. It was a long job, so I rang Tod for a life/farming update. He's in a pickle; his wife has had The Letter from HMG, saying she must not go out for the foreseeable – and that should apply to him too. Not sure how he does agronomy under those circumstances, but there we go.

The man from Mitsubishi arrived to pick up the L200 pick-up – completely unannounced, which is a bit annoying in the days of mobile telephones. We cleared out the sticks, rope bangers and long-handled clippers, and sent him on his way.

Boris' announcement of the national lockdown was a sombre moment. Much of the evening was then spent deciding how that would affect our daily lives – the verdict was 'very little'. We've got to farm, and much of what we do is in splendid isolation anyway. The vet is due tomorrow for some unbelievably badly timed TB testing, so we assume that will go ahead. Perhaps some phone calls first thing tomorrow are in order.

Jonathan celebrated a 12-week lockdown by turning his Jarvis Dupont-style manbun into a buzzcut. So it's not all bad news at the moment.

March 24th

A busy morning on the phones. In the middle of the night, I remembered I had a prescription outstanding from the Alresford chemists. I was slightly apprehensive about ringing them to see if they still had it, and if they really worried about non-virus-related medicines at the moment. I had visions of it being a bloodbath at the shop as Alresford's finest engage in pitch battles over the country's last two paracetamol tablets.

I needn't have worried. Everything sounded calm and good-natured, and there was laughter in the background as they checked my prescription. Yes, it was still there for me to pick up, and everything – apart from a limit of two people at a time in the shop – was as normal. Hazel agreed to fetch it on the morning foraging run.

The next call was to a local tractor dealer, idly asking if he had a spare machine we could hire while we've got an able-bodied boy at home, and a mountain of field work to do. Unfortunately, he had just shut down 90% his business, and only a skeleton breakdown staff remained. He was also less than happy. After a failed attempt at some light-hearted chat, I wished him to stay well, and hung up. Grim.

Then the vet rang and left a message. This morning's TB test would be late – they'd had a couple of emergency callouts. Oh, and did we by any chance have anyone showing coronavirus symptoms?

The Editor called, sounding like he was going mad after just one day in 'lockdown'. We discussed the legalities of pigeon shooting under the present restriction. Is it exercise – allowed 'once a day'? I said it was 'vital protection of food crops' and offered to write him a note to that effect. 'I, Charlie Flindt, have asked the bearer of this document to assist in protecting vital food supplies in whatever way possible...' He seemed unconvinced. Let's give it a couple of days.

In warm sunshine, I hitched off the CO3 and switched to the ST4, with a view to starting on the spring wheat. Several jobs needed doing first. I had to swap control boxes in the cab, remember where all the extra cables and pipes go, and, crucially, check the feed roller wasn't jammed – there was still most of a bag of Crusoe in the hopper, left over from the first week in February, and it can sit pretty solidly after a long layoff. I opened the bottom flap, threaded my way through the tines and coulters, and wiggled the rotor by hand. To my huge relief, it freed up. My plan to go out to Clump and sow it was still on.

It will only be a few acres, but should nearly finish the field, and will prove an interesting experiment. It's way past the official 'sow by' date for Crusoe (end of January), and will be a little patch of the farm to watch with interest. Will it get 'vernalised', or will it grow only as 'grass', without any ears? It's not a waste of 400 kg of seed; it's a public service. You're welcome.

And bearing in mind I was only sowing it as an experiment (and because I couldn't be bothered to clear it out onto the barn floor and sweep it up) it was ironic that Clump drilled as well as anything I'd done all season. Dry on top, moist underneath, and crumbling beautifully. Should've left the whole field until now – if it vernalises, of course.

Hazel made it back from the paper run with my prescription, and news that Alresford was almost deserted, apart from a long, well-spaced queue for the chemist. The patisserie was selling eggs off cheap – no baking to be done any more – and the chemist was selling home-packed packets of generic paracetamol. So she had one of those as well. Twenty more in the bathroom cabinet for when the virus gets here.

I was in the middle of calibrating for spring wheat when Tod arrived in the yard. We kept a good ten yards apart and ran through the recommendations he was going to put in after his brief walkabout. Apart from rabbits blitzing BML's, everything looks very good. Big Field could do with a roll before it gets too hard – and there's something we thought we'd never say.

Finally, I was ready to go. I redirected the lost-looking vet who finally arrived to do the TB test, and set off to Blackhouse Road. I started drilling N-S, at a slight angle to last year's tramlines, and beginning in the shortest work opposite New Pond Cottages. By the time the first bag had run out – almost as calibrated – the turns were beginning to get much longer. And, once again, the stubble was breaking up an absolute treat. That's why we love growing peas – they are the easiest crop to follow with wheat. And sometimes you get a decent pea crop, too.

Jonathan gave me a lift home, with news that the TB test had gone every smoothly, with Hazel's dopey cattle behaving immaculately, cruising quietly into the crush. The follow-up test might, of course, be different, as even dopey cattle remember that the last time they cruised quietly into the crush, some bugger stuck something sharp into them.

March 25th

Hazel had another early straw customer, and then hitched the loader onto the seed trailer for me. I took it down to Blackhouse Road, filled up the drill, took a deep breath, and set off. As the sun set, I'd done about 50 acres, most of it beautifully, and some of it not so well – the ground is getting too hard. Amazing.

There were a couple of interruptions. One of the Old Boys of Bramdean arrived in the field slightly unexpectedly, asking if he could shine up his old two-furrow match plough in one of our fields. I made a great song and dance about having nothing to work it down to a seedbed, but then rather contradicted my argument by offering a game strip to plough. He gave me a card, and I said I'd get in touch if I could think of somewhere. The truth is, of course, that in these days of 'straight in' seed sowing, the last thing we want is a little patch of plough, complete with ridges and furrows.

Just as I was shutting down for a refill, the phone rang, and it was neighbour Robert Junior, bursting to tell me of his latest encounter with the self-isolating public: a young couple, stark bollock naked, sunbathing in the middle of his wheat, in full view of the passing traffic (what little there is at the moment) on the A31. How we laughed. We never got to the serious bit of his call, because a man and a dog could be seen walking merrily through the Big Field game strips, so I hung up on Robert, and went to intercept.

"It's OK, this is a footpath," he said when I asked if he was lost. I pointed out that it wasn't. "Well, it was when I lived here 15 years ago," he insisted.

"You may have walked it, in the mistaken belief that it was a footpath, but in my 60 years here, it has never been a footpath," I huffed. There was then a certain amount of lowering of hackles, and we had a friendly chat instead. He had indeed lived here 15 years ago, at New Pond, and was now a plasterer in Alresford. He thought he'd pop back for a bit of nostalgia. I know either he or his brother broke into our grain store when they were much smaller and shot all the old bulbs to pieces with an air rifle. Broken glass in the grain, police called, words exchanged – but thought it wise not to bring that incident up again now.

I finished all the long work as it was getting dark. A good 50-acre day, with long turns and fabulous conditions. I'll need fuel to finish tomorrow, so popped into the diesel barn and put the bowser battery on charge overnight.

March 26th

With a freshly charged battery on the bowser, the tractor refuel was particularly quick, and by the time smoke was drifting up from the on/off switch, I had enough fuel in the tractor to crack on. I got the landwork of Blackhouse Road done (including the unbelievably tiresome short work on the brow opposite Joan's Acre House) by lunchtime, and started the huge headland after lunch.

There were more interruptions: another long chat with the Literary Agent, who looked slightly offended when I said he should give us a shout if he and his wife find themselves in need of anything. He pointed out that he is offering his services to others in West Meon.

Neighbour Robert Snr rang for a catch up. He's confined to his house/garden by the sound of it, and being driven bonkers by it. Not being able to pootle round the farm or do our regular Tuesday Pots visits is putting a hell of a strain on him.

Seven turns of the headland, and the biggest field on the farm was finally finished. The Blackhouse Road headland always brings back memories of when I was doing my first year on the sprayer. It was an Allman mounted sprayer, with manual-folding 12-metre booms and a 150-gallon tank, mounted on a Ford 6600 2WD. The water rate was the time-honoured 15 gallons/acre, so the capacity was 10 acres per fill. These days I do 60 per fill – and even that's slow compared to some modern machines. The first time I set off to spray Blackhouse Road, the headland was two turns of 12 m. I didn't even get round both turns before the sprayer ran out, and it was time to go home and refill. Things have moved on, thank goodness.

The next field of spring wheat was Kilmeston Road, so I came home first to refuel with diesel, tea and honey sandwiches, and ring the Editor to discuss the legalities of pigeon shooting. He's worried about leaving the house to do it, I'm sure that it is crop protection, and crop protection is part of crop production, and so it is a permitted activity. I told him to get on with it, and I'd vouch for him having been asked to help with 'crop protection'. He seemed unconvinced – again. I'd done my best.

I set off for Kilmeston Road. Down the hill from the farm, into the Folly at the fork in the road, and then out of Folly, across the road, and into Springshot. Well, that was the plan; it turned out that if you straddle that particular bit of raised road while towing an ST4, all your coulters get stuck in the tarmac. All very embarrassing, especially when you've just exchanged a curt and unfriendly "Good evening" with the arch-trespassers of Kilmeston. They must have wondered what the hell was going on, as I had to reverse carefully into the Folly with 4WD on, desperately hoping that none of the tines would break.

The only solution was to turn onto the road towards Kilmeston, then back along the road for a bit, then turn right, off the road and into the Springshot gateway. All very easy in theory, but a vast family of dayglo-clad cyclists arrived in the middle of this intricate manoeuvre, and, completely unaware that I was in the middle of a slightly tricky operation, proceeded to mill around the tractor/drill combo, debating loudly as to which way to go next. I resisted joining in and telling them where to go, as we've all got to be nice to each other in these difficult times.

Eventually, I got into Springshot, tiptoed round the flooded patch at the far end – the Itchen has crept up the valley a bit this year – and unfolded the drill.

Kilmeston Road is another field I haven't set foot – or tyre – in since harvest, and I was a bit worried about what state it was in. It was OSR last year, and large patches vanished thanks to the flea beetle, and there were clumps of tough old weed out there that I couldn't get the combine through at harvest. The two doses of Roundup we'd given it since then had done a great job; the ground was as clean as a whistle, and the tough old weed had been reduced to brittle stalks that didn't stand a chance against the Horsch. I marked out a headland, dodging the even wetter bit at the lower end, where water was running across the field, and got stuck into the landwork.

I was just contemplating how well everything was going when I noticed Tigger in the middle of the boggy bit of Springshot, up to its axles, and utterly immobile. It was baffling; Hazel had been due to drive it out, and she would surely know not to drive through the slightly enlarged source of the Itchen. Just then, my phone rang, and it was Jonathan, who had volunteered to bring it down and walk back with the dogs.

Drilling was abandoned for an hour as we worked out how we'd rescue Tigger. I did a bit more 'expert' driving to try and get it out, but achieved nothing. I then remembered the tow rope.

Not just any old tow rope. The lovely Sean and Dawn are very sadly moving out of their cottage at New Pond, and he's clearing out a lot of unwanted stuff. Almost every time I pass, he's got a bit more junk he's keen to get rid of. One day, he offered me an unusual tow rope – unusual, because it was about 100 yards long. And we were going to need 100 yards to get the 'towing' vehicle off the bog that much of the west end of Springshot has turned into.

Jonathan walked home with a flea in his ear, and Hazel arrived shortly after that with the Massey and the rope. Ten minutes later, everything was on solid ground, even if we were all a bit grubby. I kept drilling into a gobsmacking clear sunset, and then headed home.

March 27th

Over breakfast, yesterday's chaotic events suddenly gelled into next week's *Flindt on Friday*, which I'd been struggling with for a couple of days. Typed up and sent off by 8.30am. Perfect. So I headed off for a long day in Kilmeston Road with a sense of relief.

It was warm, windy and the ground was drying with every turn – although the very bottom of the field was still too soft to risk driving into. We had quite enough stickiness yesterday, thank you. But I finished the whole of the rest of the field by teatime. Hazel finished rolling Blackhouse Road and brought the rollers over, and after some more uneventful shuffling of vehicles, everything came home. A great seven days' worth of drilling: all the winter beans into TBHD and 120 acres of spring wheat in the most perfect conditions imaginable.

Even better news: the cattle all passed the TB follow-up test.

March 28th

I was cleaning the dregs of spring wheat out of the drill when Hazel got back from her paper/foraging run. On the way to the shop, she'd returned some puppy fencing that had been kindly lent to us – the return was done at great distance over a garden wall. The lender is in the medical trade, so, inevitably, talk turned to the virus, and its progress. "The tide has gone out, because the tsunami is on the way" was her message. Quite a sobering thought.

Hazel sent emails to all the puppy buyers; if things get much worse, the lockdown will be more severe. Driving across the country to pick up puppies is already a grey area when it comes to 'reason to be travelling'. There's every chance that it will become impossible. She asked everyone if they fancied getting here as soon as possible – and sod the 'eight-week' pick-up rule. They're seven-and-a-half weeks, and have suddenly become too big for the house.

Meanwhile I filled up the drill, calibrated with Planet spring barley, and set off for the Folly. I was getting cocky with the drill's calibration, and instead of putting only one bag in to check the seed rate, I put a tonne in and merrily set off. The whole tonne was gone far too early – instead of 193 kg/ha, I seemed to have done 240 kg/ha. I sat in the tractor and had a head scratch. What had gone wrong? The bags were proper commercial bags, so they were guaranteed to be 500 kg. There was no reason to suspect the doppler radar on the drill was playing up.

Then I remembered that the scales I use had been behaving a bit oddly. The tin bucket, which usually holds about 4 kg at a time, seemed to be weighing 'light'. And all the time it stayed on the scales, the reading crept up. I reckon it was feeling the cold (and it's not getting any warmer for a few days yet) and was indeed reading light. So the figure I punched into the Horsch 'Drill Manager' was too low, so the computer dispensed too much seed to reach what it thought was the required rate. Bugger.

I've used about 200 kg too much after only one fill, but there's a lot of ground to go, so I'll make it up slowly. I changed the required seed rate to 156 kg/ha, in the hope that it will actually dispense 193 kg/ha, and came home in a bit of a sulk.

Two puppies had already gone by then, and Hazel decided the best therapy for missing them was to head out to Kilmeston Road and do a couple more hours of rolling. I lit the fire and had a Saturday evening snooze.

March 29th

Three more puppies were hastened out of the door – the Yorkshire buyers arrived at 10am, having set off at 5am – and that's BST. The consolation was that by mid-afternoon, lovely reports were coming back of them in their new homes, happy as Larry.

I had another session in the Folly. My maths turned out almost perfect after yesterday's calibration chaos, and the day went pretty well – if you ignore the badger holes, the telegraph poles (both ending up on the tramline bout, dammit) and the fact that the headlands were almost too hard to be drilled. I was glad Hazel finished rolling Kilmeston Road in the afternoon, before it dried out any more.

I walked back up from the Folly at lunchtime, with a plan to take the loader and some seed down for the afternoon. Jonathan was at the door to meet me, looking slightly worried. He said there had just been a huge crash, and asked if I'd seen a tree. I hadn't come up the road – but when Hazel got in, she said that a huge chestnut had snapped off in the NE wind and fallen a good ten feet down into the sunken bend just south of the house. Anyone underneath wouldn't have stood a chance.

We rang the Trust's head gardener man, who was over in his Valtra with a huge chainsaw in moments – even though it was Saturday. He turned down my offer of help, so I cracked on with sowing. I had to take the seed out via Godwin's, down to the Drier, and back along the lane from there, but was up and running soon enough.

As I was doing the second turn of the headland, I spotted a large family strolling along Dark Lane, fully wrapped up against the cold, but took little notice of them. Then they caught my eye again: they were all lined up on the top of the bank, giving me a round of applause. How sweet it that? I confess I shed a bit of a tear, and keeping a look out for the work of the marker arm was difficult enough without having to wipe your eyes. A truly lovely moment.

My old chum Graeme rang for a catch up – there's a lot of it going on at the moment, for some reason – and I told him the story of the applauding walkers. "Don't be daft," he said. "They're just clapping you for finally getting off your fat arse and doing some work!" Cheers, Graeme.

But, my God, it was cold. That howling gale kept on all day, and flurries of sleet every so often. Despite the new longer evenings, I headed out to chop another chunk of logs and lit a good fire. Funny old day.

March 30th

It's all a bit Groundhog Day at the moment. Stunning sunrise, depressing headlines, Hazel on foraging trips, puppy buyers arriving, I set off drilling...

There were a couple of differences. Hazel tiptoed into the pharmacy and got a bigger pack of paracetamol, so supplies must be catching up with demand, and my trip to BOMS to drill spring barley ended in failure.

It was winter barley last year, and it was the one field of Tower that we didn't sell for straw. So I'd stopped swathing at harvest, and put the chopper on. Now, calling the little black device on the back of my TC5070 combine a "chopper" is being a bit generous. It's good at shattering the easy-to-shatter stuff like bean and OSR haulm, and makes a respectable job of short wheat straw, but barley straw doesn't so much get 'chopped' as 'apologetically spread across the width of the combine'.

I was halfway round the 'marking out' turn, when I realised a huge mat of straw had built up under the Horsch, and when I tried a proper cross field run, the same happened. No way was I going to get spring barley in there without some more preparatory work to the field. Disc it? Wait for neighbour Robert's Kockerling to become available? 'Sod it', I thought, and headed back to Godwin's, and made a very good start in Middle Broom. It was hard on top, but surprisingly wet underneath, and the drill was making a very nice seedbed.

Yet another sowing plan developed in my head. Perhaps spring barley in Godwin's Park, after all this dry weather, then beans in the Hangar, and cultivate BOMS – but thought it better to concentrate on the job in hand, one day at a time.

I finished Middle Broom and made a start on Child's Broom. Seed ran out exactly on time, and I headed home. Just two puppies left now, mixing boldly with the other dogs, and a rapidly dying AGA. The promised warm weather can't get here soon enough. It might, if we're lucky, bring some rain. And I never thought I'd think that a fortnight ago.

March 31st

Yet another cold start, but the wind had dropped a bit. Not a lot – neighbour Robert was on the phone early asking if we wanted any Kockerling-ing done, because he'd abandoned Roundup-ing near the village. I said that would be perfect; he could biff BOMS into some sort of submission for me, after I'd failed to get the Horsch through it a couple of days ago. He also asked if we had a spare tonne of barley seed. I'd been dithering about putting spring barley in the Hangar again, and his request was enough to make me decide: spring beans in the Hangar, and a spare tonne of barley for Robert.

The rest of the day was as the last few days. I drilled, finishing Child's Broom, and then did all of Big Broom. Hazel rolled and did seed support. The Kockerling did arrive, and showed no mercy to BOMS – that'll be ready for tomorrow. Not sure what Jonathan did. Hold on: the Aga started to get cool and smelly, so we put it out of its misery and turned it off, and he used his powerlifting skills to lift out the central barrel. Good lad.

Funny to start a diary, calling it the Brexit Year, and then find that after only two months, Brexit has vanished from the agenda altogether. The world has gone into complete lockdown – or 'meltdown' – over the coronavirus. We are blessed: we live and work in effective self-isolation, our work is considered essential, and we've got stocks of seed and diesel – and unsown fields – ready to keep us busy for weeks ahead. There was once something called the Agriculture Bill. I wonder what happened to that?

April 1st

We lasted one whole night without the Aga. The kitchen was cold and horrible at breakfast, so, after checking that drilling weather was going to continue for some days, I decided to service it. I had all the kit – new brass elbows, new wicks, and power supply for the tractor barn to power the little shot-blasting kit – and for some reason it went more smoothly than ever. It was lit and beginning to warm up again by mid-morning.

The last puppy buyer came and went, leaving only 'Tim' to start his new life with all the other dogs. Another good reason to get the kitchen warm – it's where he'll now be sleeping.

The farming frenzy continued. I did BOMS after lunch, relishing the fabulous seedbed left by Robert's Kockerling, but not quite enjoying the bumpiness caused by me going at a sharp angle to his work. Luckily, it's only 20 acres. Hazel loaded another straw buyer with half a dozen bales, and then did more rolling in Godwin's. Both straw and rolling will be much needed if this dry weather goes on.

The spring barley ran out perfectly, if rather heavily, in BOMS, leaving only spring beans (not that urgent) and spring peas (not at all urgent) on the list of sowing jobs. There's a lot of outstanding fertiliser, though, so that might take priority. Graham Tosdevine's sprayerman came in and did White Hill and Cheyney with 3l/ha Roundup, so they'll be ready to drill in a few days. A bit of rain and a day off might be in order soon.

Anthony messaged from London to say he was housebound with symptoms of a heavy cold, and had been sent home from work. He works for Enterprise car rental in St John's Wood, so avoiding the virus would be the hardest thing in the world. His list of symptoms did suggest 'normal' flu, so that's one relief. Thanks goodness for all the modern methods of mass communication: imagine the world being in lockdown without the internet.

April 2nd

Working on the assumption that the world is running short of everything, I thought it would be wise to chase up some farming essentials. First on the list was fertiliser, which will be my main job once I get the spring beans in. After a few false starts (the lines are very dodgy round here at the moment) I got through to Yara, and promptly got put into a long queue, which then went to an answering machine. This did not sound good. I had visions of a spring with no fertiliser to go with no rain. I even rang the area rep – but he didn't answer his phone, either.

I gave the Yara line one more try, and got through to a person. I explained that I needed another load of N35(S) liquid fert. "Tomorrow delivery OK for you?" he asked. This took me by surprise, and I managed to put it off to Monday – bearing in mind my tank is still half full at the moment. Another 270 acres' worth of stuff will be very handy, but just not yet.

Next on the shopping list was everything for a simple tractor service. My John Deere has done just over 500 hours since the huge 3,000-hour service this time last year, and I hate going over the schedule. Something tells me that the tractor's here for a long time, and frequent oil changes are officially a Good Thing. I like to do it at 400 hours if I can, but I seem to have missed that slot this year.

The local dealer had a chirpy skeleton staff answering the phone, and claimed that they had everything I needed, so after I'd hitched off the ST4 and left the tractor for Jonathan to pressure wash, I jumped in the Octavia and drove to Chilbolton. The roads were odd – much more quiet than normal, of course, but those who were driving were driving like idiots. I had two near misses on the stretch from the Petersfield Spur to the Winnal roundabout. It's like the races in *On the Beach*.

Having survived that, I found that they were one filter short of what I needed. They were very apologetic and said someone who lived in Alresford would drop it in on their way home.

Back home, I hitched onto the sprayer and did one tank of fertiliser on the OSR – its final dose. It looks very sick, but it's still there – which is better than many crops this year. If it warms up next week, after the promised rain on Monday, it will, I'm sure, explode into life. It was lovely being able to see out of the tractor, though.

My copy of *South East Farmer* was delivered (in the remote box for the distancing postie to use, in the middle of the yard), with my first ever paid-for advert for Book One in it. By evening, a tsunami of orders had arrived; I printed both of them off, ready for tomorrow's post.

April 3rd

The spraying contractor was due in early to put pre-emergence herbicide on the late drilled winter beans, so I did the paperwork, checked the spray store and the water tank, and awaited the arrival of the huge self-propelled John Deere. Ten minutes later, there was a slightly worried-looking operator walking across the yard. "I am supposed to be here today, aren't I?" he asked. "I'm locked out!" I knew I'd forgotten one job. Once we'd got the gates open, we chatted (at a distance) about how lucky we were to be in farming at the moment. He said it was the first time in his career that he doesn't dread driving his huge machine along main roads; there's no one to get upset. Half an hour later, he was on his way out to TBHD with a tank full of yellow stuff.

Tom the Cattle Dealer arrived mid-morning to look at Hazel's beasts. Yes, beasts. She'd mentioned that she'd be quite keen to move them on and have a break, and he was very keen. We couldn't have our usual coffee and gossip – which is the very backbone of farm negotiations – but he and Hazel stood the correct distance apart in the Back Meadow and talked money. He poked a few with a stick, as you do, and hummed and haa'ed at Hazel's price, and said he'd go away and think about it. I kept well out of it all, and instead replaced the inner cab air filters in the Deere – for the first time in its life. No wonder the air smelt a bit sweeter when I got going with fertiliser again.

I finished the OSR in Drier Field, then did some sums on what was left in the tank, and did 200 l/ha of N35 on Big Broom, Middle and Child's Broom and then had 2,000 l left. An awkward load, not enough to do Folly, but too much for that rate on BOMS. So I upped the rate to 250 l/ha and crawled over BOMS, finishing with a rinse out. The fertiliser tank is now empty and waiting for a refill. I came home, hitched off the sprayer and put the CO3 on again, ready for the spring beans. By then it was cold again, so I lit another fire. No rain in the forecast – none of significance, anyway.

April 4th

It was a fairly busy morning getting the CO3 set up and calibrated for spring beans, and all the control boxes swapped over again, but by late morning, it was all sorted. I, however, wasn't, and treated myself to a bit of a half day off. It's easy to forget we've been going non-stop for some weeks now, and all after a six-month layoff. I'm actually pleased with how well we've put up with the pace.

And, as it happened, by mid-afternoon, I was tickety boo again and drove the Deere and the CO3 out to JA/DC, did a bit of headland marking, and drilled one bag's worth of Fuego. I was so pleased that it worked out just right that I rang home for a lift and called it a day.

Hazel had been down to the curious semi-rural suburbs on the outskirts of Southampton and come home with a box of fresh chickens. We haven't restocked since Mr Fox had a pretty clinical clearout some months ago, and now seems as good a time as any to get some more. They very soon settled into the chicken house. Smallholding – here we come.

April 5th

It was very satisfying to have a mini-flurry of book orders on the strength of the paid-for advert in *South East Farmer* and the freebie mention in the Mole Valley Newsletter. I'd sent the editor of the latter a plug for it, but didn't hold out much hope of getting in, but there it was, under my original tongue-in-cheek headline of "Thrilling new book!". No mention of how to buy it, or even a reference to the title, but in these days of Google, any old fool could track it down. And a few did. Hurrah.

In the hot wind, I trundled out to JA/DC with some seed, and finished it by about six, and brought the drill home. Jonathan gave Hazel a lift out to pick up the seed trailer and the Massey, and another hugely productive weekend finished.

April 6th

Good grief – it rained. The radar showed quite a heavy shower coming through at about 3am. The ground was damp, and the buckets had a couple of millimetres in the bottom, but it wasn't really enough. It'll do a bit of good, especially on the OSR which has had its final dose of fertiliser. It's astonishing to be longing for a good soaking after the six-month spell between the equinoxes, but hey, that's farming.

I realised that the review of the Mitsubishi L200 should have been submitted a few days ago, so I dug out the copious notes I made at the time (always a good idea) and wrote it up. It seems odd to be writing up new cars while driving is all but banned, but hey, that's the world today.

Hazel went down to the Drier Yard and put the rest of the spring bean seed bags on the trailer and brought them home. We now have a free and relatively rat-free barn to use as storage for all the expensive seed we bought last autumn – but never used. There's all the Tower winter barley and the Zulu wheat. The tractor barn is heaving with rats, and it would be nice to get everything out of there and somewhere slightly better for long-term storage. Mind you, in about five months' time we'll be digging it all out again.

I filled up with diesel and headed out to Cheyney with the drill. It was sown with OSR last September, but, like White Hill, got mangled by flea beetle. Tosdevine Roundup-ed it a few days ago, so it was ready for spring beans. It went mostly very well; the far end was a bit tough, and I decided to bring the 'game strip' down the west side back into the rotation. I was driving the Horsch straight through a tough selection of grass, docks and thistles, but the Solo legs sailed through the lot. A good roll (and perhaps another pass with the drill if I have any seed left after the Hangar) and it'll be a good job. It might even persuade Kilmeston's Chief Trespassers that it's not a right of way. Come to think of it, that's the only reason I'm getting rid of the game strip – we've never shot through it. It was, ironically, full of pheasants.

I had two phone calls during the afternoon. One from a lovely lady in Worcester who had seen Book One advertised in the Mole Valley Newsletter. She wanted to get a copy, but the Newsletter gave no details at all as to how to actually get hold of a copy. So she'd rung Mole Valley, who – rather generously – gave her my mobile number. I stopped the tractor and we had a lovely chat, so it didn't matter. I told her to send me a cheque, and gave her my address. The line wasn't brilliant, so God knows where it will end up.

The other call was from the lorry driver delivering the load of liquid fertiliser. He was checking for directions (good boy) and asking if it was OK if he kipped down there overnight. I said that was fine – as long as he didn't leave anything behind. He laughed and promised not to.

At about five, I got out of Cheyney, and having popped another bag in, headed back down the road, turned left into Springshot, and trundled over to the Hangar. In a fit of enthusiasm, I marked out the headland and did an acre next to the track. I locked up, all ready for another day tomorrow, and had a lovely evening walk, and a bit of a sit-down among the sheep and lambs in Springshot. No planes overhead, no racing motorbikes on the A272, no lost walkers, just me and my empty Thermos. Unprecedented silence. Just a little moment in heaven. And in history.

And best of all, the vitamin D has finally kicked it, and my shoulders stopped hurting.

April 7th

It was rather odd, in these surreal traffic-free days, being woken by a vehicle this morning. We're used to the shepherd doing an early tour on his UTV, but this was bigger and noisier. It was, of course, the fertiliser tanker man, having rested overnight down at the Drier Yard, making his way out. It was a throwback to my childhood in the sixties, when the milk tanker would trundle its way down to the tiny Blackhouse Farm. It was still a dairy back then, not a little piece of White Settler heaven.

Hazel went off and rolled JA/DC, and I drove Tigger out to the Hangar and did a couple of hours spring bean sowing before lunch. A long session after lunch, and some instinctive seed rate tweaks meant that I finished that field by about 5pm, and then had a bit left in the drill to pop back into Cheyney and resow the old game strip, and was back in the yard just after six.

But not before I'd stopped in the gateway to Chalks to point out to a couple of lost walkers that they were, um, lost. "Oh, sorry," they said as they came strolling through the game strip. "We're trying to get back to Hinton Hill." It all made sense. The National Trust will have re-let one of the cottages in the village, and told the new tenants, in an attempt to justify the astonishing levels of rent that they charge, that all the land around is available for free walking. And, as usual, I will have a jolly few months trying to intercept these new tenants, and persuade them, as politely as possible, that Rights of Way do still apply. Today's meeting was indeed polite and friendly, and they were suitably apologetic, and seemed desperate to know as much as possible about their new home. Unfortunately, I was knackered, and all I wanted to do was head home, get cleaned up, and get to bed. I'll catch up with their questions another day.

I hitched off the CO3 from the tractor, ready for the oil change tomorrow. Only the peas left to do, and not before the legendary Kockerling has been in and worked its magic on a pretty hard White Hill.

But that's 372 acres sown and mostly rolled in 18 continuous days. Not much per day, but an absolute joy to be going flat out when in most other jobs, we'd be sitting indoors. Going quite mad.

April 8th

You'd think by now I could change an oil filter on a tractor. How many gallons of fresh oil have I poured into hard-to-reach spouts? How many filters have I carefully oiled up, and then spun on until hand tight and then another half-turn, but no more? And it had got off to a good start. I had the right oil, the right filters (always check before taking off the old ones), and after a trip round to refuel, a sump full of nicely warmed old oil.

I found an old 20 litre drum and the manky funnel, got everything into position under the sump, and carefully unscrewed the drain plug. And then dropped it into the funnel, where it got jammed in the narrow bit, despite my best efforts – with bare hands – to dive in and fish it out from under the deluge of warm, black oil that was now pouring out. I'm not saying it was a bloody mess – but I was very grateful to have a huge pile of grain/chaff/dust sweepings from the rat-infested end of the barn to eventually serve as a soak-up mix.

The fuel filters were a doddle by comparison, despite there being two of them, and one with fiddly electrical connections, and the fact they don't screw on – they have to be pushed up into their holders with slots and ridges lined up properly, and then fixed into place with locking collars. It was a huge relief when, after a minute or so to let the electric fuel pump click its magic, the Deere started first time. I still have memories of the old Fords, which more often than not needed bleeding all the way to the injectors.

One job left: blow out the multiple radiators. Luckily, we're well stocked with masks – but for how long, if they force us all to wear them? – and opened up the Rubik's Cube of cooling systems. The clouds of dust that filled the barn once I set about them with the compressor made it worth the effort, and also explained why the tractor had been getting a bit warm recently. I 'Gunked' the engine over lunchtime, and then hitched back onto the sprayer.

Blackhouse Road and the Folly both had a 200 l/ha of fertiliser, although it was interrupted by numerous phone calls referring to yet another motorbiker who'd crashed outside the Editor's house. Multiple police were there, lots of emergency crews – and the air ambulance, which landed in the gravel pit field, scaring Noel's sheep half to death, according to all the calls. Facebook pictures suggested that they couldn't give a toss. It was fortunate for the motorcyclist that the emergency services have nothing else on their plates at the moment.

The spring wheat was just coming through in Blackhouse Road, and the spring barley in Folly is only a day or two away – both fields looked magnificent in the evening light, but they could do with some rain.

April 9th

These mad days mean everyone's losing track of what day of the week it, never mind that it's Easter Bank Holiday coming up. I got a gentle hurry up from *Farmers Weekly* about next week's *Flindt on Friday*. Lucky, I had an idea in mind, and they had it by mid-morning.

I spent the rest of the morning having a bit of a faff about, trying to decide whether to carry on with the fertiliser, or do some spraying, or hitch onto the drill again and get set up for the peas in White Hill. The forecast is for heavy showers this weekend, followed by a dramatic drop in temperatures. Do peas want to be sown with a cold spell coming? I sat in the hot sun outside the back door and thought long and hard about it.

Hazel grabbed a good pair of gloves and a roll of duct tape, and had a marathon session getting all the unused winter seed down to the right-hand lean-to, where it should be more safe from vermin over the next few months. Left behind in the tractor barn and Godwin's barn were a heap of rat droppings and chewed seed. Goodness knows how many tonnes have actually been lost. It probably looks worse than it is. We'll find out when we start sowing next autumn.

Tod called in for an agronomy update, and we sat on the staddle stones in the yard, keeping the right distance apart. He was impressed with our progress – so much that he added a couple of extra spraying burdens to our workload. There was much discussion about the three small parcels of spring beans, all near houses, and all due to be sprayed with Stomp and Defy. Defy is the most pungent and long-lasting chemical in the book – days after application it leaves a foul oily smell heavy in the nostrils. With everyone at home at the moment, should we drop the Defy? Could do, said Tod, but we'd miss the whole point of putting those fields into spring beans, and the chance to have a good clean up – using Defy. And this is the year of all years to make the most of the goodwill to farmers that's quietly brewing. True, I said. But I'll wait for a westerly.

By late afternoon, I'd had enough sunbathing, and went out to Kilmeston Road with a tank of fertiliser. The spring wheat was coming through in places, but much of the field looked as though it had been raked over. The rooks and pigeons had given it a thorough working over – so much so that I could hardly see the tramline markers in places. A couple of times I jumped out and did some digging. There's stuff coming up nicely from deep, but the birds have cleared an awful lot of the surface stuff. Time to get the dead rooks out of the freezer.

April 10th

Good Friday. To think that once upon a time, this would have meant a day off. Now, we work when we can. There's precious little 8 till 5, or Monday to Friday. If there's stuff to be done, we do it. And if there's nothing to be done, or the weather's not right, we don't.

Today was fine, sunny and hot, and there was indeed stuff to be done. Hazel took Pig and Sasha, headed out to Kilmeston Road and the Hangar, and left some dead rooks dangling on sticks – the sure-fire way to scare rooks off and offend the urban locals. I took Tigger out for a drive round to check what's growing. Stuff that has been sown deep into a bit of moisture is up and away in many places, but many grains of seed are just sitting, waiting.

Back home, I calibrated the ST4 for peas, tried to sort out three punctures in the 16 following tyres, but found large holes in two tyres that meant they'd just have to run flat for now. When I bought the drill – very second-hand – this time last year, it came with the horrid puncture-proof resin in every tyre. Each one weighed a ton, and each tyre carcass had pretty well worn away, so my summer job was to dismantle the whole lot, cut out the foul-smelling resin, and get Micheldever Tyres to put new standard air-filled tyres on each rim. As I was trying to inflate damaged tyres this morning, I could see the reason for the resin.

Jonathan was hopping up and down, looking for a job, so I suggested he dismantle the 'stand by' diaphragm sprayer pump that had been sitting in the barn, neglected and lonely. I've had a run of new sprayers – two catastrophic Amazones and my present FarmGem – and I haven't kept any of them long enough to have to change or service the all-important pump. The pump overhaul is supposed to be the winter service job, but my policy is to do it when it's needed. (Old farm saying: maintenance is what farmers do when something goes wrong.) I spotted a spare pump for sale some years ago, and then ran a policy of having one overhauled and ready at any time.

I'd almost forgotten about the spare, sitting on the floor where it was dumped after the last pump change – which could have been ten years ago. So I gave Jonathan instructions to Gunk it, sterilise it (Mr and Mrs Rat have been using it as a way marker in the barn) and pressure wash it to within an inch of its life. We found a random selection of Allen keys, and I left him, suitably instructed, to give it a clean and dismantle it. And then went sowing peas.

White Hill was fantastic – very dusty, but nicely worked down by the Kockerling. The Ghost of Rough Field struck again – my low-level indicator started beeping while there was still a tonne in the hopper, and if there's one thing guaranteed to drive you crazy, it's a 'beep beep' every ten seconds for half an hour. Mind you, at least I could keep going: the Curse has caused burst oil pipes and no-reason shutdowns of control boxes over the last few years.

By six, I had nearly nine hectares done, and, working on the assumption that I'll have time to do the whole enormous field in three chunks, called it a day. I got home to find the diaphragm pump perfectly cleaned and dismantled, with all its components neatly laid out and labelled on the yard workbench. That boy is wasted at university – if it ever starts again.

April 11th

It was becoming a race against time to get the last of the sowing into seedbeds that still had some moisture in them. The Kockerling had done a great job of working up a tilth in White Hill, but in places it was baking into little bricks in the sun and the wind. Thanks to the long turns and the fact that the ground had been loosened up in advance, I was flying.

And then, of course, I reached the part of White Hill we call Rough Field, and it's very rare that the spirit of poor 21-year-old Sub Lieutenant Norman John Daly RNVR, from Bromley in Kent, doesn't have some say in what we're doing out there. He was the pilot of the Fairey Barracuda that plunged vertically from 3,000 feet into Rough Field on 13th November 1943, during 'fighter evasion exercise'. The Barracudas had a tragic habit of leaking hydraulic fluid into the cabin, rendering their pilots unconscious. So there's a high chance that John Daley died a sudden and violent death, rendered insensible by mechanical failure, and while training. And he was my son's age.

We try not to acknowledge that Rough Field is always trouble, but when set-aside came along, it was the perfect candidate for being left alone. Right back to my youth, I can remember hydraulic failure, combine fires, both tyres on one side of the combine going flat within moments – cartoon style – as they passed over something sharp, and the day I drove all the way from the combine to the grainstore with the back of the three-ton Weekes trailer open – having taken the load in Rough Field.

Even in the set-aside years, it was an uneasy place. A friend was thrown from her horse very nastily, although the concussion – which meant she became convinced she was in *Gone with the Wind* – was very entertaining. Some years ago, we brought it back into the rotation. The contractor had trouble with his machine out there, working it down for the first time in ages, and most years, issues arise. Burst pipes, control box failures – you can be pretty sure something will happen.

Yesterday, the low-level indicator went crazy and just wouldn't shut up, and today was even worse. I was heading up across Rough Field when there was much beeping and 'comms error', which was sorted – I hope – by some very scientific wobbling of cable connections, and then came the big one: I paused to do a bit of seed rate maths, and then got underway again. Somehow, in the short break, the whole feed tube had bunged up with peas, and jammed the feed rotor, with deafening results from the control box alarm.

What on earth was the solution? I could hardly disconnect the pipe in the field and dump the whole lot on the dirt. I rang Hazel and asked her to bring the two big white buckets that fit nicely under the Horsch, with the idea of 'draining' the peas into them. But over a Thermos and a honey sandwich, we had a bit of a committee meeting and decided that bringing it home was the wisest idea, and using a freshly swept section of yard as the emptying spot

I had a bit of an enthusiasm by-pass once I got home, and really couldn't be arsed to wrestle with the insides of the Horsch. It would wait until the morning. I did, however, run the compressor over some of the numerous punctures in the set of rear press tyres. Two of them wouldn't even pump up thanks to stone slashes. I half-heartedly fetched the box of sticky rubber inserts, and, more in hope than expectation, covered them in goo and mercilessly stabbed them into the tyre holes. I felt better, anyway.

April 12th

At 8.15 on Easter Sunday morning, I was already hot'n'sweaty – it was almost like a harvest morning. I'd been clambering in and out of the wings of the unfolded ST4 drill, trying to work out how to clear all the bunged-up pipes, and all the time trying to work out what the hell had caused everything to bung up in the first place.

I'd swept a clean bit of concrete ready for the horrible 'dump everything on the floor' scenario, but in the end, I didn't need it. I undid the huge jubilee clips on the short and very sturdy bit of flexible pipe that goes from the seed venturi at the bottom of the hopper to the steel vertical elbow, and managed to hammer the pipe off. The seed ran out nicely into a huge white feed bucket I'd managed to thread through the tines into position. Seed was still firmly wedged below the 'mushroom' distributor, but I managed to free it all up with an unfolded coat hanger.

As the last dregs ran into the bucket, there was a flash of silver. It was a broken off bolt, complete with its Nyloc nut. Not very big and well-polished. Could this have been causing the problem? Was it sitting in the air flow, too heavy to reach the distributor head, and big enough to interfere with the smooth flow of peas – enough to start a blockage that then snowballed? And then the bigger question, which bugged me for the rest of the day: where did the bolt come from?

But I was glad that I'd found something to blame, and even gladder to find that my cack-handed attempts to plug two punctures in the Horsch's following wheels had actually been successful. That doesn't often happen.

By late morning, I was back in Rough Field, and although the drill was working fine, life didn't get any easier. First of all, the tramlining went all to pieces – probably something to do with yesterdays' 'comms error' messages. I should have got out, paced out the 29 easy paces to work out where the next tramlines should be, and got everything back in sync. But after 22 days of continuous tractor work, I just thought 'sod it' and kept going. If I have to make new ones after emergence so be it.

The next problem was that by the time I got to the really heavy stuff, it was so dried out that I could not see my work or my mark, and more than once veered off into no-man's land. In a bit of a huff, I jumped into the Massey, hitched onto the rollers (Hazel was still at lunch) and rolled ahead of the drill. It went down perfectly, and made me wish I'd done all the heavy land ahead.

It was late evening when I did an unnecessary seventh turn of headland to get rid of the extra seed (the drill was once again under-sizing the field). I folded up, and trundled home, praying for the rain that they keep promising us. Hazel finished the rolling, and with a shuffle of vehicles and a ceremonial locking of gates on a heavenly looking White Hill, spring drilling was finished. About 444 acres over 22 days. Not a lot per day, but there were fertiliser days in there too. Not a bad few weeks' work.

And, talking of heavenly, I reckon the time has come to ask the nice new vicar to sort out the poor soul who still haunts Rough Field. Do they still do exorcisms?

April 13th

Some lie-ins work. This one didn't. All I got for my attempts to catch up on some sleep was a headache that at one stage was threatening migraine status. Luckily, some precious paracetamol (rescued from the combine cab, expiry date 9/2016) kicked in after an hour lying on a dark sofa. Shouldn't have bothered.

Once I was feeling human again, I had a long drive round, and dug up some beans – the winter ones are just poking through, and the spring ones are on the way. It was enough (once I'd had had a majestic sweary shouting match with Kilmeston's Chief Trespasser, strolling nonchalantly and deliberately through the wild bird strips with his black lab) to make me switch the tractor once again from drill to sprayer, ready to get the vital pre-emergence spray on them.

Other highlights of a quiet day were dusty dried-out drilling bogies that were almost too big to get out through a nostril. Not sure that anyone needs to know that, though. I also spent some time on the phone chasing up the cream of Hampshire's pigeon shooting fraternity to get them out here, assuring them that both the NFU and the local PC have given the idea the thumbs-up. That should guarantee the fields are free from pigeons for weeks.

April 14th

The day got off to a wonderful start, and went downhill from there. I was woken by a couple of geese passing over the farmhouse – and that's a first in my lifetime. Feeling unusually refreshed, I leapt out of bed (not really), prepared for a carefully organised day of spraying. Breakfast was a flurry of spray sheets, calculations and mental plans.

The first problem arose when, having worked out how much Stomp Aqua would be needed for the planned pre-em on the spring beans – 70 litres – it turned out that we only had 32 in stock. Numerous phone calls to Tod resulted in multiple rescheduled spray recommendations, which seemed to change by the hour. First, there was no more Stomp Aqua available, so the other chemical in the mix – Defy – would have to be increased. Then it turned out that Tod had found some somewhere, and could drop it off tonight, bless him. But that meant leaving the spring beans for another day, hoping that this morning's hard frost might slow them down a bit in the seedbed.

So I changed plans, and did the weedkiller on the forward wheats in Chalks, BML's and half of Rick/Clump. As I was rinsing out in Chalks, I rang Tod again, and casually checked if I could/should go straight into the bean ground after this chemical mix. "Er, no," said Tod. "Overnight bleach is vital, in case the beans are just poking through." Damn.

It was mid-afternoon, and I briefly contemplated a couple of loads of fertiliser to make room in the main tank for another lorry load which I hoped to order for the couple of wet days at the end of the week, and then a very late bleach fill. All very complicated. Too complicated, in fact, so I went home and filled up the sprayer with clean water and a tub of hypochlorite, and left it to soak, and spent the rest of the afternoon helping Hazel and Jonathan as they started clearing scrub and old trees in the estate yard. I couldn't help pointing out the site of the old loo, a tin shack with a telephone directory for wiping.

The fertiliser team promised delivery on Thursday or Friday, which will be perfect if I can get a couple of loads out before they arrive, and get the pre-em on the beans. It all makes three weeks of continuous drilling seem very easy.

Book One has a lovely review in *The Field*, with the reviewer grasping the whole concept of a real book about real farming perfectly. Might push sales on a bit.

There were no pigeons to be seen anywhere. Probably scared off by the geese.

April 15th

One of the least pleasant arable jobs is doing pre-emergence weedkiller on spring beans. The chemicals we use for the job are bright yellow and stink. The time of year we do it means that there's normally people about, and the weather conditions often mean that there's a bit of a hurry-up to get it on before the beans emerge.

The three fields that needed spraying this year (JA/DC, Cheyney and Hangar) are small, far apart from each other, but free from footpaths. However, they all have houses nearby – the Hangar, with New Cheriton directly to the north of it, is about as near as we get to 'urban fringe'. And, as it has been stubble for many months, it has been adopted as a walking area.

I decided I couldn't leave it any longer. The wind was a gentle east, occasionally ESE (sounds like the shipping forecast), so would take the worst of the pong away from the houses. A normal south-westerly would have been best, but, like everything at the moment, 'normal' is unusual.

As it happened, it worked out very well. I failed to spot one walker on Dark Lane – I was staring too hard at the ground, searching for a tramline marker – so I hope she wasn't too upset as I passed, noisily, colourfully and aromatically, within a couple of yards. I had hoped to catch up with her when I reached the end of the field, but she'd gone. I wonder if it was her who left a fresh bag of dog poo on the gate into Springshot.

Cheyney was a challenge: no tramlines visible at all. God knows if I managed to do the whole field, or if strips of weeds are going to emerge. And for JA/DC, I abandoned looking for the pre-emergence markers, and used last year's still-visible tramlines. By now I just wanted to get the damn stuff on. I did a wash out in Dell Close, apologised to the Literary Agent's wife, who was walking Piper down the road, and went home for a satisfied lunch.

Getting more fertiliser on the spring barleys in Folly and some of Godwin's was a doddle by comparison. I had a long virus-distanced chat with the Editor, out for his Hour, at the top of Middle Broom. The clean-air view over the A272 valley and beyond was stunning, and the main road itself is still relatively peaceful, although traffic is creeping up a bit. He said it reminded him of the early years of this century, when leading his children on horseback alongside the main road was still safe enough to be possible. It's a funny contrast of feelings: longing for the old days, while hoping things get back to 'normal' soon. Whatever 'normal' is. I headed home with half a tank; it was too late to refill now.

April 16th

With much clattering and banging, Hazel's 15 cattle rumbled their way onto the lorry, and were whisked off to Woburn. She had come to a very satisfactory deal with Tom, the Livestock Agent, and she and Jonathan got up reasonably early to load them. The lorry was originally due at eight, but was delayed, so Hazel texted Jonathan to say he could stay in bed for another hour. It worked.

It's always a relief when great big dopey moos make their way onto a lorry. Yes, they're quiet, yes, they're tame, but they will have never seen anything like it, and there's always the potential for something to go horribly wrong. Not this time, though. It was rather sad to see them go. Will they be replaced?

I did the next *Flindt on Friday*, and then headed out on more fertiliser duties. I topped up the part load I came home with last night, and then did the spring barley in Big Broom and BOMS, putting them to bed – fertiliser-wise, anyway. Just as I was finishing Big Broom, the tanker driver rang for directions, saying he'd be here just after lunch. That would be perfect, giving me a chance to drain the big tank first. He listened very carefully to my detailed instructions in the way that only someone who has no intention of actually remembering them can. I could tell he was driving, and so there was no consulting a map going on.

Sure enough, just I was draining the main tank there was another call. "I've got to the main farm; where do I go now?" So I went through all the details again. "There's someone here, I'll ask him," said the driver. Luckily, the 'someone' was Jonathan, fresh from a long session bagging up the last of the chicken/pheasant corn, left on the floor of Godwin's barn after harvest. But I was still relieved when the huge lorry joined me in the Drier Yard.

Rain is still promised, so I cracked on with another dose on the forward wheats.

It was hot and a bit scorch-y, and the weedkiller had already tickled it up a bit on the overlaps, but it seemed important to get another good dose on in case the forecast is right. I did Chalks, the good half of Rick/Clump, and then called it a day. A fantastic anvil cloud could be seen far to the south, and the radar and lightning detector said something big was heading this way from France. We'll see.

April 17th

Not a drop of rain. Dry as a bone. A monumental storm had petered out as it crossed the Channel. If you'd told me four – or even three – weeks ago that I would soon be having a bit of a sulk because we'd missed out on rain, I don't think I would have believed you. Luckily, there was more wet weather on the way, and as spots started to fall mid-morning, I headed out with a large dose of fertiliser to BML's. By the time I finished, the rain was proper 'wipers on' rain. This'll do some good.

Heading back down the little track from BML's and out onto the road at Joan's Acre is always a bit of a worry, and my Guardian Angel (who has had a busy year this year) whispered in my ear to be extra careful. Good advice; just as I was nudging the front of the Deere blindly out onto the road, a little black Fiat 500 shot past, inches from the front link arms. (Yes, I know the arms should have been folded up safely.) I just had time to recognise the 'Raimes English Sparkling' magnetic sticker on the driver door as it passed. It was neighbour Robert Jnr's wife, out delivering bottles of their wildly successful bubbly. (Have to make sure we use the correct terminology, of course.)

On the totally irrational assumption that there would be no more traffic, I followed her out into the road, and drove home through some lovely puddles. I rang Robert Jnr to get my pre-emptive apology in for nearly opening up the little Fiat like a sardine can. We laughed about it, and he said he'd be up in the yard shortly to drop off the Kockerling-ing bill, and pick up the huge tine that his magic cultivator had left behind in White Hill, and which Hazel had spotted while rolling. The value of the tine wasn't far off the cost of a couple of acres of Kockerling-ing, so he was very grateful it had been found.

He was also grateful that we had good stocks of lovely big square bale hay. We went mad on haymaking last year, giving the pastures the most monumental few weeks of TLC. Mind you, we had all the arable side of the farm under control this time last year. The grass fields had spray, fertiliser, a good slit, and a good, but very slow, roll. Rolling 80 acres of pasture very slowly with an eight-foot-wide roller redefined patience. Hazel and I did it in long shifts. But, my word, it was worth it. We filled the barn with a mountain of fantastic hay, and a lot of it is still there. We also baled more straw than we thought we could ever get rid of at harvest, but Dad's old saying – "you can never have too much hay and straw!" – is, once again, proving true. Robert is after a couple of trailer loads for the horse livery business. He'll have to organise it between the little loads of straw that keep vanishing from the barns, too. All of it is very useful cashflow.

Robert arrived in the yard and there was a virus-distanced exchange of invoices and huge metal tines, and then we stood, correctly spaced, in the log-barn with Jonathan (who was having a firewood session) and moaned as only farmers can. We moaned about growing oilseed rape, we moaned about the frosts playing havoc with his vineyards, we moaned about the RPA inspection he's found out he's having; one thing we didn't moan about was the rain overflowing the dodgy gutters. And that *is* unusual.

What was also unusual was the feeling of having nothing to do. After a glorious flat-out month of tractor work, there's nothing leaping out from the 'to do' list. Yes, there are shooting strips to cultivate, another dose of N could have gone on the late-drilled wheats (although they've hardly grown enough to take up the first dose), and there are still barns to be blitzed after a long winter of seed and rat storage, but I'll leave that to Hazel and Jonathan. The rain was set for the afternoon, Jonathan had brought in another heap of dry beech, so there was only one solution for a couple of hours: the sofa.

By evening, the rain had cleared, and I did my favourite Clump walk for the first time in weeks. Last time I did it, only a couple of fields had been touched, and the view south from the top of BOMS was grim. It was a different picture today; if they weren't greening up nicely (or yellowing, in the case of the rape), they had that 'just sown and rolled' look. BOMS itself looked best of all. All that Kockerling-ing had been worthwhile. Funny old world.

Best of all, another huge heap of rain was promised overnight, and as Sasha and I nipped out to check on a car that had driven very slowly past, the lightning over the Channel was spectacular. Sasha decided very quickly that the car was just being driven quietly to avoid the curtain twitches (and the fact that we were out there showed that it had failed in that respect) and trotted off indoors. She's a miracle, that dog. I watched the storms for another ten minutes, and then headed off to bed.

April 18th

There was no lightning or thunder overnight, and, judging by the fact that I slept through and well, no rain either. I was all prepared for another weather-related huff until I drew the curtains. The world was drenched. The radar showed it had been long and steady overnight – the perfect follow-up to yesterday's rain. Perfect for a quiet Saturday.

The only problem is that there's nothing else to do. No sport to watch, no driving allowed, no pub trips. A couple of hours watching Australian Border Control documentaries was quite enough, and I headed out in Tigger for a bit of a 'state of the farm' tour.

The forward wheats are quite scorched, but otherwise looking healthy, and loving the rain. The winter beans are through nicely in places, but quite badly notched on the leaves. The weevils were obviously enjoying the hot spell, too. Spring beans are just coming through, so I'm glad I got the spray on in time.

The spring barleys look fantastic, and the spring wheat, although patchy in places, is looking better by the day. In a warm, wet seedbed, all that late germinating seed will be cracking on now. The only problem is the peas, which are racing towards emergence, but haven't been sprayed. The wet spots in White Hill won't be any drier after all that lovely rain, though.

After lunch, I decided it was time to start giving the shooting strips a good working over – a job that should always be second in the queue after farm jobs. So I hitched onto the disks and gave a couple of them a session of tillage. It always takes longer than you think, and by the time I'd done the home 'S', I was ready for tea, and headed home from the far end of Roe Hill via BOMS and the Clump track – there were a few fallen branches on the path that needed to be pushed back.

"Hello trees, hello sky!" I thought, once I'd done my good deed and made the footpath more passable, and headed off north up the track, shutting the grab at the same time.

Or so I thought. I was actually lowering the grab, still open and slightly tilted down, towards the ground. The next thing I knew, the tractor stopped dead, as the row of bottom tines suddenly dug in – and I had been travelling at a fair lick on the smooth track. Actually, it's all a bit blurred: I can remember a monumental collision, jarred teeth, a ferocious blow to the rib cage, and looking down to see a distinctly funny shaped steering wheel. As usual, the first thing you do is check that no one witnessed this moment of monumental stupidity. Luckily, there was no one about.

Next, assess the damage. Apart from the steering wheel, everything else seemed OK. No teeth had broken, and the ribs were sore as hell, but not broken or popped. Both a great relief – who would want to be finding a dentist or travelling to A&E at the moment? I limped home and managed to get some sympathy – when the laughter had died down. It'll make a good *Flindt on Friday*, anyway.

April 19th

Another lockdown Sunday, and the first one we've really noticed. Up to now, there has been enough frantic activity to ensure we're kept busy. But the fields are too wet for spraying, the papers are running out of things to say, but there's a reasonable selection of films on television. I had another drive round (still feeling rather tender), and for the first time since the September equinox (when the six-month rain started) decided that the farm looked officially 'good'.

In a fit of enthusiasm, based on the fact that we might have a harvest after all, I tried to start the combine, which had been sitting untouched since the last day of harvest. The longer warmer days would be perfect for the annual pressure wash and service. It tried to start, and then the batteries gave up – they're still the originals, from 2010, so I shouldn't complain. There was then a jolly half hour hunting round barns and sheds for the 50-metre extension cable and the charger, both of which had been ruthlessly tidied away by Jonathan, and were therefore almost untraceable. Once they were found, I rigged everything up to charge overnight (the three-pin sockets down at the main barn are getting very dodgy), and came home via White Hill, which I decided was still too wet to drive over – although there's another race against germination to get the pre-em on. Rather curiously, I could find peas that were on the point of bursting through, and peas that looked straight out of the bag. Odd, I thought. The forecast suggested a windy few days were imminent, so I thought I'd give it a go tomorrow.

April 20th

An early visit to the combine suggested that the batteries had charged OK (in other words, hadn't exploded overnight), so I disconnected the charger, but left it there just in case. The extension cable stayed too, ready for the pressure washer. And on the way back, White Hill felt firm enough to carry the weight of a tractor and trailed sprayer.

The worst time to find out that the wind is a bit too strong to be out spraying is once you've got out into the middle of the field, you're spraying bright yellow Stomp (again), and the tracks and paths are full of people taking full advantage of the new government advice to drive out to the countryside and have a walk. I shut the tractor windows, adopted my grumpy farmer face and just pushed on.

In the end, it went well. The only muddy mess was in the far south-east corner (always a wet spot), the satnav found me some new tramlines to make up for the out-of-sync ones laid down during drilling, and my hunch that I would have too much in the sprayer if I didn't push the rate up was spot on, and I ran out on the last ten yards of Rough Field. I have a horrible feeling that I managed to flush out the booms on the bits I'd deliberately left for shooting strips, but there we go.

I hitched off the sprayer and back onto the ST4 with a plan to get rid of a leftover 500 kg of spring wheat up in Clump. Every single surface of the Deere was yellow-coated after the spraying – horrible. Must get the pressure washer up and running. I calibrated for 200 kg/ha and headed out via the Godwin's fields.

Half of Clump was quite respectable forward wheat, from October. Then there was a strip from a dismal attempt to sow in the late winter, which had mostly rotted, and finally a few acres of very late sown Crusoe, done as an experiment to see if it would come to ear. I resowed the rotted strip with spring wheat, and then started on the north and west headlands. By the time the seed ran out exactly on cue (2.5 ha/496 kg, according to the onboard computer) there was a little patch of 'experiment' wheat, and the rest looked fantastic. A quick roll, tomorrow, and that should, at last, be the end of sowing. Fantastic.

My joy was short-lived. In among this morning's letters (the postie leaves them in the virus-approved plastic box in the yard) were two from the company that supplied our pea seed. I opened them in the wrong order: the first was an envelope full of 'replacement' seed labels for the bags of seed, along with a hand-written note, saying we should keep these and destroy the old ones. I wouldn't know where the old ones were if you paid me – probably out in the yard, still attached to the now empty bags, stacked up in Godwin's silo waiting for recycling to restart. Hazel and Jonathan had just finished a monster broom and bucket session in the tractor barn, sweeping and cleaning up, so the bags c/w labels had only just been gathered into bundles.

The second letter explained it all. A re-test of the seed's germination had come up with a dramatically low figure: 70%. What was really odd was that the letter seemed unconcerned. "Yeah, we know it's illegal [I paraphrase], but we're sure it'll be fine." And what was really, really odd was that they'd found out the terrible germination rate two days before it was shipped out – and I do seem to remember being taken aback at the earliness of the delivery, and the short notice we got. Almost as if they wanted it out of the way as quickly as possible.

And then there's the really, really, *really* odd bit: the letter breaking the news was dated three weeks ago, but only arrived today. It's almost as if they wanted it all in the ground before the bad news got out.

I rang Tod, who was astonished. I rang Crop Advisors, who said they'd heard about it, and would be looking into it further. I managed to track down the man whose name was at the bottom of the letter. He was a curious combination of wary and belligerent. Their agronomists would be liaising with ours, and everything will be fine, but if not, everything's insured. Hmmm.

It might explain why, in my digging session in White Hill, I often found ungerminated seed alongside nearly emerged plants. This one, I think, will run and run.

April 21st

Too windy for spraying, and all the drilling done, too dry for working shooting strips; what's a man to do? There's a danger of letting the lockdown get to you if you don't find something. Luckily, the parts for the old sprayer diaphragm pump had arrived, so I had a long morning reassembling the crankcase with squeaky clean new diaphragms. Amazing after all these years (the heads were stamped '2006') that everything seemed to fit together OK. The insides are a bit gooey with all sorts of gunk, so my next mission will be to find something to flush it through with. Either that, or I'll just use standard oil and change it after a few days.

And for the afternoon, I set about the combine with the pressure washer. It started on the button, and I reversed it slowly out of the barn. Three hours later, it only needed another couple of hours to be finished. I'd done most of the complicated bits under the covers – the bits that delight in sending the jet of water straight back into your face. When I couldn't focus any more, I headed home.

This harvest will be its tenth. According to the 15-year plan (pay over five years, run cheaply for five years, run expensively for five years, and then sell) it's about to enter the more troublesome spell of its life here. Let's hope Luke the Combine Wizard works his magic again this year. I rang Garwood's once I got in to check that combine servicing was still ongoing. Good news – it is.

Even better news: the peas are coming through strongly. I'm glad I got the spray on the other day. And they look thick enough to allay concerns about germination – so far. A loop round Kilmeston Road was less encouraging, though. The spring wheat looked patchy and very poor. So much so that I drove back through the farm into Springshot, climbed over the gate into Kilmeston Road and had a closer look. For some reason, it looked a heck of a lot better from close up. There's a lot of seed only just germinating after the hot rain the other day, so if the rooks can give it half a chance, it should thicken up.

Another Tuesday evening, another one without our once-regular pub trip. But Robert still rings for a catch-up and a gossip. It's nice, but still not the same without four pints of Perridge and a couple of pairs of packets of peanuts.

April 22nd

One more outstanding job, and everything will be up together – for a bit, anyway. The forward wheats (Chalks, some of Rick/Clump and BML's) need a healthy dose of fungicide and some straw shortener. I'm warming to the idea of quite low water rates, so with 29 hectares or so to be sprayed, I set the rate to 110l/ha for the 3,200 litre tank. There was a lot of chemical to pour in, and you always worry it's going to make a gooey mixture, but 100 litres in 3,200 isn't really a problem. There's more of a problem getting all the empty cans into an old seed bag that was empty only a couple of days ago. The quicker the recycling gang get their act together, the better. At the moment we can't get a squeak out of them about opening times, and the yard doesn't get any emptier. The virus is playing havoc with everything.

I was very pleased to run out on the last tiny turn of BML's, had an in-field wash out and came home. Hazel rang just as I was finishing, asking if I was OK. That's the problem with doing a heck of a lot of acres in one tank, especially over three different fields. You're away for ages.

Hazel went off in the afternoon with the loader and had a long session putting all the anti-poacher telegraph poles back into position across gateways. We've had all the fields lying wide open for ages while we've been flat out, and we reckon we might be pushing our luck. One night the buggers will arrive back and make a monumental mess of the newly sown fields. Mind you, the ground is baking hard again, and the police are thrilled at the lack of night-time traffic, which makes a dodgy Subaru stick out like a sore thumb.

Meanwhile, I had a quieter afternoon cleaning out the diaphragm pump a bit more, and pressure washing the Stomp off the tractor. Bloody stuff gets everywhere.

The Editor rang in the evening in a state of high excitement. He'd been on pigeon patrol, and spotted them coming into White Hill at last. We hatched a cunning plan to get him up to the Barracuda dell for the afternoon tomorrow. He's finally relaxed into the idea of being out shooting, now that I have written confirmation from the police and the NFU that it is allowed. It still leaves the tiny issue of getting him anywhere, bearing in mind his brilliant mind is totally unable to process map information and directions. Tell him how to get to Dell Close, and there's a high chance he'll ring from Darlington. I think I'll escort him to the dell.

April 23rd

Yet another hot sunny day. I got a bit cooked washing off the combine the other day, so haven't done any more to it. Instead, I got the 'bent steering wheel' saga written up as the next *Flindt on Friday*, which seemed to go down well.

It was too hot and a bit early for a second dose of fertiliser on the late wheats so it was a fun DIY Thursday. I needed some bits for the last stages of the diaphragm pump overhaul, so Jonathan did an online 'click and collect' with Screwfix in Winchester, and then set off to get them – M6 x 22 Allen screws and a five litre tub of proper degreaser. He got a great welcome (if a virus-distanced one) – he worked there for months during his year out, and many of his workmates are still there. He got a lovely handwritten 'best wishes' note on the receipt.

I then got him going with the chainsaw-on-a-stick, and he set about the dozens of sycamore suckers that have grown all around the garden and yard over the years. His mission (I told him) is to make it possible to see the Back Meadow from our bathroom window – as we used to be able to do when we moved in, in 1997.

The Editor arrived in the middle of a delicate sharpen, and I escorted him out into the peas, round the north and east edge of White Hill and Rough Field, and up to the Barracuda dell, where I left him scanning the clear blue sky for pesky pigeons, and making half mumbled plans about flight lines and where to leave decoys. It's his definition of heaven.

Back home, with the mixed musical accompaniment of a Makita two-stroke and a blackbird singing "you've got to stay indoors!" I set about the pump, filling it up with degreaser and turning it by hand for five minutes using half an old PTO shaft from one of the shelves in the barn. A couple of hours later, I drained it, and filled it with fresh oil. And then remembered that the oil refill is the last thing you do on a refurbishment. Oh well. I'll work out how to tip it on its side (to fit the manifolds) without spilling oil everywhere later.

One noise noticeable by its absence was gunfire. Sure enough, the Editor rang late afternoon to say he'd had hardly a shot, and apologising. I told him off for apologising – news that there no pigeons to be seen is welcome news for farmers – but he'd be welcome any time.

Tod the Agronomist arrived, and we had another staddle-stone based virus-separated chat. He was happy with most things – only the OSR concerned him. The flea beetle larvae have been taking out many stalks, which is why it looks so stunted and pale, and the big frosts last week didn't help with the flowering. Oilseed rape's days are pretty well numbered.

But what do we replace it with as a break crop? I mentioned that neighbour Ashley is looking for maize ground, but Tod was cautious. In theory, it makes a great entry for winter wheat, but four years out of the past five, the weather has meant maize fields being left rutted and unworkable until the next spring, when barley tends to be the best option. Which sort of defeats the purpose. He said we'd have to look closely at our tenancy agreement, too, and also how we'd work it with buying chemicals and fertiliser through our buying group – maize is very hungry for both. Suddenly, OSR looks like less of a hassle.

I remembered that today I was supposed to be at the big press launch of the new Defender – a proper two-day freebie. Cancelled, of course. I had a very rare silent curse at the virus.

April 24th

The Editor's uncanny ability to keep pigeons off fields of peas wasn't to be taken for granted two days in a row, so I set off, armed with boxes of rope bangers and some long-handles secateurs, to try and keep the fields safe. At the entrance to Roe Hill were two elderly walkers, looking lost, so I paused to offer help.

Inevitably, a long chat ensued. He was an elderly chap, but both he and his wife were sprightly, and setting off to the bluebell woods using some fairly scanty directions on their phones. They read out what they thought they should be doing, and I did the classic "I wouldn't start from here if I were you" routine. More chatting revealed that he was an ex-builder and had worked on many buildings in Hinton Ampner in the early sixties. He was part of the team that rebuilt the House after the terrible fire, and said he'd done work on Joan's Acre House, too. He remembered a few of the old characters from round here, but didn't mention Dad.

After half an hour of virus-distanced gossiping, I sent them on their way over Roe Hill and down to New Pond, and on to the Joan's Acre Woods. They thought it sounded like a bit of a hike, but set off.

Luckily, the pigeons hadn't discovered the peas in the meantime, and I cut some 'pea sticks' in the copse at the entrance to Springshot, and drove out across White Hill, siting three sticks and associated rope bangers in what I hoped would be the perfect triangle of deterrence. Good band name.

The combine beckoned for another session of pressure washing – probably the second session of three. As usual, it's very satisfying working slowly – and gently – over the black dust, restoring it to New Holland yellow. I exchanged jolly greetings from on top of the cab with various walkers and riders, although the view into the oilseed rape in Drier Field wasn't quite so jolly. It seems to have decided that its pathetic efforts at flowering are all we're going to get this year.

I mentioned the bluebell walkers to Hazel when I got in, and she said they were probably heading for the much closer Broom Wood bluebells. Ah – that would make sense of their directions. I had a mini-crisis about sending them on a five-mile round trip instead of their intended one mile one. I'm sure they've forgiven me.

April 25th

There was an inexplicable surge in Book One sales on Amazon (five in about an hour), so I sorted those out while Hazel put more bangers out on the peas on her paper run. The flatcoats reckon it is the best fun in the world (apart from real shooting, of course) because there's smoke, bangs, birds flying, and even a dead pheasant on the brow, being cleaned up by a couple of red kites. It made their day.

I was in shooting mode, too, deciding to have another go at cultivating the shooting strips after last week's slightly painful debacle. I'd been meaning for weeks to assemble my dream tilth-buster, and finally got it done just after lunch. I've got the three-metre heavy discs, but I've also got an Opico Varitilth, which is a set of six quite deep cultivating legs on a frame which goes between the tractor and the discs. They came in a set with an Opico Varidisc, which was a great machine in theory, but terrible in practice. Too many complicated settings and a billion grease nipples. I sold that at the West Meon Crap Sale and bought the much simpler Proforge version a couple of years ago.

It took an hour or so to get the two machines to mate up successfully, and the finished product is fairly long and heavyweight, and it made the Massey work a bit in the hot weather (must give the drop-nose radiators a blow out), but it did a fantastic job. I worked down the two strips in Big Field, the tiny one behind the narrow wood in Big Field, then Roe Hill and Chalks.

On the way from Big Field, I spotted two people wandering around in the oilseed rape, so made a detour to ask what they were up to. I was then treated to one of the finest sets of comedy excuses I've heard in a very long career of asking people to keep to the Right of Way.

"You seem a bit lost," I started with (my usual opener) as they emerged out of the crop and rounded the end of the barn.

"Oh, can we not park here?" asked mother of teenage daughter, gesturing to where they pulled off the road into a mini-layby.

"Of course you can park there," I replied, "But I'm worried that you were out in the crop, which could easily have just been sprayed with insecticide and fungicide."

"No, we weren't."

"Yes, you were; I've just been watching you from that field over there," I pointed out somewhat wearily.

"Oh. Well, we were looking for the footpath out there," she grumped.

"Madam, if there was a footpath out there, there would be a path cleared through the crop, and a sign saying 'footpath'. The footpath is over there." I very nearly added 'as you well know', because I thought I recognised her and them as locals. But I can never see behind their shades.

"We wanted to see how tall the crop was," was the next justification. I'm afraid I burst out laughing at this one. Not least because the distinguishing feature of that particular field is that the oilseed rape has given up growing and flowering after reaching a pathetic 18 inches. So, if they were a couple of budding agronomists, that would have been a valid excuse. But they weren't, so it wasn't. I asked if I could use that last one in an article, and the mother got a bit cross. "You don't understand. We're looking to make a music video for my daughter – she's written some songs. She's played at Open Mic Nights with your band, the Old Gits." And she then said who she was – and they were indeed locals.

But, for goodness sake; why didn't she say that to start with? I would have been delighted to let her scan the whole farm for possible filming locations. We have atmospheric barns, sweeping rural vistas, post-industrial abandoned grain cleaning plant – and even pathetic oilseed rape crops. But by then, the atmosphere was a bit strained, so they went their way, and I went mine. I should really pick up the phone and invite them back. Perhaps later.

April 26th

The two shooting strips on the west edges of Long Field and Pipeline tend to get neglected at this time of year – but only because I'm too idle to make the long trip up there. But it's worth putting the work into them, because they've provided lots of entertainment over the last few seasons, if not many birds. The Editor writes regularly in *The Field* about the mysterious 'Pipeline Twelve' who evade us week after week.

All the other strips had had healthy doses of Roundup and been cultivated, so I thought the time had come to get up there – even if it was Sunday morning. So I loaded up with a couple of hundred litres of water, some wetter, and a healthy dose of glyphosate and set off. It all looked a bit neglected up in Stanmore. It was originally booked in for winter barley, but the weather put paid to that idea, and the last time we were up there we were slipping and sliding in ankle-deep mud. And that was only months after being up there in the combine, relishing a joyous and bountiful – and rock-hard – harvest. How the farming year goes round.

Then it was time for the last lap of the combine wash, with the more gentle hosepipe and a soft brush. Finally, I stopped pushing harvest grime from one end of the machine to the other, and it started to look relatively clean. I left it with its sides up to dry and called it a day; I'd had my fill of hot sunshine for a bit.

It is a joy having Jonathan home during the lockdown. I think Hazel and I ran out of things to say to each other some years ago. (That's why long-married couples buy dogs, I reckon.) He went to bed before us – which is quite unusual for a 20-year-old, although he is doing monumental high-speed walks round the farm every evening with Sasha, who is his new best friend as a result. Seeing his light was still on as I passed his door, I asked if he was OK, if he needed tucking in, if he needed his tummy tickled and a cuddle and a hot Ribena.

Some moments later, as I dozed off, I relished the thought that I if did the 'Grandpa' and died suddenly overnight, there would be enormous solace to be found in the fact that the last words we exchanged were "Do you want your tummy-wummy tickled?"; "Just fuck off, Dad!"

April 27th

It was a busy morning on the phones. We had a letter from North's garage reminding us that the Octavia Scout's MOT has run out. We booked it for the end of the week, with perhaps a full set of new Falken tyres. The backs are getting perished, and the fronts have worn down a lot since being part of the sale deal a year ago. Trouble is, it's a hoot to drive, and heavy right feet cause extensive tyre wear – front and back.

Next up was APM for some agricultural bits and pieces. I managed to get more rope bangers ordered, but there was a laugh at the other end of the line when I asked about stocks of dust masks. I think the NHS has commandeered the lot. We'll have to use the few we've got carefully, and hope supplies get back to normal come barn-sweeping time.

I then chased up Bright's Seeds by text about the cover crops for this season. We've used a mix with kale in for some years, and it's time for a break. The reply was instant but with a lot of options. I'll get my head round them later. It was easier in the days of the big shoot, when it was maize and millet, and that was it.

Last up was Garwood's, to tell them that the combine was as clean as I was going to get it, and so it was ready for Luke the Combine Wizard to do his pre-season check and service. That, too, was booked for first thing Friday. That, along with a very wet weather forecast, was my cue to pop down the Drier Yard and put the clean(ish) and dry combine back in the barn. I had to get my way past two mysterious SSE electricity vans which have a habit of parking up in that yard – and the one at home – and doing bugger all. I've never worked out what they're up to, but we had a polite chat about the combine, and they furtively drove off. One of them looks astonishingly like Julian Assange, which might explain a bit.

With rain on the way, I thought I'd have another session on fertiliser, and put the second dose on the spring wheats. Blackhouse Road looked good, Kilmeston Road looks very poor – the rooks have done some serious damage. Let's hope tomorrow's rain and another 70 kg/ha of N will kick it on a bit.

You could tell a serious change in weather from the hot'n'humid to something more unsettled was on the way: we were invaded by a massive bee swarm. Robin the Bee Man was summoned from his den in Godwin's yard. He said it was too big and active to be dealt with then, but he found the queen, put her in a box, and left the rest to follow her in overnight. He's very welcome to them.

April 28th

A 'good' rain is slow and steady, but wakes no one – and that's what we had last night. I woke from yet another dream-infested sleep (in the most dramatic, I had to get to one of the northern unis in a great hurry, with only an ill-sounding Fiat 127 at my disposal) thinking the rain must have missed us.

It hadn't; the yard was full of healthy puddles, and the whole world felt nicely washed. I celebrated with a quiet day, mostly in the office, and partly on the sofa. It was only as it started getting late that I remembered the sprayer MOT test first thing tomorrow, so I gave the sprayer a good clean out (nozzles, filters, etc) and unfolded it carefully in the yard. I got drenched in the process by another bout of 'good' rain, although I was less than complimentary about it when I finally got back in.

April 29th

The man doing the sprayer MOT arrived on the dot of 8.30, and the next few hours were taken up with a pretty comprehensive front-to-back checkover. All the pipes, connections, pivots and booms were given a thorough inspection, and, apart from a bit of chafing where the outlet pipe leaves the pump, passed with flying colours. We then fired it up, got the pressure in the booms to 3 bar, and he worked his way along the nozzles, armed with a stopwatch and measuring cylinder, checking output. I sat in the cab and kept dry, he got drenched. Once again, no problem. We did a bit of investigation into why chemical takes so long to reach the end on the booms, when it's supposed to have built-in recirculation, but found nothing amiss. I'll go back to the main dealers and ask them.

He even had a spare lid for the oil reservoir on the overhauled pump, and took away a set of six diaphragms from one of my old AR pumps, which I found lurking in the back of the barn, unused. That'll be worth 50 quid off the bill. I hope.

The rain came on heavy again, so I took the chance to give the Octavia another blast, ready for its MOT on Friday. The furthest place I could go for AdBlue was Hunt's at Chilbolton, so, after I'd rung to check for stock, I had a lovely high-speed drive up the A34 and the Roman roads. Traffic was heavier than the last time I dared to venture out, but still well below pre-lockdown levels.

A late evening walk with Sasha in sudden sunshine showed most crops looking fantastic, and the spring wheat in Clump up and away spectacularly, after only ten days. We had a stand-off with a huge fox in Roe Hill – it was tucking into something (probably one of Hazel's pheasants) and didn't see us sneaking up on it. It looked at Sasha, and Sasha looked at it, and I bet both thought they were looking in a mirror. After a moment or two, it ambled off into the trees with its catch. I cursed not having the .22 slung over my shoulder, as one did in the old days. There would have been one big dog fox less. Who am I kidding? There would have been one big dog fox scurrying away laughing, and a .22 heading off to Bramdean somewhere.

April 30th

More lovely rain – which was lucky, because I spent much of the day struggling with the next *Flindt on Friday*. I'm trying to do a rare deadly serious one, and they're actually harder than the silly ones.

It was another busy day on the phones. After my visit to the Deere dealer yesterday, I dropped an email to the rep enquiring about replacing my much-loved 6630P after eight years and 3,600 hours. He was on the phone early with a rough figure for a 2020 'model year' 6155M, which Deere has wisely made remarkably similar to the old and hugely popular 6030 series, and news that there was an 'early bird' scheme being run by John Deere, worth another couple of grand – and, guess what: it ran out today! Much as I'd love to agree the world's fastest tractor deal (three minutes), I said I'd look at the quote properly (if he emailed them through), and that I felt confident that we could come to a deal that would match the 'early bird' scheme.

It took ages for the email to come through, because the internet died. It was a bit iffy last night, and it was useless this morning. It's only then that you realise how utterly dependent we are on it. Even trying to find details of our internet company – Fleur – involves an instinctive reach for Google followed by a self-admonishing slap to the forehead. Luckily, stacked deep in the pile of files on the office shelves is paperwork from the last time it died, and Fleur's contact details were on it. Curiously, after I'd spent 20 minutes in a queue on the landline, the internet started again, and went well all day. I never did get through to them.

There was much discussion about who's at fault. Is it an intermittent fault, or someone doing maintenance or an upgrade further down the line? The landline works – and it has never been so busy – and the router and its cables work well some of the time; if they were knackered, they'd never work. There's the horrible feeling of having to ring Openreach, who will suck their teeth and tell you off for not being with BT, and then charge you a huge fee if there's nothing wrong with their equipment if they come out and look at it. And everyone is short-staffed at the moment.

Worst of all is the fact that Jonathan is doing some hastily cobbled together internet-based exams to end his first year at Newcastle Uni. He managed to message assorted lecturers from his course who replied that they know all about useless rural broadband, and there are systems in place to deal with that problem. It's a shame he switched his chosen degree to Economics and Politics from Computer Science during his 'A' levels. Imagine how handy that would have been.

On a more muddy and mundane level, I place the order with Bright Seeds (after some highly successful haggling) for the game cover. 'Broad Buster' for the nearest strips which need some weed control, Radical Pheasant and Finch for the other strips (except Big Field) to give them a break from kale, and something with sunflowers in for Big Field – which will no doubt look lovely and result in a thousand people a day trampling through it. So maybe not a very wise choice. We'll see.

We dropped the Octavia down at North's for its MOT. It was quite lucky that the government have given everyone another six months on their MOT deadline – we'd forgotten all about it. When the reminder came through from North's it was a bit of a shock to realise we've had that car for a year. It was only yesterday that an exciting car hunt ended at a Mitsubishi dealer in Downton, who had just what we wanted: a reasonably low mileage Octavia Scout in silver. We got a far better deal by not trading in our old 1.9PD model, although there's always the slight worry about trying to sell privately. So we asked the team at North's if they'd put it in their yard with 'for sale' on the windscreen. They politely declined, but only because one of their team happened to be looking for a car just like it. So the world's quickest private car sale was done.

There was one tiny issue when they rang up a few days later and asked where the spare keys were. We could have sworn we'd put them in the car, they swore we hadn't. I wouldn't say that things got heated, but there was an odd feeling that something wasn't right. So there was much relief a few days ago when Hazel, in the middle of sweeping the garage, found the spare keys down among the leaves. I rang North's with the news, asking rather sheepishly if they'd spent a fortune on getting a replacement set. Luckily, they hadn't, and they were much relieved to see the spares when we dropped them off today.

All this non-writing activity did the job, and just after tea, the next column finally clicked. It's guaranteed to upset the ecofascists, but that's no bad thing. I celebrated with a Drier loop walk with Sasha (her fourth walk of the day), although there was a bit of false start when I got halfway to the tennis court and had to turn round for a sweater, a coat, a cap and some gloves. Where's global warming when you need it on the last day of April?

So that's three months of post-Brexit Britain done. And how has it been? Life has changed in ways none of us could possibly have forecast – but it's nothing whatsoever to do with Brexit, of course. It's the coronavirus which has resulted in lockdown, social distancing, closed shops and pubs and the prospect of a trashed economy. Boris has had the virus and looks to have mostly recovered, people are being unbelievably compliant and thoughtful, and the government is handing out money here there and everywhere. The man doing the sprayer MOT said he'd got a cheque for ten grand, which was very nice, but he'd put it safely to one side in case he got another message to say they wanted it back.

Having said all that, for us life hasn't changed at all. The virus arrived with some fine weather, so we've been going flat out for weeks, loving every minute of it. We're essential workers, so we go about our daily business untroubled. The traffic has gone, and most walkers have vanished. We've not got the whole farm sown, but there's only about 140 acres untouched, which isn't bad, considering the state of the place after six months of almost continuous rain, equinox to equinox.

Our subsidies will be starting to taper this year, but it will still be a sizeable sum. Who knows what has happened to the Agriculture Bill? Will it still feature a lump payment to help farmers quit?

Even if it does survive and make it through the House, I suspect that generous lump sums may end up being slightly less generous as the tax demands soar to recoup the government handouts.

But perhaps farming's fortunes will change, too. There's much talk of people shopping more locally, and rediscovering stuff about their food. The home-baking frenzy has helped the wheat price, and this harvest will certainly be lower overall than it has been for many years. Perhaps better times are on the way, and it would be a shame to miss them. Perhaps ordering the new tractor would be wise after all.

Meanwhile, we have a big house, a 920-acre garden, and a new puppy to add to the torrent of flatcoats (and Sasha) who consider it their divine mission to be relentlessly cheerful. The weather has been fantastic and the farm looks good. Anthony is doing well in London, being one of the few in the company kept in full-time work and being given more responsibility, and Diana is in a fantastic industry for a lockdown – video gaming. Hazel said she was beginning to tire of working from home, but there are worse places to be stuck than Cambridge in an English spring. And Jonathan is home, still managing to do uni work, and keeping cheerful too – when the internet works. We count our blessings.

Oh yes – Brexit. We're told that things are still going on behind the scenes, but the Remainiacs are of course demanding it be delayed or scrapped. What a surprise, said no one, ever. The good news for Leavers like me is that the EU has been shown up as a completely ineffective and superfluous organisation, and the virus has resulted in national governments springing into action to look after their own. The EU has been flailing around looking for purpose, and failing. For those of us who loathe it with every fibre of our bodies, that can only be a good thing. Meanwhile, the sun shines and the crops grow, and the blackbird in the yard continues to sing an infuriating 'diddley doo di-doo' every 20 seconds. I have a theory that he's singing "you've got to stay indoors!" but hasn't mastered the words yet. I hope the lockdown ends soon, if only for his sake. I'll shoot the fucker soon.

May 1st

May got off to a busy start. By the time I got down the Drier Yard to fill up with more fertiliser, Luke the Combine Wizard had arrived, backed the combine out into the yard and got her opened up for 'winter' inspection. We chatted for a bit, but I thought the quicker he got on with his methodical and unbelievably thorough front-to-back checkover, the better.

We'd had more rain than I thought, and the fresh drilling up on top of Clump was a bit slippery with a full load, but I persevered. I did all of Rick and Clump (trying to keep track of what bit has had what in the mosaic of different wheat crops is a hell of a challenge), and did another tank on Big Field. By then all the moisture had gone, and a howling hot gale meant that fertiliser scorch was now the problem, so I gave that job up, and had an early Friday finish.

Hazel spent a long day rolling the Back Meadow. It had taken a hammering over the wet winter with her cattle and needed a bit of TLC. Unfortunately, the long dry spell meant it was too hard to do anything with, but the last couple of proper wet days have softened it up a bit.

We have a very old – probably 1950s – 3.5 ton heavy roller, made up of heavy metal rings filled with concrete. It has clonked and clanked its way round the farm for all these years, sometimes being very busy, sometimes not used for ages. It had a full season last year, when we decided to give all the pastures, except the Back Meadow, a proper going over. They were harrowed, sprayed, fertilised and – somewhere in the middle of all that – were given a good slit and a roll. We put the heavyweight pasture slitter on the front of the Deere, and hitched onto the roller (you need a bar between the lower linkage arms to take the only narrow pin that fits the roller) and did all the pastures – very slowly. Luckily, this time last year we were all up together, and we took it in shifts.

It paid off, though. We had a monumental hay crop, which Hazel is selling very lucratively now. Some to the horsey crowd, some to cattle owners without grub. And even 12 months on, the pasture looks green and lush.

So it was lovely to see the Back Meadow, having missed out on all the attention last year, coming up in alternating green grass stripes as Hazel trundled back and forth. And some of the stripes were nearly straight.

Back in the mid-80s, pasture rolling was Ken's job, and he took it very seriously. His concentration to keep those lines straight was famous. One day, he was out in Hinton Ampner Park – land we gave up two decades later in a major shuffle of fields (and lucrative cheques) – working his way between the many copses and trees out there. He'd made it up to just below the Hinton Ampner cricket pitch, which was situated on the top of the ridge just west of the House. The views, if not the cricket, were magnificent.

Ken was concentrating so hard on his work, or perhaps enjoying the views so much, that he failed to notice that the central shaft of the roller was working its way out, and the individual segments of roller were becoming free. By the time he did notice, he was dragging the frame alone across the grass – a sort of flat chain-harrowing.

His brother Ernie noticed somewhat earlier. He was out doing some spraying in the Hangar, downhill from the cricket pitch. Life was hard enough for the sprayerman in those pre-tramline days without having to dodge sections of heavy concrete and steel – each weighing four or five hundredweight – which had refused to simply fall over in the pasture, and were rolling at pace down the hill, down across the Park, down the bank, through the fence, and through the crop of spring barley that was in the Hangar.

Ken's face when he arrived sheepishly back in the yard was a picture. He got a major bollocking from Dad, of course, but then attention turned to finding all the sections. Four or five had made it into the Hangar, and we spent the best part of a day driving round with a trailer and the terrible Ford 6610 loader, picking them up. Two lessons were learnt: Ken probably looked behind him while working a bit more frequently, and I discovered that trying to lift a four-hundredweight section from flat to vertical using fingertips will knacker all the tendons on the inside of both forearms for days.

The Octavia sailed through its MOT, and North's had also replaced all four tyres at £100 each, which seems very reasonable. If only we had somewhere to go in it.

May 2nd

Another stunning spring morning, so while Hazel did her paper run, which includes walking across the peas in White Hill and lighting a selection of rope bangers, I sat in the sun outside the back door and entertained the puppy. It took me back to spring '95, when I sat outside the bungalow French windows and entertained another small animal – Anthony, who was then only four months old. Back then, the Trust had done little to popularise Hinton Ampner, even after nearly a decade of ownership, and the footpath along the bungalow's south boundary was pretty well unused. The mania for loud bikes hadn't started back then, and I'm sure the skies were quieter, too. It was a nice hour of nostalgia in the warm sun.

Tod's last spray recommendations included an insecticide for the winter beans if they were being nibbled, so I drove out to Hurst Down to check; they were indeed being nibbled – some of the smaller plants were being hammered by weevils, struggling to get up and away. So, with Saturday's afternoon TV being, once again, utterly uninspiring (much as I'd love to watch the Coventry vs Spurs FA Cup final replay), I filled up the sprayer, put two litres of something unpronounceable in it, set the water rate to 118 l/ha, and headed out there after lunch.

It's a long haul out to Hurst Down, especially with the lanes now heaving with cyclists, walkers and horse riders, and 66 acres being done at speeds that minimise the bumpy ride (I'm crossing last year's uncultivated tramlines) meant it was past four when I got back. My conscience was cleared for the day, although I'd noticed that the top half of Dell Close looked terrible. A quick check of the drill book showed that I'd popped in a bag of 'old stock' Fuego at that point. I knew I should have mixed it in with the new stuff when we were recleaning and bagging the fresh stock. God knows when that old stuff was delivered. Probably when I had Anthony bouncing on my knee.

It was quite entertaining to find the remains of a compass in Dell Close. Not sure whose it was, but it was in several pieces, and a long way from any right of way. I think that's proper 'irony'. I also think there's a fungicide called 'compass', too, just to confuse things further.

May 3rd

A quiet Sunday – 'quiet' as in work, not 'quiet' as in the lockdown, which seems, to all intents and purposes, to have been abandoned. The farm lanes are once again heaving with people – and quite right, too. We take it all for granted.

I did little more than wash Hazel's Octavia and Jonathan's i20, and have a long evening walk in stunning sunshine. A suburban Sunday.

May 4th

My phone rang quite early. It was a farming neighbour, and when she rings, you can usually guarantee 30 minutes of silly 'banter' (as young people say). But not this time. She sounded weary and utterly fed up. She'd been 'furloughed' from her part-time job and had just about had enough of being at home, by the sound of it. If this lockdown is getting to the farming community, then you know it's serious.

The day didn't get much better when I thought I'd get the fungicide/insecticide mix on the oilseed rape. The insecticide refused to rinse out of the can (it's somewhat oddly named 'Aquaflow'), and you're left with a dilemma. Just how long are you supposed to persevere? I used the rotary nozzle in the bowl, I put fresh water in the can, put the lid on and shook vigorously, but nothing would shift a stubborn pale yellow slick at the bottom.

What do you do? Shrug your shoulders and say "Well, I've done my bit", and throw it in the recycling bag? Some poor bugger has got to process it further down the line, and there's always the chance of being in trouble for not washing cans out properly. I rinsed for as long as I could put up with it, and sent the cans to the bag – the sprayer was filling up too fast to hang around much longer.

Mind you, I needn't have hurried. The next chemical to go in was a fungicide, in two 5-kg boxes. Out comes a heap of brown powder that sets in a lump in the induction bowl, and gradually, slowly, reluctantly turns from powder, to porridge, to slurry, to paste, and then finally, to a solution that vanishes through the grid at the bottom. I suppose you're meant to trickle it out of the box while the flushing nozzle is at full blast – but it was too late once I'd tipped the whole lot in at once. Ho hum.

The oilseed rape cheered me up a bit, though. Given another dose of rain and some warm weather, it looks like it might make it to a crop. Only a few weeks ago I was almost writing it off. If I'm going to go through all the palaver of converting the combine for only 50 acres OSR, it had better yield well.

After lunch, I switched to Roundup, having seen the blackgrass romping away in the Stanmore block the other day. I got Pipeline done, and half of Long Field, and then headed back for another agronomy chat with Tod, three of us (he brought his son) sitting on the staddle stones. He, too, seemed a bit fed up. He'd had shouting matches with some normally cheery clients, and things had gone a bit pear-shaped on the weed control front, too; we couldn't use what we'd hoped to use on Blackhouse Road on a technicality. Infuriating, after thinking we'd have a great chance to nobble the blackgrass out there. We agreed to switch to Topic, which is cheap, but probably won't work, and then pencil Blackhouse Road in for another spring crop next year. Funny old game, farming.

We had an email from the co-captain of the White Hunters Cricket Club. It was nothing to do with cricket (alas, cricket's died a death, too), but said that he had a bag of spare hawthorn saplings, and would we like them? We'd been puzzling on how to persuade the good people of Kilmeston that the gap into Long Field isn't gateway, and suddenly a line of hedge planting seemed like the perfect solution. Less militant than a gate or wire, but, we hope, a message forcefully put across. Hazel popped down to his little store in a neighbour's yard to pick them up. We'll buy him a beer if the pubs ever open again.

May 5ᵗʰ

Just for once, the forecast was spot on: a band of rain crept slowly over the Channel, but fragmented as it got to the Isle of Wight. It was a shame, because I was planning another chunk of liquid fertiliser on the wheats, and a drop of moisture would have been handy.

I had another day in the office, trying to get my head around the next Single Farm Payment submission. It's odd; it is such an important part of the farming calendar, you'd think it would be dead easy to remember what you did last year, and how you filled in the online forms.

Not a chance. I dug out the files from last May, and they looked completely alien – almost like the thermodynamics exam papers from June 1984 I found in the attic. I did them once, but I'm damned if I remember how. Hazel and I spent a couple of hours trying to reinterpret all the codes and working out what on earth we'd submitted for our 'greening'. Lots of hedges and trees had been measured, and there was a 720 m length of 'buffer strip', too. It was in a field with a number, which, even after all these years, still means nothing. More cross-referencing gave the field a name; it was White Hill, and the buffer strip was alongside the road. It's a good start, I suppose. You can tell 'real' farming jobs – they're the ones that you fall back into effortlessly.

Hazel went up to the Long Field gap and tried her hand at hedge planting. As usual, she was an expert in moments, and soon two smart lines of hawthorn could be seen, lined up in smart guards and secured with stakes. A drop of rain on them wouldn't go amiss to get them started.

I decided the rain wasn't going to arrive and did a couple of loads of fertiliser in the cool of the evening. The main tank was now empty, and I could have a long session adding up the final 'where's had what?' chart, and ordering the last of the season's nitrogen needs. Maybe over breakfast.

May 6th

I did indeed do my fertiliser sums over porridge. I'd need another 16.5 cubic metres of N35(S) to give everything what I think it needs, and then some more for a splash on the Back Meadow to bulk up the grass a bit, and a bit for the shooting strips. Round it up to 19 m³. Yara weren't open until eight, but I managed to get my order in over the phone. At least, I hope I did. It was like an episode of Harry Enfield's Polish Café – she was lovely and charming over the phone, but the accent barrier was quite substantial. I think she said they couldn't do delivery until after this odd upcoming bank holiday weekend. I said that wasn't a problem – I needed a weekend off.

Assorted spray deliveries came during the morning, once the drivers had rung to find out where the farm is, and then ask why they can't get into the big container in the yard. The answer is very simple: the big container isn't the spray store. It's temporary accommodation for all of Colonel Guy's stuff. When he (finally) left the army, he had nowhere to store a lifetime's worth of possessions, and he asked if we would host a container – once used, lightly dinged on one side, so therefore no good for shipping any more – and let him fill it. It was delivered by a one-man-and-his-lorry operation, sited perfectly in the yard, and even came in my favourite dark green. People who know the yard very well walk past it and hardly realise it's there. The Colonel did several trips up here from Dorset, and filled it to the brim with eclectic paraphernalia; mostly DIY and car maintenance related, but sofas and white goods, too. Certainly no agrochemicals.

He then set off for a bucket list trip to Southern Africa, overland in a highly specced VW Transporter. It was all very open ended ("When will you be back?" "No idea!") until the virus came along. He managed to wangle a rescue flight out of God knows where using connections in the German army, and headed to the wilds of Scotland to re-join his wife. I haven't heard a squeak since. I promised to look after his fabulous blue Legacy 3.0, which is still sitting in the yard. I had a plan to insure it and enjoy it, but that's all binned, too.

One day the Colonel will find somewhere else to put his stuff, and I'll buy the container off him, and it will be the proper spray store. Until then, I'll keep on using the not-terribly-good spray store that forms the north end of the old stable block.

In between guiding spray deliveries to the right part of the farm, I tried, and failed, to come up with the next *Flindt on Friday*. It's amazing how much you need to be out and about to get ideas.

Hazel and Jonathan were much busier. We'd finally got in touch with our plastic recycling people, and several loads of seed bags, spray cans, feed bags and cardboard boxes made their way up to the Monkwood recycling centre on the back of Tigger's trailer (once all the tyres had been pumped up.) I can't decide if I miss the trips over to the Chalks dell with a mountain of plastic, which was then burnt. You had to give it 'close supervision' as it burnt fiercely – which was another way of describing enjoying a couple of cigarettes while sitting in the heat.

Putting Roundup on Stanmore had been halted when I ran out of the vital water conditioner – or is it vital? The glyphosate manufacturer used it as the excuse for a lack of effectiveness decades ago, blaming our hard water. As the price of Roundup has dropped, the price of ammonium sulphate has risen, though, Funny, that. Anyway, one of the deliveries included more conditioner, so I filled up the sprayer for another trip out. I finished Long Field, did Broom Field, folded up to 12 m and did the Barracuda game strip (greening up nicely with weeds and peas where the ST4 had been a bit incontinent on the headland) and then headed into Roe Hill. Roe Hill went really well – the Roundup was much needed – until I ran out of spray with a bit of short work left, probably about the same area as the Barracuda strip. Bother. No doubt I'll be out with glyphosate again soon.

May 7th

An email from *Farmers Weekly* pointed out that Friday is a bank holiday, and they'd like the next column a bit lively, like. Luckily, I had just worked one out, and they had it within an hour.

Hazel got back in from her round of getting the papers and setting rope bangers with a less-than-cheery face; some horse rider had been all over the Stanmore fields, and, worse, had mistaken her beautifully regimented hedge plantings for a jump, and, even worse, made a right hash of the jump. Tree guards and stakes had been splattered everywhere.

That was our cue to load up Tigger with posts, barbed wire, the mallet, a hole-making bar, pliers and hammers, and head up there for a world first: erecting a barbed wire fence that's not meant for livestock. A couple of hours later, a reasonably smart three-wire fence stretched across the gap. It probably won't stop the most militant of trespassers, but we'll just keep fencing whenever they've made new holes. They're coming through and heading over to where one of the rides emerges from the wood, so we drove over there, repaired the 'no access' sign that the Trust had put up some time ago (and which has mysteriously vanished), and put up a row of posts ready for one of the lengths of chestnut paling we bought ages ago. Lunch beckoned – thank goodness. My shoulders were dropping hints that that would do for now. Hazel was keen to keep going with the project, so grabbed Jonathan in the afternoon and went up again with the paling and finished it off.

I was about to go and do some spraying – weedkiller on the late wheats – when I thought I had better check it with Tod. This hot weather is all very well, but it can sometimes inflict a bit of scorch with lively herbicides. He agreed and suggested waiting for things to cool down – or to go out at eight in the evening. I told him to bugger off.

Out there in the outside world, news that the key academic advisor on the unbelievably strict lockdown rule and regulations was breaking all the rules and regulations to boff his glamorous young mistress, who just happens to be a lefty activist and Extinction Rebellion supporter, didn't really come as a surprise at all, somehow. I must get a copy of *The Long March through the Institutions* and see if it has a chapter on the value of pillow talk.

May 8th

One of the worst side-effects of the six-month equinox-to-equinox rain was an explosion of rats. The barns near home were stacked full of bags of seed, just waiting to be nibbled into. We finally got much of it into the ground, and had a blitz on the rest, carrying it and stacking it down at the Drier Yard, where, thanks to a contract with a proper pest-control company, there are no rats. For now, anyway.

So the rats that are up here are getting a bit pissed off, and are beginning to chew anything and everything they can get their vicious little teeth into. We don't mind about the odd cardboard box, but there's always the fear that they'll start on cables and engine bays. It's time to start a counterattack, and a really good start is to round up all the old-fashioned rat-traps I could find, and set them in the tractor barn. After a couple of hours hunting, I had six traps loaded with a mushy peanut butter and porridge paste placed round the inner walls of the barn. That'll get 'em.

Next stop was the old calf pens, when you only have to leave a bag of feed or seed for ten minutes and it'll have a hole in it. The buggers had already started on our bags of game strip seed which were delivered only the other day. So we had a session lifting them out of the way, and then trying to flood the rat holes with the hose pipe. All this proved was that the caverns under the floor are bigger than we thought. Daft idea.

Sasha and I had another majestic walk in the warm evening sunshine, with skies full of purple and reds as the sun went down. There's supposed to be a big change to cold weather this weekend – we're going to miss this. We took a short cut through – well, let's just call it 'the wood where lots of badgers live' – and sat on a log to watch them running around and playing. Sasha sat and huffed and grumbled, not quite sure what to make of these black-and-white dog-sized creatures which were ignoring us completely. If we weren't cattle farmers, we could grow to love them.

May 9th

Not a single rat in any of my traps. One day, we'll discover the perfect bait, if there is such a thing.

My computer decided it didn't want to talk to the internet. Hazel's did, so it wasn't the internet at fault, and running a spare cable through the house from the router didn't improve things, so it wasn't the old exterior cable causing the problem. I dug out my old computer and plugged that in; it worked fine. So it had to be my not-very-old Acer computer. I did half an hour of fruitless cookie wiping and cache clearing, until Jonathan got out of bed. He sorted it in about thirty seconds – his explanation of what he'd done took longer, even if it made no sense to me at all. Another one to make the ghosts of this old house shake their heads in bewilderment.

It got hotter and windier – not spraying weather at all, so I didn't.

May 10th

A quiet Sunday – to start with, anyway. I contemplated a tank of herbicide on Blackhouse Road, but it wasn't long before the north wind got up, and it suddenly got very cold. Arable work was off the menu. Lighting a fire and watching 1973 Rugby League and *Minions* was a far better idea.

Hazel was kept busy with her very productive straw trade, loading another trailer-load down at the cattle barn. These buyers had found a couple of iffy waxy bales in their last load, so Hazel was happy to do a bit of retrospective haggling with them. They weren't unhappy about it, because they'd been warned it might happen. Last harvest, when we were filling every barn we could with bales of barley and wheat straw (to go with the monster crop of hay we made in June), there was a batch of barley straw that was a bit on the damp side when Mac baled it. They were bound to turn up sooner or later – we were lucky they didn't ignite in September.

She rang Mac to ask if he had a moisture probe she could use to try and find the dodgy bales in advance. He had one, but wasn't sure it would be able to spot excess moisture after all these months. That didn't stop him jumping in his truck and kindly bringing it over.

We had a long socially distanced chat in the yard about life, the universe and everything, but mainly the straw trade and our plans for harvest. The long six-month washout cleared out the nation's barns, and everyone is crying out for fodder. One dealer is doing trips to Devon to source hay. Mac asked about our plans for swathing or chopping straw, and I told him I hadn't really thought about it yet. But it sounds like the chopper will be pretty-well unused this harvest.

As we talked, he was fighting off a pack of adoring dogs. Sasha, who thinks he's the bees' knees, was continuously dropping off tennis balls at his feet, the two big flatcoats were nuzzling and pushing at his arms (bit awkward when he's trying to work out how to get the probe to fire up) and Tim the puppy just bounced up and down going "Me! Me! Me!" and getting crosser because he was being ignored. He's never been ignored before, bless him. By the time I got back to my warm sofa, I'd missed the important plot twists in *Minions*, but it was so nice to have a very important socially distanced business visitor, I didn't mind.

May 11th

My phone rang well before nine. It was the Literary Agent ringing from the far end of the farm to say yet another tree had come down in last night's oddly strong winds. It had fallen across the bridleway/footpath/Trust walk just next to his house. The thing is, I know what these literary geniuses/genii are like; geography and cartography are not high on their list of skills. Exhibit A: The Editor, who will spend 40 minutes studying the world's clearest map while being given directions to the best place to shoot pigeons, and then ask innocently "and where are we now?". So I thought it would be worth driving out and double checking exactly where the tree had fallen. It was exactly as described.

The National Trust have kept on one employee at the House and gardens, who seems to be having a lovely time tending the deserted lawns and flowers, and, when called, jumping into his Valtra with his trusty chainsaw. I rang him, and the first thing he said was "another tree down?". He promised he'd deal with it later in the day.

The gale kept on, so I thought I'd start work on the two uncultivated shooting strips, Long Field and Pipeline. The hefty dose of Roundup they had the other day had done its job, and a pass with the deep legs of the Agritilth and then the Proforge Inverta discs did a reasonable job. After lunch I did them again, and they looked even better. I did Barracuda and the strips in the Folly, and these last ones could have been drilled at once – but something tells me we ought to wait until there's some rain forecast, and there's none on the horizon.

On the way out the first time, I lit a couple of rope bangers to keep on scaring off the pigeons, which have vanished altogether. Where have they gone? I was summoning the cream of Hampshire's pigeon shooting fraternity a few short weeks ago; now there's not a bird to be seen. Not complaining though. I *was* complaining about the rope bangers, which have gone from being a bit of rope with bangers in, to a bit of rope, lots of plastic labels with warning instructions on, a four-inch fuse and a box of tapers with which to light the fuse. I never bother with the tapers, though, and just light the fuse with a lighter.

Trouble is, on a windy day like today, you have to shield the flame to keep it going, and poke the end of the fuse into your cupped hand, and when it ignites, a burst of flame shoots out. I managed to comprehensively cook the left side of my right thumb, and there's no pain quite like the pain of a flame burn. Usually there's a bottle of water lurking in the cab somewhere, but not today. It was a big 'hello' to Mr Sudocrem (still lurking in the bathroom after proving invaluable on small children all those years ago) when I got back in.

Luckily, I could still use the phone, so thought I'd do another diesel order, ringing round my three suppliers for quotes to top up the nearly empty tank. I was quite pleased to get an order in before the lockdown, which saw us through a frantic spring, and the prices I got from two calls suggested that this next batch will be the cheapest for many years. I couldn't raise the third quote, so left details and asked for a call back tomorrow. Everyone is answering their phones from home, and you can tell there's hurried opening up of computers and pressing of buttons as the call starts. But it seems to work. Just.

The driver with the last load of fertiliser rang to say he was on his way from Dagenham and wanted to check directions – good lad. He was actually standing still, and checking on assorted navigation devices, rather than ringing because he'd been told to ring, and then going "uh-huh, yup, I see" all the way through the complicated process of being told how to get to our tank, and then ringing again, lost and confused, once he gets here – which is the normal process. In fact, he could be accused of being over-keen on directions. I was checking over the little three-metre box drill that we use for sowing game strips (£300 on eBay a couple of years ago) when he rang again. He'd sneaked past silently, and was now down at the Drier Yard, looking at an empty fertiliser tank. "Is that the one?" he asked. Tempting to say "No, it's my beer storage!", but sarcasm isn't appreciated at the moment. Not that it ever is.

I popped down in Tigger to say hello and collect the paperwork, and a curious thing happened. "Can I use that hose pipe to wash the bugs off my windscreen?" he asked. Odd. We've been told for years that such a thing is impossible due to climate change's insectapocalypse. The world is confusing sometimes.

May 12th

We had a dead rat in one of the traps. It's a start.

The last fuel company finally rang back, and their quote was the best, so I went for it. We're now down to about 38p/litre – I must go back through the files to see when it was last that cheap. I paid in advance using the bank debit card, which is a relatively new thing here. It saves invoices and cheques and all that palaver. What will they think of next?

I spent much of the morning and the start of the afternoon deciding to get the Mountfield mower going. It starts OK, but then surges horribly. Luckily YouTube is full of incredibly easy 'hacks' on how to get the Honda GCV135 engine running smoothly. None of them worked, and I gave up, smelling sweetly of petrol and Easy

Start. The mower was heading for the scrap skip – or, even more cruelly, the West Meon Crap Sale, if it ever takes place again.

I needed some brake cleaner to give the carburettor a good blast off before I started dismantling, and a trip back into the barn to where I was sure a can lived revealed nothing but two young rats tucking into the body of this morning's victim, which they'd dragged, complete with the trap, under the shelves. They are the most hideous creatures. But no cleaner. So I popped up to Rod Gaskin's at lunchtime to get some more of it, and it was nice to see and hear a tractor dealer in almost full cry – even if stuff we'd bought had to be left outside on the table. I made a casual enquiry about dust masks. How everyone laughed.

Mind you, I was having a better day than the Massey dealers (not the same ones as in Book One, please note) who came out for yet another repair job on our 5713S. It was to replace the roof lining which had got a bit floppy and mouldy thanks to all the water leaking into the cab. They've had to make quite a few trips out now, what with the 4WD problems, the loader problems, the wheel setting being wrong and the brakes jamming on. It's quite a hike up here from the south coast for all these warranty jobs (even though we've crept out of the warranty period now), and it's not made any easier when they've brought the wrong replacement headlining. There was an apologetic phone call about an hour later, saying they'd come back another day. Made me feel a lot better about that carburettor.

By late afternoon, the weather was more suited to spraying, so I did something for the first time; I applied a tank of expensive chemical in full expectation of it not working. It was Topic – or a generic version – which five years ago would have clobbered the blackgrass in Blackhouse Road. Nature has struck back, and Topic is usually useless, but no other product would be legal, so Tod and I decided we'd give it a go. You never know, it might work.

The fuel company rang asking if they could deliver early tomorrow. I asked just how early they meant – we'd be up and about by six-thirty (a huge lie, of course). "Perfect," he replied. Bloody hell – that means I'll have to get up at six-twenty.

The day ended more cheerfully with a Book One order (the first for a week), and another invitation to speak at a dinner, this time in Essex. I'll have to check if I've told my joke that far away first. I was so cheered that I bought a Chinese knock-off carburettor for the mower on eBay for the grand total of £14. At that price, it'll probably be as effective as that Topic.

May 13th

As I staggered across the yard at just after six, I could hear the rumbling of a lorry somewhere round the back. Our diesel delivery was indeed early. He was delighted to be let in ahead of schedule, and was in and out in no time at all. No sign of a ticket when he'd gone, though – he mumbled something about 'contamination' as I was unlocking the barn. Hmm. Not having that – I'd like to see some proof of what has actually been delivered. Call me suspicious and old-fashioned.

I rang Tod to see if the spraying tickets from some days ago were still valid, but he was in a bit of panic. We ordered huge stocks of soon-to-be-banned chlorothalonil last autumn, in full expectation of having plenty of opportunities to use it up constructively this spring. However, it hasn't quite worked out like that. Thanks to the almost total lack of sowing possible over the winter, opportunities to spray it onto nice forward crops have been non-existent. And as the deadline for its legal use approaches, the farm is mostly sown, but no crops are really in a position to justify it.

The Great and the Good have been lobbying furiously to get an extension for its use – just like the RPA have given us another month for our SFP forms, and the MOT tests have been deferred – but the CPD, the body responsible for such an authorisation, have refused.

The result is absurd. If we don't want to pay for collection and disposal of our stocks by a fantastically expensive processing company, we are going to have to go out and apply all our chlorothalonil to our crops just to get rid of it by the deadline – May 19th – whether they need it or not.

Then there was another complication: we appeared to have more in stock than Tod's records said we should have, and Crop Advisor's records backed him. But I was standing in the spray store staring at three stacks of chlorothalonil: one of Bravo, and two of Rover, when it should have been one of each. Tod said this made no sense at all, and if we were going to get rid of the extra 70 litres of Rover, there would have to be some very convoluted and slightly iffy spray plans – and we wouldn't want that. We agreed to all go away and run through the paperwork. I'm fine with that – I've not got much else on, but I'm not sure about Tod. He sounded at his wits' end as it is.

While all this was going on, Hazel and Jonathan had a long first session on muck cart from the back barn. A rather more simple kind of farming activity.

May 14th

During the odd half-wake half-asleep time between the bloody dawn chorus and the alarm going off, a thought hit me. Back in the dismal wet days of last autumn/winter we had indeed had two deliveries of Rover fungicide. At the time, it struck me as being a bit odd, but I thought little more of it – my grasp of agronomy leaves a lot to be desired, and if a van drives into the yard and drops off a load of chemical, I assume that it's supposed to be doing it. Far better than a van driving into the yard and making off with a load of chemical, anyway.

I was rummaging through the big box of delivery tickets in the spray store astonishingly early and found one for the Rover. Ten minutes later, I was rummaging through the huge pile of delivery tickets on the shelf in the office – where tickets often, but not always, end up. Much to my surprise, I found the second. Same order number, same company, same quantity, same chemical – just different dates and different sale number. Very odd.

Tod was very relieved when I rang him as early as I dared – his records weren't at fault after all. He even had a simple explanation: the company involved had fallen victim to a 'ransomware' attack, and having failed to pay the hackers, had had their computer system destroyed. The result – apart from much embarrassment and an updating of a system security – was a lot of repeat delivering. Hence the second delivery of 70 litres of Rover.

When I rang the company, armed with my carefully smoothed out delivery tickets, they came clean at once. Yup, that was exactly what had happened. And they'd be out tomorrow to pick it up and take it away. I rang Tod again with that great news, and he could then set about some thoroughly above-board spray recommendations to get rid of the heap we were supposed to have in the first place. I could now finally put the phone down and get back in the tractor.

I did two long tanks: Rover on the winter beans in TBHD, and Bravo on the spring wheat in Blackhouse Road. I wonder if organic farmers would have these problems? Probably not, if they didn't use pesticides, but they do, so they probably do.

Team Muck Cart decided they fancied a day off – after only one day on the job – so the Massey dealers were able to fly out with the correct headlining for the tractor and fit it. I told the cheery fitter (/sarc) to leave the 6' by 6' box; it would be perfect for Tim the puppy to shred.

I had to chuckle, as I ran through the chemical-related events of the last couple of days. How unlucky do you have to be to get a free load of spray delivered that you can't use because it becomes illegal?

May 15th

Bizarrely, after last night's closing thoughts, I finally got the next *Flindt on Friday* finished. It was a day late, and all about how lucky we have been this spring. They seemed to like it.

Then it was a full-on spraying day. More Rover on the three geographically diverse spring bean fields, JA/DC, Cheyney and the Hangar. They looked an absolute treat, even on the chalky bits. And after all the fuss and bother about rooks cleaning out beans in the Hangar, it was completely untouched. Mind you, they'd pretty well wrecked the spring wheat in Kilmeston Road. The wind was perfect for doing the Hangar, too, a light north-westerly taking the pong away from the road and the houses. And the track stayed empty all the time I was out there.

On the way to Cheyney, I met Hazel and little Tim, out for his first 'proper' walk away from the house, on a lead. Very bold he looked too – around tractors and cars, anyway. Hazel's noticed that he's a bit wary of people, though; after all, thanks to the lockdown, he's only known the three of us. Normally, a farmhouse with puppies is jam-packed with visitors. But these are strange times.

Cheyney looked even better, with the old game strip on the west side (a good idea at the start of our shoot, but never really of any use) coming up well after a good dose of Roundup and some double drilling with spare seed.

The crops I visited after lunch weren't quite so impressive. Big Field, and the late wheat in Rick/Clump was more weed than wheat in places, and when the weedkiller gets to work, many of the green areas will turn back to brown. Still, where the wheat is good, it's surprisingly good.

The spring barley in the Godwin's fields looked even sadder. There are gravelly bits that are drying out and dying, and the ST4 seems to be drilling to an uneven depth. The right-hand side is sowing shallower than the left, and the shallow stuff is dying off, too. It took me some time to work it all out. The poor strips are eight metres apart, perfectly matching the down/back drilling system. In the tiny field right alongside the A272, which I always sow round and round, the weakest strips were four metres apart.

In a normal year, it wouldn't have been a problem, but that Godwin's gravel – so handy in a wet year as the sort of land you can actually get to work in earlier than the clay – has dried out too quickly, not helped by the run of blistering north winds and hot easterlies. Strange times, indeed.

Team Muck Cart were happy. They'd finished the back barn – taking longer than they thought, of course – but it was done and (not quite) dusted, and the tractor ventilation system had finally started blowing cold air, so that had been worth mentioning to the cheery fellow doing the roof lining. I pointed out to Team Muck Cart that they hadn't finished the job. There was two days' worth of sloshing buckets of water out of the trough and onto the floor and hours of hand sweeping with a stiff brush to be done yet. That's how we did it in the old days. The reply regarding where a stiff brush would go is unrepeatable.

Sasha and I walked down the huge hedgerow on the south side of the Back Meadow, looking for somewhere to put a little gate. The problem with the first drive on our little shoot is that we occasionally put someone in the meadow while the rest of us beat through the north edge of Chalks, who then has to walk half a mile to get back out of the meadow when we're done. A little gate would be perfect to nip through the hedge and into the strip.

There is a perfect gap – not quite central, but still handier than the long walk, especially when carrying armfuls of pheasants. Mind you, if we don't get any rain soon, the strips won't be any good, and there won't be any pheasants. And the Back Meadow itself was lethal, with hoof holes baked dry – Hazel's rolling a few days ago had missed that magic two-hour slot when soggy turned to rock-hard. Even fleet-footed Sasha had to take it steady as we walked it. Seems odd to be wishing for rain after that winter, but there we go. It's what we do.

May 16th

After a short Saturday morning lie-in (otherwise the headache kicks in for the whole day), I decided to try out the new Chinese knock-off carburettor on the mower. It went on surprisingly easily, and there was even enough 'spare' gasket paper connected to the old carb to fashion a new one to replace the one that had disintegrated. A couple of puffs of Easy Start, and away it went properly for the first time in about six years. I did a few random cuts across the back lawn to test it, and it was running smoothly and evenly, sweet as anything. To think that we nearly spent a small fortune on getting it serviced professionally – or were going to send it to the crap sale and buy another one.

It still bewilders me that for £14 I can buy a carburettor assembled in China, sent over to the UK, and sold to me from a housing estate in Coventry. I assume everyone gets a share of that £14, but I dread to think what the poor man assembling the butterfly valves gets for his troubles. I suspect it will work for a year and a day, like all Chinese imports – except the coronavirus, of course.

Jonathan is turning into his grandfather; he was so upset with my random test mowing lines that he mowed the whole lawn to get rid of them. Good lad. I never even got to do an oil change on the old mower. That'll have to be another day.

I still had itchy feet about getting rid of the chlorothalonil before the ban kicks in, so headed out with another tankful (added to a very complicated mix of three other fungicides) to do the early 'good' wheats in Chalks, most of Rick/Clump and Behind My Love's. I had one of the most accurate finishes I've ever done in my long career of spraying, as the 'low flow' beeper went off within a couple of yards of finishing the last turn of BML's. Hugely satisfying after 3,200 litres and 75 acres to get it that accurately.

Today was the second anniversary of having the hip resurfaced. It's easy to forget the pain of sitting with what felt like an open penknife in my right pockets. The last test vehicle we had before the op was a big Mercedes estate. I managed to get the driver back to Petersfield station, but only just made it home. I didn't manage many miles in it during the test week. And now? I can get through the longest spraying days without even a twinge. A bloody miracle. I'm missing the post hip op hot pool swim therapy though – although that has become a social jolly more than a medical necessity. It's a sign of how good it feels when you find yourself asking 'how long will the new hip last?', as if counting down the days.

May 17th

I had planned a quiet Sunday. The spraying got procrastinated again, and I spent a lovely post-breakfast half hour soaking up some much-needed vitamin D. One of the side effects of the wonderful Questran powder that I live on is a lack of Vitamin D – I've run out of supplements, and every joint is slowly seizing up.

But I couldn't sit around for too long; Hazel arrived back from her rounds looking slightly shocked. There were, quite suddenly, rats everywhere. The old calf pens were heaving with them – big ones, small ones, baby ones. I went out to look and they were all over the back of the tractor and the sprayer, after the barley awns and seed that had got lodged in there during pre-harvest Roundup spraying last July. And the tractor has been parked there on and off for ten months without being touched.

The world's scariest thing (for a farmer, anyway) is rats chewing away inside a tractor somewhere, so I backed it to the other side of the yard – four rats ran out in that short journey. I was on the phone at once to the Editor. He has a magnificent Weirauch under-lever air rifle of mind-boggling accuracy and consistency. I borrowed it for the first time a couple of years ago, when the Drier was invaded by white doves, and even mild-mannered Luke the Combine Wizard pointed out that he'd rather not service the New Holland when it's plastered in dove shit. A couple of afternoons spent down there with the Weirauch, and I'd shot 42. The combine still needed the mother of all wash-offs, though.

The Editor was delighted to lend me the gun again, so I popped down to his place and did a socially distanced pick up. Several hours in lovely May sunshine later, I had seven kills, and six confirmed by bodies. And I'd topped up my vitamin D nicely, too.

May 18th

Another fine but hot and windy morning – no good for spraying or fertiliser. I stood in the yard and got a few more rats, although the numbers have dropped amazingly since we declared war on them. I also got more sunburn. Ouch.

Tod arrived for a socially distanced agronomy chat in the yard after lunch – thank goodness for the shade under the red oak as we sat on our staddle stones. It seemed slightly cooler by mid-afternoon, so I brought the tractor round to the tank again (I'd parked it out in the back barn to avoid rat damage) and filled up another load of chlorothalonil – the huge stack of it was getting smaller and smaller.

The phone rang just as I was getting to the last stages of filling the tank. I didn't recognise the number, and should have left it, but answered it out of curiosity. It was the Valtra dealer that had done a couple of quotes for new tractors last year. Their old rep, who we've known for decades, then left them, so all went quiet. It was the new rep on the phone, keen (of course) to perhaps shift us over to the Finnish brand, and asking if he could pop out for an appraisal of the Deere. I said he was welcome to, and then had to cut him off as the water level reached 3,200 litres. Mind you, the Deere might benefit from having some of the dust, grime, Stomp and crap washed off it first. At least the rats have stopped running all over it.

Kilmeston Road looked better than it did the last time I was out there, and I was just coming to the end of it, going "hello trees, hello skies, hello hares, hello lapwings – nice to see you back – hello skylarks" when the tractor started to feel a bit odd. Then there was what sounded like a gunshot echoing back from the L plantation, and the left-hand side of the tractor dropped suddenly.

Typical. Bloody typical. A flat tyre, about as far away from home as it's possible to be, and a third of a tank of spray still on board. What to do? Driving all the way home would surely wreck the tyre – although the 'blowout' suggested it may be beyond keeping – and it was just past office hours for Micheldever Tyres. They have an emergency number, but I didn't feel like calling them out late.

So I did a sort of compromise; I limped to the gateway into Springshot, shut down the tractor, and managed to get hold of Tod, who was still here, just finishing his inspection rounds. He gave me a lift home. I wasn't sure if I should climb on the roof or hang off the Freelander's tailgate to maintain social distancing, but I reckoned I was sufficiently topped up with vitamin D to chance using the passenger seat instead. I certainly felt slightly over-cooked.

May 19th

After a drive out to Kilmeston Road very early to double check the tyre's size (so many joggers out there at 7.15!), I got through to Micheldever Tyres just seconds after eight o'clock, hoping to be first in the queue for jobs. I was too late – they already had two repairs lined up, but promised someone mid-morning. I had a nervous morning trying to get our SFP up together, while scanning prices of new 18.4R38 tractor tyres – surely the tyre wouldn't be repairable after that spectacular blowout?

Just as Hazel and Jonathan set off to get some new doors they'd organised for one of the stables that Jonathan has turned into a home gym, the distinctive Micheldever Tyres pick-up came hurtling along the road, with the mighty Dale at the wheel. I sent him on his way to Kilmeston Road, and headed back indoors and did more tyre porn. Should you stick with one of the established makers – Good Year, Continental, Michelin – or try one of the newer 'bargain' makes – BKT, CEAT, Ping Pong? (OK, there isn't really a make called Ping Pong, and even if there were, it would be Chinese, and I think we should be avoiding everything from them for the next ten thousand years.) A Good Year would be about £1,500, a BKT about £800, and it would be wise to replace both back ones at the same time, so...

The phone rang. It was Dale. "All done, Bud. Couple of splits on the inside gave way. I've patched them up." What about the 'blowout' – surely the tyre is knackered? "Nah – it'll be fine. I'll knock you up some prices for new ones if you want, but there's no hurry!" The man is a miracle worker.

After lunch, Hazel gave me lift back down to Kilmeston Road in Tigger, but we had to pause in the entrance to Springshot, where a whole family, spotting that the gate was unlocked, had set up a complete picnic, with rugs, tables, children and granny, out among the sheep. Our fault, I suppose. Leaving a gate unlocked means it's fair game. I was a bit ruder than I needed to be while asking them politely to fuck the fucking fuck out of our fucking field, but fuck it; I felt better for it.

I also felt better when the tractor started (I hadn't left all the control boxes on all night), and better still when the spray flowed out of the booms. There's always a risk of a 'suspension' chemical bunging everything up solid unless it constantly agitated. But, no, it flowed OK, and I finished Kilmeston Road, drove round to BOMS and did that one, finally emptying a much-delayed tank. There was another half tank of straight chlorothalonil to do on the Folly, and then a big cocktail in the late sunshine on Big Field and the late-sown half of Rick/Clump. A quick in-field rinse out, and, after 50 years, the last litre of chlorothalonil had left the boom. Bizarre, bearing in mind that it has been doing a great job for half a century, and some of the 'science' behind the ban seems decidedly iffy. But that's the way of the world these days.

And all day, I tried to get my head round the 'blowout'. It made no sense at all. Perhaps one of the picnickers had a gun with them and decided to take revenge on me for asking them to leave so politely. Yes, that was it. I was being shot at, at exactly the moment the tyre went down.

The lockdown can't end soon enough.

May 20th

Hot. Very hot. A haymaking hot. And windy too. So no spraying (not that there was any to do) and certainly no liquid fertiliser. That will have to wait – again.

The chlorothalonil ban is definitely worthy of a *Flindt on Friday* column, so I spent the morning getting that together – even doing some proper research into the 'science' behind the ban. It was a great joy to discover that the most-frequently quoted condemnation of this much-used and much-loved fungicide – "It is not possible to exclude that some chlorothalonil by-products do not have a long-term negative effect on health" – is actually, if you read it slowly and cull the double negatives, a compliment. It's just that no one seems to have noticed before. I sent it off to *Farmers Weekly*, half-expecting the green lobby in their editorial ranks to veto it.

The new, young, keen rep was round from Valtra to look at the Deere. As usual, it was a struggle to talk the spec of any replacement tractor down – all I want is manual spools, a good radio and a seat with no armrest. And, no, I don't need 200 hp. We'll see what he comes up with.

When the day finally cooled, I filled up the sprayer with 1,000 litres of water, wetter and Roundup, and set off round all the shooting strips. Some needed it more than others, but they all need a good load of rain before we think of putting the game seed in. Seven-thirty on a cooling May evening is about as lovely as England can get. A joy, even from the tractor cab.

I was back very late, and then ate too much too late. After an hour lying in bed trying to let my insides sort themselves out, I got up and watched the preposterous end of *The Martian*, and some of the original *Robocop*, which, compared to *The Martian*, was the very model of credibility.

May 21st

That delicious and enormous steak pie hung around for most of the morning, so I sat around feeling sorry for myself. It didn't help that plans to get that last dose of fertiliser on everything were once again scotched by scorching temperatures. I had several fruitless goes at starting the next opinion piece for *British Farmer and Grower*, and even more goes at trying to sort out the Editor and his chosen shooting dates for next season. After an enthusiastic reply to the first 'what dates would you like?' email, choosing dates A, B and C, he'd checked his 'other' diary and couldn't do B and C after all. Trouble is, D, E and F have been snapped up by the other member of the 'syndicate' – so the Editor had to make do with A and G. Silly sod. His diary keeping is a bad as his map reading. God help him if he ever got into a situation where he relied on both at the same time.

There was talk of the wind getting up tomorrow, so – feeling a bit less full after lunch – I thought the time had come to put the little skid sprayer on Pig and mark out a few footpaths before the good people of Bramdean start firing off letters to Hampshire County Council Rights of Way team.

I bought an 'ATV sprayer kit' off eBay some years ago, and, of course, it turned out to be the bare minimum possible to be defined as 'a kit'. A spare afternoon with an old pallet, lots of jubilee clips and some home-made booms turned it into a useful slide-in six-metre sprayer. I've used it once or twice with non-Roundup herbicides, but Pig's a bit short on PPE, so I now only use it as a Round-upper, with the boom reduced to one metre.

Jonathan was busy in his new mini-gym in the old stable, so I collared him and he helped me get it all mounted and strapped into Pig. A few gallons of water and a bit of wetter, followed by a splash of Roundup and I set off across the Godwin's fields, trying to mark the paths as straight as possible, while hoping that the wind – which was getting up – wasn't going to widen my hoped-for yellow strips across the fields.

An ex-neighbour left a message on Facebook, desperate to get out for a bit. If he drove up to Hinton from his house with some beer, could we sit in the garden for a couple of hours and chat? I thought about it for all of two seconds and told him to get up here. So we sat on the lawn, all distances correctly observed, and shared, probably incorrectly, a few bottles of beer, and some top-notch sausages that Hazel knocked up. If you've read Book One, you'll know who he is when I say we sat and agreed furiously about everything until he thought it wise to head home. But we probably need to keep it secret. Shame really.

May 22nd

As well as being blessed with my own column in *Farmers Weekly*, I recently was asked to do occasional columns for *British Farmer and Grower*, which is the monthly magazine for NFU members. They only want something every three or four months, and it works quite well; I can send them something that wouldn't be quite right for *FW*. This morning, for instance, I did 650 words about being driven slightly loopy by the lockdown and imagining that the birds in the garden were deliberately winding me up. I doubt *FW* would print that – it was hardly a hard-hitting opinion piece.

It was another hot, dry and windy day– still useless for any spraying or fertilising, so I rang Hunts to see if they had parts for the Deere ride-on mower. The drive belt is getting loose, and the engine could do with a service. They did, so I then rang their tractor rep to see if they had any of their 2020 'model year' M Series tractors in the yard.

I have no idea why I'm contemplating a tractor replacement. We have unsown fields, crops dying from drought, and the subsidies start being culled this year. But if we're going to keep farming, we need the kit. And it's great fun, too.

There was a 120M in the yard, so, having picked up the belt and filter for the mower, I opened it up (using the ten-year old key for my 6630P – great security, Mr Deere!) to inspect the cab – which, as all old farmers know, is now the most important part of a tractor. You can forget power, torque, lift capacity, and all that techie stuff; how comfy and practical is the cab? Can I change radio channel in a hurry when Ellie Goulding comes on? Are the heating and ventilation controls easy to use?

Unfortunately, Mr Deere has gathered all the important buttons and knobs and put them in a low row below the right window (although having windows that open is a bonus these days). And he's made the buttons really, *really* small. And I don't drive my tractor while wearing reading glasses. A real shame – I had thought that the new cab would be like my old one.

The old 6630P might have to plod on for a bit yet. Looked after and serviced, they're good for many hours – and mine hasn't even reached 4,000 yet. I might end up giving it an expensive set of tyres and forgetting all about replacement. All good thinking material on the drive back from Chilbolton – and I had longer to think, now that the roads are back up to about 80% of pre-lockdown business, and giving the Skoda's tubes a high-speed blast is slightly harder.

The man from Valtra rang to say he hadn't got the quote together yet, but it would be done next week. I told him not to worry, but I would be docking £100 from the quote every time he used buzzwords like 'touch base' or 'ducks in a row', and that he'd just saved me £500. Poor chap.

Sasha and I did a late walk round the beans – the spring beans are in danger of overtaking the very late drilled winter beans, but at least they're growing well and filling out. I drove home via Chalks and noticed that the early wheat is coming into ear. It always happens around now, but always takes you by surprise.

May 23rd

It would be very easy to get a bit fed up with this weather. I've got one simple job: get the last bit of liquid fertiliser on the forward wheat, and the last thing that job wants is hot windy weather. But that's what we got – again – this morning. What made it even more frustrating was the promise of showers that would be perfect if they arrived just after application. I wasn't brave enough to chance it, though, and even sat in the tractor for a bit and double checked my figures to make it easier to chicken out: the forward wheats have all had about 210 kg/ha of N, and they all followed beans, so there should be about another 20 kg/ha of 'residual' – possibly more. It depends on how much was lost in the six-month deluge. That's quite enough N for yield – any I put on now (I was planning another 40 kg/N) would be to get protein levels up – and that can wait.

Having used this high-level agronomic reasoning to persuade myself not to go out in the tractor, I adjourned to the sofa for some lame Saturday TV, only for some spectacular thunderstorms to roll in from the west. Most of their torrential rain just missed us and headed south, and I had a very enjoyable nerdy couple of hours watching the lightning strikes and radar on the internet. Once upon a time, we would have run round the house disconnecting all electrical appliances (and putting knives away) at the first sign of lightning. Now, I can watch the thunder wave approaching and count down the seconds to a rumble. Fantastic.

A long walk in the evening showed that the south of the farm got quite a good dose of rain after all – there were roadside puddles at New Pond. I could have got a bit of fertiliser on. But, hey ho, that's farming.

May 24th

Another hot and windy Sunday.

Hazel had the full dog training gang round for a socially distanced session in the Back Meadow, and it was nice to see Tim the puppy slowly, ever so slowly, getting a bit bolder with strangers. He takes his cue from Sasha, who – once all the other dogs are safely out of the way – greets everyone adoringly. People always find her greeting special, because it usually starts with the most terrifying display of snarling and barking through the kitchen window.

I enjoyed some highbrow culture on the TV (*Carry On Up the Khyber*) and went for a long walk. The oilseed rape is pushing on majestically, taking us all by surprise, and is full of bees. A tad ironic, as OSR's days in the nation's fields are numbered, thanks to the ban on the neonicotinoid insecticide that – it is alleged – kills bees. I hope they find something to replace the bright yellow flowers that they're feeding on now.

May 25th

The Monday bank holiday was completely overshadowed by politics, and the Leftwaffe's attempt to 'get' Dominic Cummings. They have never forgiven him for Brexit, Boris winning the last election, and Magic Grandpa failing to become prime minister. A monumental storm has erupted about Cummings' drive to Durham while the lockdown was on. The hideous Remainer pack in full cry was truly something to behold.

DC was due to make a lengthy statement in the garden of No 10, and I had a sinking feeling about it; it seemed that Trial by Twitter was going to win, so went for a yomp to get away from it. After all: no Dom, no Brexit.

It was immensely cheering to get back and find that he'd very politely told the baying mob to fuck off. So cheered, in fact, that I set off at eight in the evening and did a late tank of fertiliser on BML's, and the forward bit of Rick/Clump. My reward for working at dusk on a bank holiday evening was the most stunning sunset and a sliver of a new moon. Fantastic.

May 26th

It's a good thing we've got a big yard, because we seem to be collecting cars. There's the '16 Octavia Scout (mainly Hazel's), the '07 Terracan (mine), the '17 Hyundai i20 (bought as a children's runabout in the Black Friday sale at Richmond Hyundai for an astonishing £7,995). There's also Granny Flindt's yellow Lupo – sitting unused but not worth selling, and the Colonel's fabulous blue '07 Subaru Outback 3.0 H6 which we were supposed to be babysitting while he's on his travels. We're still babysitting it, but his travels were curtailed by the virus, and he's back with Mrs Colonel in the wilds of Scotland.

Every so often, I go out and fire up the Lupo and the Scooby, and give them a run round the yard. Today, though, neither would start – it's probably been far too long since I last did it. Two hours on the charger, and the Lupo started first time. The Outback was more awkward. I disconnected the battery – after all, it's not my car, so I thought I should do it properly to avoid damage to the electrical system.

That's all very good and worthy, but as soon as I reconnected the negative lead, all the alarms went off – the Subaru's security system is somewhat more sophisticated that the Lupo's. Mind you, that's not difficult. After three or four futile attempts to beat the alarm with door locking/fob pressing/foot stamping, I left the battery unconnected and decided that an evening on the internet was the best answer. It's lucky that, out here, a car alarm is completely useless.

I thought I'd stick to slightly less sophisticated technical jobs, and concentrated on taking the 100 litre tank off the Pig sprayer pallet, and mounting it solo with a couple of ratchet straps to the Kubota's little tailgate. Hazel has started doing the rounds of all the pheasant feeding stations, and there's not a drop of water for the existing birds out there. She has been using half a dozen old 20 litre plastic cans, but it seemed sensible to rig up one bigger tank – with the pump and a little dispensing tube, normally connected to a sprayer nozzle. Best thing is that there's room for the ever-increasing ranks of flatcoats and Malinois to fit in, too.

Apparently, and this is only a rumour, in the evening, four country types gathered on a farmhouse lawn, wielding plastic 'take outs' of beer from the Flowerpots (and half a dozen packets of peanuts), and enjoyed a much-needed and much-missed evening of silly comments and putting the world to rights in the warm May air. But it's very important to stress that this is only a rumour. Who would do such a thing under these circumstances?

May 27th

I didn't feel too good this morning. God knows why. It's not as if I overindulged in several pints of Perridge or anything like that last night. That would have been very irresponsible. Who would do such a thing while the national emergency is still on?

Once my head had cleared, I trawled the internet for advice on getting the Subaru Outback started, and most wise heads said that the key's the key. If you open up manually, put the key in the ignition and turn it to 'on' and then reconnect the battery, the car reckons you must be the owner, and won't go mental. The wise heads were nearly right; if you do that, the alarm is delayed for about fifteen seconds, which gives you time to reconnect the battery, slam the bonnet, get the key out, slam the driver's door, and lock/unlock with the now-functioning fob. Success. A couple of turns, and the flat-6 coughed into life.

A couple of minutes trundling round the yard just to give the wheels a turnover and get the rust off the brakes, and I fell in love with it all over again – I do every time I drive it. One day, I'll persuade the Colonel to sell it, and I'll buy it off him. It'll need to be a good harvest before I do, though, with £500 for tax, and 23 mpg. But I'd love to give it a proper run on the open roads – ideally before they fill up again. But it might already be too late for that.

It was too hot and sweaty for spraying, but I needed to get the last fertiliser on the forward wheats. I'd done BML's, Rick and Clump the other evening, and I drove out in Tigger to see if my 'late night' policy had paid off; it had, for there was very little scorching to be seen. Based on that, I had an early tea and set off at about seven to do another couple of tanks, one on Chalks, and all of Big Field. Another fantastic sunset was fine reward for working so late.

May 28th

Another very quiet day. It got so hot that we decided there was only one thing for it: put up the metal-frame pool that has been sitting, disassembled, on the old tennis court. It's a lot of tubing and support legs, and a big plastic central liner. It's cheap, it's cheerful, and it has done us really well for many years. It never went up last year for some reason, but the year before it was the best thing in the world for kickstarting a very sorry-feeling pelvis after the hip resurfacing.

The forecast – both long term and short – is hot and dry. There could be a hosepipe ban (although mid-Hants usually escapes them), which would scupper plans to put it up, so the time is now. A tentative foray through all the bits revealed a few missing clips and fasteners, but after an hour on the internet, it became pretty obvious that anything to do with swimming pools has been sold out for weeks.

Only one solution: Gorilla tape. A couple of hours later, the main frame was safely assembled, the support legs were all laid out, and all it needed was some muscle to help with the final lifting and assembly – but he's too busy revising.

And we all know that the only reason for putting it up is to make it rain for the next two months.

May 29th

Funny to think that this year's diary was to be all about Brexit, the biggest news to hit the UK (and farming) in generations. Well, that all went very quiet when the virus came along, and that has been the news-hogger for months. But the virus' significance has fallen off a cliff-face – and now the farming news is about drought. Crops are wilting, harvest predictions are dropping, and pastures are going brown – which explained today's visit.

Graham Tosdevine's Land Rover wheezed into the yard, so I ambled out to have a quick socially distanced chat. Hazel had mentioned to Luke – Graham's shepherd – that the Back Meadow was available for grazing, if he needed it. Our plans to give it another dose of fertiliser and a spray of weedkiller had fallen by the wayside, so it was open for offers. It took Graham all of ten seconds to say 'yes please' when he saw it. He said he'd tell Murph – who rather confusingly actually owns the sheep – to give Hazel a ring and discuss it. That suited me – I like to keep well out of these discussions.

Our attempts to break the drought continued with assembling the pool. After an hour's swearing and heaving and pinching our fingers in all the connectors, it was ready, and a selection of hosepipes was finally connected, and a dismal trickle of water started. Water pressure up here on the top of the hill is always poor, and the pool is a hundred yards from the tap at the back door, but it was still pleasing to see the water flowing. Give it another ten days, and we might have a pool full. And it'll probably be raining.

I did another late-night tank of spray – this time, all of the Godwin's block of spring barley. It's looking a bit better in places, but slightly worse in others. Where it has been cultivated twice (overlaps and so on) it looks a treat. Memo for next year: book neighbour Robert's Kockerling to do the lot.

May 30th

A Saturday that summed up the moment. Very windy, very hot, and another very late tank of spray, this time on Folly and BOMS. Jonathan had another end-of-year exam, done online, and he seemed pleased with it. I can hardly remember my first-year exams. Mind you, it was 1982, and I'm not even sure I turned up for some of them. But don't tell him that.

May 31st

A quiet Sunday to end the month. I watched a re-run of the successful launch of SpaceX's mission to the Space Station with Jonathan on his computer. He was amazed by it, but somehow it was old hat to me. My generation grew up being slightly aware of the Saturn rockets, then being gripped by the Apollo programme, and then, while doing physics A level, following the Space Shuttle development week by week, one non-sticking ceramic tile at a time. By the time STY-1 launched and landed, I had left school, but I still remember sitting in the farmhouse, watching it all on the television. That landing – the tension: had the tiles done their job? A 'simple' rocket launch doesn't have the same level of drama.

We had a great life update from Diana in Cambridge, still working from home, but still working. And going flat out by the sound of it, and her video gaming company enjoying a boom time. She had lots of exciting stuff she couldn't tell us about new products, but did say she reckoned her prospects were very good – even if they don't reckon the offices will be open again until September. Hope she can endure home working until then.

June 1st

Flippin' 'eck, it was hot – again. So it was a lazy day, with a nice stream of visitors, socially distanced, of course. Tod came round for an update, and we discussed the crops while sitting on the staddle stones. Mac popped round for his straw moisture probe, and spent an hour hanging through the kitchen window with his engine running, telling us what a hurry he was in, and how he couldn't possibly stop for a chat or come indoors. And one of Jonathan's friends from his Cheriton school days walked up from the village to have a go in his new gym.

Highlight of the late afternoon was a phone call I made to a complete farming stranger in Shropshire somewhere. His wife had ordered a copy of Book One on the Friday before the last bank holiday, sure that it would get to their house by today – his birthday. I got the order and printed the label on the Friday, but didn't get it to sleepy little Cheriton Post Office until Tuesday after the bank holiday, and posted it 2nd class. I had a worried message late last week saying it hadn't arrived, and now the Post Office had dropped Saturday deliveries, there seemed little hope of it getting there in time.

She asked if I could ring him up and wish him a happy birthday instead. Why not? You can't beat something as daft as that. So I rang, sang 'Happy Birthday', and chatted for a minute or two. It became obvious quite quickly that he'd missed my name when I said who I was, and thought he was talking to some nutter – it was made worse when I asked if the book had arrived, and, of course, it hadn't; so he had even less of a clue as to what I was on about. He handed me over to his wife, who chatted for a bit, and then handed me back to him, and after another minute or two, it all became clear. How we laughed. We did, actually.

Once it was cool enough, I did another very late tank of spray, this time on Blackhouse Road. It was encouraging to see what little blackgrass there was out there looking extremely sick, and even sparse enough to pull by hand. I'll suggest it to Jonathan once his exams finish – and then duck for cover. The numerous ash trees at the southern end of the field look equally sick, as if the leaves have been shot blasted off. It's no joking matter – I think it's the ash dieback sweeping through woods and forest all over the country. Very sad.

June 2nd

Rain is promised, and I needed to get the last of the 'needs bleaching out afterwards' weedkillers on the spring wheat, and it's still very hot. The only answer was a rare early spraying session, and I was out in Kilmeston Road by just after nine. The wheat out there has recovered from its mauling at the hands – or beaks – of the rook population reasonably well. In places, it's weak, but in places it's quite a thick crop. The summary is that it will all need combining, which, this year, is as good a result as we could hope for.

The pool was nearing full, so I had a lovely session digging out all the 'Pool

Nazi' kit – in other words, all the stuff needed to clean it. There are pipes, filter baskets, brushes on long poles – when properly assembled and working properly, it's fantastically therapeutic to spend an hour methodically working your way over the whole pool floor, contemplating life. I've got to be careful; at the posh house in Alresford where I spent many hours swimming as a young teenager, our host would spend all day cleaning and pampering his very smart pool, and made it quite clear that he was not keen on children enjoying themselves in it. He was phenomenally grumpy, tut-tutting as we ran round shrieking. Mind you, Dad was boffing his missis at the time, so you can't blame him.

Another Tuesday evening in the 'Faux-erpots' on the lawn. I'm not sure if it's legal yet to say there were four of us enjoying take-outs of Perridge and Pots ale, and peanuts, and a lot of silly talk, so I had better not. Not just yet.

June 3rd

At last, a cooler day, with some welcome, if light, rain. I was three days behind with the motoring column for *The Field*, so that had to take priority over the last dose of fertiliser on the spring wheats. It wasn't made easier by the fact that we haven't had a test car out here for months thanks to the virus, so I did a piece of the sadness of the fantastic new Suzuki Jimny being withdrawn from sale by Suzuki on EU CAFE emissions grounds.

Once that was done, I sent it off, got back in the tractor, and had a good slow run in Blackhouse Road and Kilmeston Road, putting a final 70 kg/ha on. Not everywhere looked like it justified it, but I pressed on anyway. And it rained gently for the whole day – perfect for that job.

Just as I was finishing Kilmeston Road, I had a phone call from a new ACCS inspector. Could we organise a 'virtual' farm inspection by next week? I was disappointed that it wasn't our usual inspector, who has been checking us for what must be a decade. We have a good laugh and a gossip, and shout at each other about the EU – he's a fanatically pro-EU Scot – and then he gives the farm a clean bill of health. It's all done quite properly, of course. The online system will be slightly less personal. The new chap said he'd email through a set of instructions, with lots of talk of Facetiming and portals and uploading documents – it was quite a relief to end the call and get back to driving up and down a field in a tractor.

The next job would be herbicide on the peas and beans, so it was time to fill up the sprayer, flush it all through with hypochlorite and leave it for the night – and that was spraying done for a day or two, by the sound of the forecast.

Jonathan finished his first year 'at' uni, with the last of his online exams safely done. He seemed quite relieved, but at a bit of a loss as to how to mark it. If he were still in Newcastle, I think we all know how he and his mates would be honouring the occasion. It's grim that he's missing out on all that.

One thing he – or any of us – certainly can't do: jump in the pool. One of the

U-supports in the corner somehow missed its concrete slab base during assembly, and was on bare earth. As the pressure built, the corner drooped. As the corner dropped, the water poured out of the corner onto the bare earth which got softer, and the support sank lower, and more water came out... We spent an hour in the evening trying to rescue the situation by forcing a slab under the support. After much digging and swearing, we decided that after all that effort (and waiting for the pool to fill) we'd have to drain it to take the weight off. Good thing the hosepipe ban hasn't started yet. And when Jonathan pointed out two pinhole leaks spouting water on the other side of the pool, I had a bit of a hissy fit and said we should throw the whole lot in the skip.

Luckily, wisdom prevailed, and we decided to empty it slowly by syphon rather than attack it with a Stanley knife.

June 4th

We all were a bit under the weather for some reason, so it was a quiet day. I did the next *Flindt on Friday*, which came out a bit lame, but they seemed to like it. It was too windy for spraying, with the odd shower to reinforce that decision.

The pigeons have discovered the peas – annoying after all those weeks untouched. So we're back hanging rope bangers out in White Hill. They're attacking the chalky brow, where the crop is thinnest after the drought. On the heavy land, the peas are looking fantastic. This could be one of those 'heavy land' years.

A long walk revealed the Crusoe in Big Field coming out into ear, so we now know it has vernalised. The fact that it is only a foot tall might make getting those ears into the combine a bit of a challenge. And Luke the Combine Wizard was in the Drier Yard, getting stuck into all the service jobs he'd spotted a few weeks ago. It may not manage to get the low hanging heads, but at least it shouldn't break down while failing.

The pool continued to drain even more slowly than it had filled.

June 5th

It was cold and windy, with spots of rain, but nothing useful. Jonathan and I had another go at stopping the corner of the pool from sinking into the mud, but after an hour with ratchet straps, tyres levers and a bottle jack, we had comprehensively failed to get the key support leg back onto its concrete slab, and decided that the only answer was the tractor.

"Back in a minute," I said to Jonathan, as I strolled off towards the yard. Inevitably, it wasn't a minute. On the way down the hill, I spotted an Audi parked slap bang in the middle of the Folly gateway, so rather than turn left into Chalks and head up towards the pool, I went on a driver hunt. There were families heading down towards Springshot, and I thought I might catch up with the owners.

"Anyone own that black Audi? It's blocking my gateway!" I shouted as nicely as

I could out of the back of the cab once I'd managed to get past them. There was a mass outbreak of innocent-looking faces and shaking of heads. Mind you, I doubt the real owner would have owned up. I tried to do a three-point turn and head back without losing any dignity, but failed.

By the time I'd got back to Chalks, driven up the side of the field and got to the old tennis court, Jonathan was looking slightly baffled. He'd been standing there waiting all the time, and couldn't understand why I'd apparently headed off round the farm for no reason.

Five minutes later, after some careful lifting with the Massey foreloader and some straps, the pool was fully on its concrete bases, where it should have been where we started. And as for the pinhole leaks – well, we'll sort them out later.

Hazel went off with one of her dog team and Bella to a private training ground – 30 acres of woods, fields and ponds up near Whitchurch. I assumed it's safe to do that sort of thing, but her companion works for the NHS, so it must be. The virus panic is collapsing more and more with each day; it won't be long before everything is back to normal. Unless the dreaded second wave starts, of course.

I did another long session getting all the fields in order for the Single Farm Payment application, pencilling in a session tomorrow morning while the internet might be a bit quieter. It needs a good hour of concentration, and no interruptions while we lose connections. With that done, I had a drive round, and met the Editor right at the top of Big Field. Like all sensible middle-class Englishmen, we're a bit baffled at what's going on in the wider angry world at the moment, so we exchanged views and tut-tutted a lot, but in the end the cold wind got the better of us, and we headed our separate ways.

June 6th

If a very dodgy pick-up arrives in the yard during the first week in June, loaded with multiple orange crates, it can only mean one thing: our ex-layer pheasants are here. We've kept going with buying ex-layers for the five or six years we've been running the shoot, and they seem to do what's needed; not bugger off, not die, settle in well and fly over the handful of guns when required next winter.

Jonathan was dragged out of bed to help Hazel load up the crates, seven at a time, into Pig, and set off round the farm to disgorge the birds into their temporary accommodation. I felt a bit guilty at not helping (the new hip is playing up very oddly at the moment – honest) so made another cup of tea and got on with the online subsidy application. In the end, it took about fifteen minutes, changing what was growing in which field, making sure I took out of our 'Environmental Focus Area' fields that were fallow but I had sprayed off already. It was all remarkably easy. I printed off a copy of the complete form, we double checked it over lunch. And I pressed 'submit' shortly after lunch. Simples, as young people say.

Mind you, I thought exactly that last year, when I put all our pulses into EFA but completely forgot that we couldn't spray them if they were in EFA. And because we were fully cropped last year (lovely weather, unlike this year) it was a bit of a panic session measuring hedges and trees at the last minute – I pressed 'send' on 15th May. This year, of course, thanks to the virus, we've been given another month.

What was odd was that I'd got it all correct in 2018, but it was in the weeks leading up to the hip replacement, and those times have been wiped from memory. All very odd. It was only a chance mention of my pulse plans in the Pots with Robert last year saved me from serious trouble.

It was cold enough for a fire in the evening. But still no rain. Many showers came south – big ones with thunder, but they cruelly skipped round us.

June 7th

With the minimum of government approval, life is returning to normal. Dominic Cummings' act of lockdown defiance has driven a cart and horses through the fake science – anyone would have thought he did it deliberately. Hazel was off quite early to a Sunday morning dog-training session with Evie – at least, I think it was Evie; so many flatcoats, it's hard to tell any more.

I could have gone spraying to get the last three tanks done, but the lanes and roads were heaving with Trust visitors, so I took a chance on the forecast of 'fine' for the next two days, and did bugger all. I played with the pool for a bit, setting up the second pump, which died and blew all the fuses, and then finding a third one tucked away at the back of the calf pens. This one's a bit bigger, so needed some creative use of gaffer tape to get all the pipes to fit, and also pumped the water so fast through my DIY black pipe heat exchanger that it didn't do any warming at all. Or may be that's because the days are so cold at the moment. At least the water will be clean.

Hazel can't do 'bugger all', of course, and went off in Pig to let a few birds out of the cages and top up feed and water. The badgers in the Folly had had a bloody good go at getting into one of the pens in their wood. Luckily, they hadn't got in, but there were a lot of traumatised birds and evidence that some had been attacked through the wire. Hazel let them all out.

You know it's June when the lambs and ewes in Englands start to wander away from each other, and then get separated, and then start shouting for each other in the depths of the night. I even got out of bed, grabbed a torch, and checked that the lamb wasn't stuck somewhere – their heads are now perfect for getting jammed in the sheep wire. But no, they were just either side of the Englands fence, and the idea of retracing steps to the open gate was too much. Still, it was a lovely evening for a jim-jam stroll, and Classic FM did a good job of smothering the noise.

June 8th

A good spraying Monday – or it should have been. I rang Tod early to check that all his recommendations were still valid, and Hazel set off in the tractor to move the telegraph pole 'coursing barriers' blocking the entrances to Joan's Acre and Cheyney. She had a bit of a shouting match with the occupants of a Freelander parked squarely in the gateway to Joan's Acre, who couldn't for the life of them understand why they should move. They were togged up, locked up, and just setting off for their long walk. Why should a farmer needing access to his field take priority over their easy parking slot?

When she got back, she asked if we'd got her text. No, Jonathan and I were having a lovely morning natter, but we had not checked our phones. She'd had a text from Luke the shepherd asking for help getting all the sheep from Englands to the Back Meadow, so she'd texted Jonathan. The trouble with texts (call me old fashioned) is that they have to be read to be effective. Not to worry – within a few minutes we were all ready to help with the sheep.

There was more chaos caused by National Trust walkers than wandering sheep. The Trust car park and the gardens are open, and there's a steady stream of visitors setting off on the Dutton Walk – which just happens to coincide, for about a hundred yards, with where we wanted the sheep to go. We tried to rope in several walkers as gate and road blockers, but no one would join in, rather disappointingly.

But with the combined force of we three, the shepherd and his assistant, and two good dogs, we gently eased the flock out of the Top of Englands, across the road, over the tractor barn grass and into the Back Meadow. All very satisfying.

My spraying plans were delayed by an hour, though, so the first tank didn't finish till one o'clock, and by the time I'd done the long-distance haul to TBHD, it was five o'clock. I looked at the clock, l looked at the weather forecast, and decided I'd have a relatively early finish.

June 9th

Hazel set off in Pig to let the last of the birds out of their cages. This time, the badgers had got into the cages in the Folly, and it looked like something from a horror movie. She reckoned we'd lost between ten and twenty, but somehow the mess made it look a lot more. Memo for next season: don't put cages in the Folly.

I went out with the sprayer and did the three small fields of spring beans – JA/DC, Cheyney and the Hangar. They all looked very well, flowering nicely, but they'll love the rain if it gets here. I had to chuckle at the western boundary of Cheyney, which for five years has been 'gamestrip' and then fallow. To bring it back into the rotation, it had a huge dose of Roundup – and that was it. The Horsch CO3 bashed its way through the dead foliage, and now there's a fantastic crop of beans. I can remember Dad tut-tutting about set-aside (as fallow was known back then) and the impossibility of getting land back into crop production. He was brought up in the days before modern chemicals, I suppose.

After a rinse out, I did the shooting strips with a good dose of Roundup – again. It seemed silly to waste a chance to knock the thistles on the head. We all know how much the beaters moan if they have to fight their way through them. It got a bit windy in a couple of places, so I hope I didn't wipe out too much of the neighbouring wheat as I made my way up the narrow strip with the boom folded to 12 metres. Especially as milling wheat is hovering around the £210/tonne mark for November delivery. I finished in Pipeline and did another rinse out on the stubble up there, and came home. Just need some rain and I can get the strips sown.

With that in mind, I hitched off the sprayer – at last – and hitched onto the third drill in my extensive collection: a little Sulky 3 m, about as basic as you can get, with instructions for its previous operator taped onto the inside of the lid. I bought it on the internet a few years ago, after struggling to use my Horsch CO3 to do game strips. It was only a few hundred quid, and has proved invaluable for sowing the odd selection of game and cover mixtures that are guaranteed to provide great homes for the birds, and great shooting for us. At least, that's what it says in the seed catalogue. I shut off three out of every four coulters, and the spacing is then just right.

It's also a lovely throwback to old drilling. There's no PTO, no hydraulically driven fan – the feeding is driven by two land wheels on the end. It's almost silent. The big Deere hardly notices it's there of course.

After a quick grease up and tyre pressure check, it was ready for calibration. But not tonight.

June 10th

It was a full-on office day, gathering up as many documents relating to ACCS as we could find, and uploading them to the not-entirely-comprehensible Red Tractor portal. Many of them are documents we haven't seen since our last inspection. There's always the fear of one being out of date, or expired, or invalid. We uploaded them all anyway.

I spent the late afternoon getting the little drill calibrated for game strips, in the full knowledge that nothing will be drillable until we get some rain. All the showers are mischievously skipping round us. Bastards.

June 11th

It was a good thing I'd done all that ACCS preparation yesterday; I could concentrate on coming up with the next *Flindt on Friday*, and that took a good few hours in the morning. Trouble is, when there's not much going on, there's not much to write about. Luckily, last week's shenanigans with the deliveries going missing was enough. Once I'd done that, I uploaded a few more important sounding documents to the 'Red Tractor' portal, and awaited the phone call from the inspector.

It didn't get off to a good start. His original email from a few days ago suggested that a 'virtual tour' of the farm was one of the options, but once we got chatting, it became clear that it was actually compulsory, and the first thing I was going to have to do was upload something called 'WhatsApp' to my phone.

This is all very well, but I hadn't got a clue what he was on about. I've heard of these things, of course, but I dogmatically stick to using my smartphone for calls, texts and magnificent photos – and it's only the astonishing quality of the photos that keeps me using it.

That cut no ice with the inspector, who insisted I find a way of uploading it and become an expert sometime within the next few hours so we could get the inspection done, and get the points; and points mean prizes (i.e the legal ability to sell corn).

Thank God Jonathan is here at the moment. I went and prised him out of his gym, and pleaded for help. Two minutes of flashing fingers, and I had something called an 'app' on my phone, and I could now 'WhatsApp'. Hurrah. So I talked him through the spray store ("Need a new sign on the door"), round the sprayer and the filling station, and then headed down to the grain barns – where there's no phone signal. Half an hour of interruptions and broken conversations later, he agreed he'd seen enough, and 'we' headed for the office to go through the uploaded documents.

Most of them he was happy with, although my fertiliser records were a bit bewildering to the untutored eye. I talked him through what – to me – appears to be a logical system of keeping track of what's gone on where and when, and he was reasonably happy.

The biggest hiccough was trying to find records of when I'd washed the combine. In the end, I showed him a copy of the *Flindt on Friday* which mentioned it; with a slight harrumph, he approved it. And it was all over. We could get on and sell our stuff legally.

As usual, I made a huge list of things to make sure the whole process is easier for next year's inspection. As usual, I will completely forget them. Let's just hope the mad Scotsman comes back, and we can get back to eating Hobnobs and arguing about Brexit; that's what a proper ACCS inspection is all about.

June 12th

Another odd Friday that felt like a Saturday. No farm tractor work to do, inspections all done, deadlines all met… so I hitched the Massey onto the cultivator with a view to biffing the dried-out shooting strips into a slightly finer tilth.

Then at last, a storm arrived, with a good dollop of rain and a rumble or two of thunder. I waited for a bit, and when I finally got out to the strips, they went down like the proverbial onion bed. I did the Chalk and Roe Hill strips, and then Big Field – which, by the time I got there, had dried out a bit and dust could be seen again. As I finished, the southern horizon went black, and another line of heavy rain crept up from the coast, arriving just as we sat down to tea. Perfect. I'll get the strips sown this weekend.

June 13th

After most of the morning nattering in the yard with Hazel's dog-training gang, it turned out to be perfect weather for a bit of Saturday shooting strip sowing. I did have to get through the inevitable weekend National Trust visitor experience, though. I trundled down the hill with the Deere and the little drill, hoping to start in Chalks, only to find a car parked slap bang in the gateway on the left. And off to the right, out in the middle of Englands, was a complete family having a picnic, having climbed over the locked gate with their tables and chairs. I confess I went off on one again, suggesting rather curtly that 1) I needed to get through the gate to Chalks, and 2) They needed to get out of that field rather promptly. Yes, I know they're our 'customers', and I know that we get subsidies from them and blah blah blah – but all I want to do is get a job done and not have to retrieve food wrap from sheeps' insides. Not too much to ask, in my humble opinion.

Once I'd done my bit of disastrous PR for the industry, the drilling went rather well. I did the 'home' drives with 'Broad Buster' and had a bit left over to start the Big Field strips from the outside. Once I'd run out, I went home and recalibrated with 'Easy Grow' – a mix that we haven't tried before, and includes sunflowers. Not sure how that will work in full bloom while we spend all our time trying to keep folk out of the strips, but there we go.

Meanwhile, Hazel set off in the Massey with the cultivator on the back and did all the other strips, ready for tomorrow. A real 'get the shoot ready' type of day. And another shower added to the feeling of satisfaction.

Anthony finally got time off work and drove down from London for a few days break. No one seems to know if that's legal any more, but, frankly, no one cares.

June 14th

The shooting theme continued. Hazel and Evie set off to Andover for another intense training session, and I calibrated the drill with 'radical pheasant and finch'. I didn't feel up to a long morning session, so set off after lunch, and got Barracuda, Long, Pipeline, Folly and Bob's Wood all done, with seed left over. Most of them went splendidly, although the heavy ones had already shed the rain. No harm in having half a bag left over to redrill if needed.

Once back from training, Hazel got the rollers out and rolled behind me. She didn't do Folly and Bob's Wood, as the track of the Dalbo roller's transport wheels is far wider than 72", and would trash a lot of spring barley getting to the strips. We'll hope for some heavy rain in the next few days to firm them down a bit. Mind you, after multiple discing, that light land drilled so well that rolling probably isn't needed.

The daily threat of showers vanished, and it got proper hot for a bit, so to celebrate a productive weekend, I finally got my kit off and spent an hour in the pool, trying to remember all the exercises we do in the Chandler's Ford pool. It wasn't the same, though; the water was freezing to start with, and full of flying ants, and the woggles had been chewed by rats. You don't have to put up with that in a Spire hospital pool.

June 15th

My Monday morning alarm call was Cain the cat and Tim the puppy romping up and down the green stairs outside my room. Cain then announced, with a long "Yowwwwl", that it was time for me to let him in for a cuddle. So I opened the door to let him in, and he shot under the bed, obviously still in fighting mode. Next thing I knew, he flew back out from under the bed and attacked my foot, wrapping himself around it like a claw-filled slipper. We had a little exchange of views, but ended up having a snuggle for five minutes, with everything forgiven. I would have spent longer with him, but he started licking his bottom, and I needed an urgent pee.

The rest of the day was rather more productive. I wrote up a piece for Tim Relf at *Farmers Weekly*, which is a 'ten questions about how you published your book' article, but will also double as a massive free plug for it. Better than 'free' – I should get paid for it, too.

I then cleaned out the little drill, realising, by the amount that came out, that I had probably drilled the game strips a tad light; luckily they've gone in perfectly, and rain is forecast. I've got a spare bag of seed in case any need resowing. Next job was to hitch it off, put the sprayer on, covert it to 12 m fertiliser application, and give all the shooting strips a proper dose of nitrogen. Arthur at Bright's Seeds recommended 100 kg/ha, and it dawned on me that we've never put anything like that on before. It might explain the lacklustre strips we've occasionally had over the seasons, I suppose.

It took ages, of course; all the folding and unfolding, and the 300 l/ha rate meant a bit of a crawl in the tractor. And I stopped for tea and honey sandwiches when doing the Chalks strip. No wonder it took so long. The 2,000 litres I'd put in ran out exactly as I finished, which was very satisfying, and I did a rinse out on the way back through the wheat. A good wallow in a still slightly cool pool finished the day nicely – even if the scratches in my foot were still a bit sore.

June 16th

Whomp (a gas banger). Whomp. It's 4.50am, for fuck's sake. Yes, it's light. Yes, the pigeons might be working your shooting strips – whoever you are down the other side of Kilmeston – but how about you set the 'delay' timer for the morning start so we can have a bit of sleep. Not a great start to the day.

I knew there was about one cubic metre of fertiliser left in the tank, so I checked with Hazel if she wanted it on a corner of pasture somewhere. She didn't, so I put the last dregs (1,100 litres – not far out with my record keeping) on the late wheat in Rick/Clump. Come to think of it, that's where it should have gone on in the first place. I think. So much for my record keeping.

I had a long session with Tim at *FW* getting the book plug – sorry: interesting article about how to get a book published – sorted out. It looked just right and should shift a few more copies.

And the day was finished off nicely with a 'beer on the lawn'; the Editor's wife joined us this week. They brought their own wine, so we drank far too much beer. I did worry for a moment about neighbour Robert heading home on auto pilot. If he confuses our house with the Pots, and follows the 'same' route home (out of the drive, turn right, then right again) he'll end up with the de Klerks. I wonder how long before he'd notice.

June 17th

This is proving to be the most bizarre weeks for early mornings. This time, it was a van driving up and down the road just before 6.30. Experience tells us that this is not always a good sign – our white van cousins think nothing of patrolling the countryside at this hour of the day, seeking anything they like. Through the overgrown hedge I could just make out it was the fruit and veg company that Hazel has signed up to. They pop out every couple of weeks with a fantastic selection of all sorts of stuff. All packed chaotically into a big cardboard box, and no guarantee of what you're going to get. "No onions!" is the only request Hazel makes every time.

I shuffled out in slippers and dressing gown to see him, by which time he'd dropped the box in the drive just inside the gate. I casually asked what time his watch said, and he was slightly apologetic, but pointed out that he had numerous drop-offs at golf clubs and hotels to get in. And I suppose they think a farm will be up and running well before six-thirty, which is a fair assumption, I suppose. Or would be, if I hadn't had so many pints of Perridge last night.

It was another hot and lazy day. We sent the two boys out with Pig and the chainsaw-on-a-stick to do some tree lopping along the bridleway, and they managed a couple of hours before being defeated by the heat and humidity. Storms brewed up nicely, then decided they'd wait until they got to north of the A272 before dropping any rain. I'm sure we'll get some eventually.

The other highlight of the day was moving on a nice lady who'd parked her car in Cheyney gateway, and then set up camp in the field itself. She was having a lovely day, sunbathing in the entrance to her tent, and couldn't quite understand the idea that we needed to get into the field. I think we're losing the battle against public access.

June 18th

Cain is obviously quite taken with the 'sit outside the bedroom door and yowl' idea, because he tried it again this morning, and it worked – again. I got up, let him in, and invited him onto the duvet. He was drenched – but at least that meant we'd had more rain, which is a good thing. I left him licking his bum – again – and started preparations for a rare and welcome long drive.

At last – a day off the farm. Diana needed a few days away from Cambridge and her intense lockdown 'working from home', so I volunteered to drive up there and pick her up. Being old-fashioned, I gave the Skoda Scout a bit of a checkover – oil and windscreen washer under the bonnet, and then the tyres. Luckily, they're nearly new, so needed no pumping.

After a quick chat with the pheasant supplier who had arrived to take his empty crates away, I set off. I thought I'd go the long way up there, via Oxford and Milton Keynes, confident that the roads would still be quiet.

In the early 1980s, I used to reckon it was an hour to Oxford, even when we had to go through the middle of Newbury, before they finally built a by-pass. Then it got quicker with the high-speed dual carriageway, then slower again as traffic expanded to fill the roads available. (I'm sure there's a law there somewhere). Today, the roads were still quiet, and I flew through the Winnall lights without stopping – and that can often add 15 minutes to the journey.

Despite a terrifying thunderstorm that had us all slowing to 30 mph, and me giving thanks that I was in a 4WD car with brand new tyres on, I passed the Oxford radio station (not sure if it's still a radio station) on 52 minutes, and stopped for a pee after one short stretch of the M40, just after the hour. Not that I'm nerdy about these things or anything.

The roads get a bit more varied and stop-start once you turn east and head towards Cambridge across country, and massive roadworks just south of Buckingham held everything up for about twenty minutes. There's also the farmers' nightmare of driving past prime agricultural land, and seeing it being permanently destroyed. Vast warehouses (the John Lewis one is a jaw-dropper), whole new housing estates, new roundabouts and link roads – and we farmers get stick for damaging the soil. I finally wheeled my way into Diana's smart new-ish housing development at 1.30, feeling slightly melancholy – three hours on the dot.

Her house – which she shares with two others – is part of a huge modern development, built in a cod-Georgian style round a square. The modern way of getting lots of houses in a development is to make then incredibly narrow and tall. You wonder, as you approach the stylish front door, why the next front door is only feet away. Once inside, you realise that the house is about five stories, with cosy (shall we say) rooms on either side of a steep staircase. The best floor was the basement, which had all the extra room afforded by only one bit of staircase. It had a relatively roomy living area and a door out onto a tiny but well-loved square of garden. A big rambling English farmhouse it was not – but Diana felt at home in it. I knew it was a house full of girls when the loo seat wouldn't stay up during a vital visit.

I couldn't be arsed to meander our way home again via the multiple roundabouts of the A421, and decided we'd get onto the M11 and chance the M25. It was a dream; the rain had gone, the traffic was light, and we were door-to-door in two hours without a break, although I was just beginning to flag as we got home. Five hours of quite high-intensity driving after all those months without any is a bit of an effort.

We had a first full family meal since Christmas. A joy. But probably illegal.

June 19th

Another big shower woke me early (one day I'll sleep to the alarm), but, once again, it was welcome rain. Yesterday's long drive hit home just after breakfast, with a monumental headache (the one that comes with the blurred eyesight). We all helped Luke the shepherd get the massive flock back from the Back Meadow to the Top of Englands, and that was as much as I could manage until after lunch.

Anthony set off back to London, complaining of earache, so maybe there's something doing the rounds – but we all avoided saying the c-word. Tod was round for a last (possibly) crop walk, and was very complimentary about the state of everything. Everything has freshened up and pushed on after the rain, and his next ticket will be a last (possibly) rush through everything with a fungicide – and that should be it. Gate shut, holiday beckons. Not.

While Tod and I were doing our socially distanced crop review, Jonathan came staggering out of his gym (aka the old stable) looking dusty and slightly shocked. One of the thin planks lining the roof (an old version of insulation, I suppose) had come away, and tumbled into his sweaty workspace, bringing many decades' worth of debris with it – including a complete owl's nest. Not very pleasant – and one of his old chums was on her way up to use it later in the afternoon. It took him an hour to get the place tidied up.

A day nursing my head made me realise that I couldn't put up with my absurdly long hair a moment longer – it has been months since my last haircut. I summoned Hazel and Jonathan's clippers, set them to 16 mm, and said, "get on with it!" The final result didn't look too bad – a tad dramatic, and perhaps slightly risky with the 30-degree heatwave due next week, but it felt brilliant. Not sure I'll keep doing it, though.

June 20th

A bit of a rough night: poor Jonathan picked up something nasty while cleaning up the debris in his gym, and was up all night ejecting from both ends. Probably aged owl droppings. Apart from the frequent visits to the loo, he seemed well, which is a relief.

Apart from all those bodily functions, it was a quiet Saturday. Diana had an old school friend round, and they did the Trust loop round the farm, and reported a dead buzzard placed on a post up in the woods. This is not good news – and not just for the poor bird. The nature warriors who frequent National Trust properties will have it all over social meeja in moments, and guess who'll be to blame. Hazel and I decided we'd pop out in Pig with a plastic bag and quietly retrieve it. I half hoped it would be fresh. Many years ago, Granny Flindt found a red kite dead in the hay field, and kites were still very rare back then. It made its way swiftly to the freezer.

A couple of phone calls later, a delighted taxidermist arrived in the yard, and after all the relevant official disclaimers and declarations had been signed to make it all legal, he went off with the frozen bird, and we put a couple of hundred quid in the beer fund.

Alas, the beer fund would not be topped up by today's specimen. It was very old, well hollowed out in the eyes and body, too much of a challenge for even the best stuffer of dead animals. We removed it anyway, and took the chance to do an extensive tour of the shooting strips, which were loving the hot wet weather. Another couple of days of wet and then the heatwave next week, and they'll be well away.

Jonathan seemed better in the evening – well enough to eat some scrambled eggs, but not convinced that he'd be up for the drive to Cambridge. I told him not to worry, and I'd do the drive again if needed.

June 21st

As we anticipated, Jonathan was still not fully recovered, so I volunteered to do another six-hour drive to Cambridge and back. Luckily, I love driving.

There's the usual choice at the bottom of Hinton Hill: left for A34 north, or right for A3 and M25. I chose left, and it wasn't long before Diana and I were steaming towards Oxford. And it wasn't long before we were told via the signs that the A34 was shut at Oxford. So we hopped onto the M4 at Newbury and headed east to pick up the M25.

Unfortunately, Oxford is the traditional pee break venue, and as we crawled along the M4 – being converted to 'smart' motorway – we both confessed that having a loo break was rather urgent. The endless miles of high-sided concrete barriers add to sense of claustrophobia, and as soon as we saw a turn-off for Reading, we shot down it, Diana scanning her phone for service stations.

The first garage didn't have functioning loos, but we spotted a branch of Aldi on the way to the second; much relief all round. It was odd seeing the general public and their assorted degrees of security against the virus. Some wore masks of varying levels of conviction, some wore nothing, and one chap was so wrapped up in so much protective gear that I nearly asked him what fungicide he was spraying today.

We finally crawled the rest of the way along the M4 and hit the M25. For there it was flat out, round to the M11 and up to Diana's house.

There's an old friend lives west of Cambridge with her family whom I haven't seen in years – and I needed to have a proper sit down out of the car for a bit. Two texts later, and I was heading into the non-cliche bit of Cambridgeshire countryside. Gone were the huge skies and endless flat fields; this was a land of winding roads and brooks. It was lovely. Almost as nice as the tea and cake and gossip and general catch-up I was enjoying five minutes later. The perfect bit of r'n'r before setting off south again, nicely fed and watered.

The satnav took me through more lovely villages before turning onto Ermine Street, which was slow – but picturesque. The A505 was faster but somewhat less pretty, and the A1(M) and M25 were strips of tarmac infested with idiots in BMWs. I lost count of how many times I pressed 'keep the last 30 seconds' on the dash cam. The clips will be of no use to anyone, but doing it made me feel better.

I was home in an insect-splattered Skoda just before eight. A quick scrambled egg and a shower, and I was in bed. Too tired to contemplate how the insects got onto the front of the car; we've been earnestly told for some years that such things don't happen anymore.

June 22nd

A busy Monday. The first stage of relaying the oil pipeline through the farm started: the archaeological bit. Dozens of pits are going to be dug on the route (through BLM's, JA, DC, and then up and over Hurst Down) to check out anything of historic interest. It's going to make a monumental mess of my only good crops, but the four-figure sum that arrived in our bank account as compensation will go a long way to make up for it.

I had a relatively early session putting bangers on assorted game strips, and another high blood pressure moment on finding hoof prints across the middle of one strip. Whoever it is who makes it their business to roam free across the farm at weekends is obviously home at the moment.

George the landlord's agent was already in the yard when I got back, and he had brought his replacement with him, and, yup, she drove an Audi. It's a very sad moment for a tenant farmer when the agent with whom you've established a fantastic working relationship moves on. We've got to go through all the rigmarole of 'breaking in' a new one – the most significant moment will be when she calls in one day for a chat, and will look at us with a sense of gravitas and earnestness and say "Now, Charlie and Hazel. We want to work with you."

It's a scene we've witnessed what feels like a thousand times since we took over the farm in 1991, but it's probably only half a dozen times. But we have a response all prepared. "Thank you very much, Mr/s Trust Agent, but we don't want to work with you. We'll pay you a large cheque every quarter, and in return we'd really prefer not to see you at all unless it's urgent." Luckily, we didn't reach that stage today. There was a slightly stilted cup of tea on the lawn, and that was that.

Tod's massive chemical order came through, so I had a session in the spray store making some space by folding down a huge heap of empty boxes. I was just finishing when the next test car arrived, driven by what appeared to be a surgeon just out of the theatre. He had gloves and a mask, and spent ten minutes wiping everything down before he'd even open the door. It meant there was no signing or paperwork to do, and he had another car coming to pick him up, so all we did was a key handover. I left him scrubbing and wiping and had a long early wallow in the pool – now warming up nicely in the heatwave.

June 23rd

Worth mentioning that it's the fourth anniversary of the Brexit vote? Probably not.

A seriously hot day, with spray deliveries trickling in, but there's no way I was going out in the tractor in these temperatures. Another quiet day indoors beckoned. Until, of course, Hazel pointed out the Facebook posting by the Flowerpots, saying that the BBC would be broadcasting live from their car park. Well, who can resist the chance to head down there and stock up for tonight's 'beer on the lawn' *and* tell the BBC what a hideous bunch of scum they are?

Of course, I chickened out when I got there. The car park of the best pub in the world while they're trying to do a live interview is neither the time nor the place to air one's visceral loathing of the BBC. So I rather meekly stood in the 'takeaway' queue in the background, and generally behaved sensibly. Somehow the vicar appeared at my elbow, as if to prevent any childish behaviour, and it worked. I came home with a four-pint takeaway of Perridge, so it wasn't a wasted trip.

Mind you, those four pints didn't last long during our 'beer on the lawn' session, which is in danger of becoming a permanent fixture. Warm evening sunshine, good company, lots of silly chat, and no one having to produce their papers to buy a beer – which is what the authorities are suggesting will be the protocol for entering a pub when lockdown starts to ease. This is Hampshire, not Vichy France.

June 24th

The long saga of the dodgy pea seed was finally put to bed. The man from Agrii came out, had a stroll through them, pronounced that they looked fabulous and he was very happy with the plants/sq metre count. I was about to launch into my 'that's irrelevant; they were discovered by you to be 70% germination instead of 80%, and you carefully forgot to tell us until we had them drilled, rolled and sprayed!' routine, when he offered to refund us one tonne as a goodwill gesture after the paperwork cock-up. One free tonne in eight would correspond perfectly to 70% germination instead of 80%, so I said I was very happy with that, and off he went. I wasn't actually terribly happy – I had a fantastic article lined up if he'd decided to play awkward, slagging off the seed industry. Shame, really.

Ex-neighbour Ali (now in Bosham after leaving Blackhouse Farm, sadly) came round in the evening to look at the old shoot shed, now standing rather neglected and forlorn in the old estate yard. She's looking for somewhere to start a 'studio' for her latest enterprise – doing photography courses for school children. She reckoned it would be absolutely perfect, once we had put in parking, loos, decent walls... The huge windows were perfect as they were, though. I said I'd get my pet builder to come and have a look. Mind you, the idea of two dozen Tarquins and Olivias being dropped off by Audi SUVs while I'm trying to drive tractors around the yard doesn't fill me with glee.

June 25th

This hot weather isn't just driving us to distraction; the sheep and lambs in Englands are going a bit mad. All night, they bleat and blare, as if they've all lost each other. I kept turning Classic FM up last night until it smothered the noise, and finally drifted off, dreaming of sitting out there with a high-powered rifle picking off the noisiest... not very Christian thoughts, but I got to sleep.

As a result, I was a bit bleary this morning, and struggled to get *Flindt on Friday* done. After four of five failed attempts to write up the two lovely drives up to Cambridge (and not actually being sure that they were legal) I switched to the BBC's visit to the Flowerpots, and with only the slightest embellishment, got it done and sent in.

Tod was round for an urgent check on the oilseed rape. Most of his clients' crops are turning rapidly in the heat, but ours looked to have another week or ten days before we should wade in with the Roundup to prepare it for harvest.

We decided to abandon sitting out on the staddle stones, and he came in for a cup of tea – just like the old days. Mind you, what should have been a brief meeting went on for far too long as a result. Still, with not a lot else to do at the moment, that's how we like it.

The radar and the lightning detector suggested that a serious dollop of rain was on the way, just leaving the coast of France as we went to bed. It didn't stop the sheep shouting, though. Where's my gun?

June 26th

Inevitably, there was no rain. Not a drop. Not a single flash of lightning, not a clap of thunder. Just more blaring sheep. But it was still hot.

Hazel jumped in Pig and did a big round of all the pheasant feeders, topping up water and wheat, and I jumped in the test Mazda CX-30 and decided I should do some miles in it. I had a phone call mid-pm organising a pick-up time for Monday, and I realised I hadn't even sat in it.

I went to the pool spares shop the other side of Petersfield to get some more chlorine – the first new item I've had to buy for the pool this year – and then did a nice long loop from Petersfield to Selbourne, over to Alton and back via Four Marks. First impressions of the chunky SUV weren't brilliant, but I'll give it some more miles over the weekend.

The evening suddenly went cool and breezy, and my swim was relatively brief.

June 27th

We had a good rain over night, and more showers flew through on strong winds, so no farming to be done. I took the Mazda out for another spin, this time to Winchester, Three Maids' Hill, Hill Farm Crossroads, Stockbridge, Andover, Bullington Cross and home. And I managed to resist the McDonald's magnet. Amazing.

June 28th

More of the same – windy and showers – and actually beginning to be a bit of a worry, now that the forecast has changed to being unsettled all next week. There's a pile of fungicide clogging up the spray store that should be out on the crops. Ho hum, nothing to be done.

I gave the Mazda another blast, and actually warmed to it a bit. My journey was to the West Meon Hut, then Chawton, Farnham, nearly to Guildford but taking the A325 to the M3, then south to Winchester and home. Three good drives, half a tank of fuel gone, and enough opinions to form an article. Excellent. Mind you, I felt like death warmed up all day. Probably lack of sleep.

June 29th

Well, that was an exciting Monday morning. A white Mercedes convertible drove slowly into the yard as I was gently stirring my porridge on the Aga. The driver asked if we knew who owned two chestnut horses that were running loose on the A272. I said I hadn't a clue, but summoned Hazel – she can usually name an owner from a short description of any animal. But this one stumped her. We thanked the chap for the info, and Hazel got onto the phone to the usual suspects.

Much of Bramdean had been on the case for some hours apparently, chasing and reporting the two horses as they made their way round the parish. But a combination of Chinese whispers and dodgy phone masts meant that there was no solid information.

We needn't have worried. About half an hour after the Merc had gone, there was a curious noise from the yard, and Sasha could be seen on her look-out post up at the kitchen window, with a look on her face that said, "I think you need to come and see this." Two beautiful dark – not chestnut after all – horses were ambling round the yard, and had just found Hazel's plant pots. We shot out to try and stop them going any further, but there was no panic; they were calm, quiet, and quite pleased to see someone. It looked like mother and foal, and I chatted to the bigger one while Hazel fetched a dog lead (our horsey kit vanished years ago) and a bowl of chicken nuts. She fashioned a halter of sorts from the lead, and we lead them gently out into the Back Meadow – the youngster following faithfully – and let them go, safe and secure.

Back on the phones, the owner had been traced, and a Defender piled into the yard with her, her daughter, and the Editor's wife, who as ever, was a brilliant horsey helping hand. The daughter was mighty upset, so we made it crystal clear that we were delighted to help (it's what you do in these situations). A bottle of quality plonk was thrust into my hand nonetheless. The daughter and the Editor's wife set off across Godwin's, two lovely horses in proper halters, and the owner stopped for a chat in the yard, and there was much discussion at how these isolated horses were let out. A finger was being pointed at a well-known community of caravan dwellers who are in the parish at the moment – but I'm sure that any suggestion that they might be involved is scandalous and unmerited.

Meanwhile, the team from Mazda arrived to pick up the CX-30, and the team from Hyundai delivered the new Santa Fe. All go. By the time I got to my porridge, it was cold.

The rest of the day was cold, and a gale blew. No chance whatsoever of spraying, so I checked shooting strips and put out rope bangers to keep the pigeons off for a bit longer. Hazel and the picker-up team went off into the woods and up into Pipeline for a bit more training, and came back chilled to the bone. The days must be getting shorter.

There was a worrying moment while I strolled down the Chalks strip with Sasha, Evie and a getting-bolder Tim: the wind dropped. I looked at my watch. It was 8.50pm. Sorry, I'm not getting the tractor and sprayer fired up at that time of night. Mind you, by bedtime, the wind had picked up again, so my conscience was clear.

June 30th

It was a fine calm start. Full of enthusiasm for spraying, I strolled out into the yard very early, and turned on the hose pipe to top up the water tank. I even dug out the spray recommendations and a calculator to work out doses of chemical per fill – at which point heavy drizzle and a strong wind arrived and continued for most of the day. Certainly not typical end-of-June weather. Enough to make you get a bit fed up.

But then we had a 'count your blessings' episode with brother-in-law Noel and his wife. They keep livestock all over Hampshire, bit of grass here, pastures there – anything he can get his hands on. He has a herd of cows, calves and a bull on pastures some way south of here.

This bit of land is frequented by a walker who has – shall we say – a reputation for belligerence and shit-stirring. She walks a very large pack of dogs of a certain breed – I won't say which – and I've crossed swords with her a couple of times when she has ventured up this way. The reason (she explained to me once) she was perfectly entitled to walk in the fields rather than the footpaths was that her dogs are too dangerous to be around people and other dogs. Why, of course, madam. We ended up having an almighty row.

Not long after that, there was a Facebook post from Alresford by someone whose spaniel had been attacked by the same pack and badly injured. Did anyone know who it might be, pleaded the victim's owner. We gently pointed the lady's name their way, and the police got involved, but I don't think it got any further.

Mid-morning, Hazel had a text from Anna, in a right panic, because the dog walker was claiming she'd been hospitalised – and many of her dogs injured – by Noel's cattle while walking through them on a footpath. There were threats of prosecution, and lawsuits, and personal injury claims – all really unpleasant stuff.

What do you do in these situations? We immediately asked who the cattle were insured with, and luckily it turned out to be the NFU. That's a good start; they will know how to handle these incidents – even when the 'victim' is telling the Gospel truth, and experience suggests that she might not be telling the whole story. Apart from that, there was little else we could do, except see how the whole saga develops.

The rain and wind put a stop to Beer on the Lawn, so we rescheduled for Thursday.

6th February   Winter wheat under a February moon

8th February   Bella and her batch of puppies

16th February   The February gales claim another tree.

7th March   Another Big Field horse shoe.

23rd March   A peck of March dust…

26th March   A rare sight: a Terracan stuck.

1st April   Just Tim left – and his friend Henry.

18th April   Steering wheels – the new airbag?

19th May   Opportunistic picnickers.

25th May   A late evening doing fertiliser.

8th June   Moving sheep to the Back Meadow.

21st June   Mystery splats on the numberplate.

23rd June   The BBC arrive at the Flowerpots.

7th July   Manor Farm's first ever purpose-built bowser.

23rd July   Pre-harvest fuel-up.

3rd August   The pool on an August morning.

18th August   Beer goes better with a brazier.

25th August   Worrying bits of combine.

5th September   September harvesting and baling.

16th Sept   It's not the murder; it's the disposal of the corpse.

16th Sept   Whose chair is it anyway?

3rd October   A lot of rain, however it's measured.

16th October   Autumn sunset in Chalks.

19th October   Sieving the lumps out of seed barley.

6th Nov Cleaning out the bottom of the seed drill.

13th Nov Hurst Down – again. Not as dusty as March.

14th Nov   Sasha guarding the Roe Hill rain pond.

1st December   Late night bean cleaning.

27th Dec   More tree damage up Roe Hill

16th January   January sunset

21st January   Temporary window repair.

24th January   The obligatory snow scene.

July 1st

Noel's issue with the dogwalker had been troubling me a lot overnight, so I thought I'd just drop a line to the NFU in Winchester, detailing the troubles we'd had with the same lady. The reply was almost instant: they'd pass it on to the Alton office, who were already on the case, and we shouldn't worry; the NFU are indeed the masters of sorting these things out. That was genuinely reassuring, but I thought we'd make sure we were available to help in any way possible.

The Colonel was due to drop in today for a check on all his worldly goods in the container in the yard, and pass his eye over his beloved Subaru in the yard, so I spent the morning charging the battery and (having gone through the correct protocol) getting it going and having a drive round the yard.

We both burst out laughing when he drove in the yard in a battered old Golf; he, too, had had the lockdown buzzcut.

A really good afternoon catching up with news followed. His trek to Africa in the 4x4 VW van had, of course, been stopped short by the virus, although he did contemplate holing up in Sierra Leone. The British Embassy finally got him a slot on a German military-chartered plane, but with only what he could carry in his rucksack. The beloved VW, and all its contents, had to be parked up and left behind, supposedly in safe hands. No wonder he spent so long in the container in the yard, inspecting its contents.

He showed me videos of his trip, including 'diary' reports to camera, that sounded less than cheerful. He pointed out that his Parkinson's takes away much of the ability to smile and laugh; fair point. I did suggest the book of his travels should be called 'Motoring with Marvin' after the depressed robot.

He moved a few bits and pieces out of the container, had a little drive round the yard in the Subaru, and then went on his way.

I had a quick look at the rainfall radar, and decided I'd take a chance on the weather. The long finger of rain that had been pestering everything north of Alresford seemed to be dying, so I did a tank of fungicide on Chalks, BML's (dodging the pre-pipeline archaeological excavation trenches) and much of the forward wheat in Rick and Clump. As the 'tank empty' warning beeper went off, a heavy drizzle set in for about ten minutes but then cleared. And later in the evening, a huge shower skimmed us to the south. So I may have got away with it. Just.

July 2nd

It was windy and cold and grey, so not a lot of outdoor work to be done. I did next week's *Flindt on Friday*, using Monday's episode with the loose horses as inspiration. They seemed to like it.

Beer on the Lawn was quieter – the Editor and his wife had gone to the Isle of Wight for an awayday and wouldn't make it back in time. As a result, we had far too much beer – left over from Tuesday.

I gave neighbour Robert the article from *The Times* about the Ineos Grenadier – the new 4x4 machine much-touted as the real replacement for the Land Rover Defender. It's a machine that both Robert and I have a personal interest in, and not just because as farmers, we don't know what to buy next as a farm vehicle. We've both looked at the new Defender and gone "oh dear".

A couple of years ago, when word first got out that Ineos were planning this new 4x4, I did an article listing all the things it should have, and all the things it shouldn't have. Hose out interior, big buttons, tiny wiring loom – good things. Absurd menu choices for suspension and drive train, pathetic jack, woeful handbrake – bad things.

Next thing I knew, *Farmers Weekly* were forwarding an email from Ineos' commercial director. Could he meet up for a chat? I rounded up Robert and Rufus (when he still lived locally) and we three Land Rover owners and ex-owners (I was going to say 'enthusiasts', but I'm not) were treated to a very long and boozy pub lunch in the Pots by Mark from Ineos. In return we subjected him to a barrage of suggestions and requests for our ideal vehicle. By the time we all stumbled into the car park, Mark had a very full notebook. And when the alarms on Robert's 90 all went off spontaneously, we all said, as one "See? Dodgy electrics!". We were accused – wrongly – of setting the whole thing up.

But now, Ineos have released the first official exterior shot, and it looks quite superb. "Looks right, is right," as they say. Robert took the page from the newspaper, looked at it, looked at it a bit more, mumbled a lot, looked at it for a bit longer, and then gave it back. "I'm going to cash in my pension and buy one of those!" he announced. I took great pleasure in emailing that to Mark once we'd cleared the beer and glasses.

It was only as we were heading for bed that I noticed how calm the evening was. I could have got another tank of spray on. But sometimes, Beer on the Lawn is more important that an earwash fungicide.

July 3rd

Not surprisingly, the morning was slightly woozy. Even so, I looked at the dry sky and the relatively low winds and thought I ought to clear the day for spraying. I rang Woollhead's to cancel the appointment we'd made to look at what work needs doing to the shoot shed. They were fine to reschedule next week. Half an hour later, a monster gale blew up.

Highlight of the morning was an almost anonymous text saying, "Hi Charlie. You made me laugh today! Jon." I texted back, thanking him for the nice compliment, but asking how I had made him laugh, and who he was. He replied that it was today's column in *Farmers Weekly*, and he was from the seed cleaning company. Ah, it all made sense at last. I thanked him again and promised to save his number for further gushing compliments.

The gale continued, but it was dry, so Jonathan drove the Deere X105 ride-on mower round to the lawn and we set about a bit of a service. We bought it in 2017, as part of the deal to buy a Deere 5125R loader tractor, and, as often happens, it hasn't been over-lavished with servicing. In fact, I'm not sure we've even changed the oil.

Jonathan and I had a long afternoon lowering the cutting deck – so many guards! – and changing the drive belt. We then got the blades off, with much grunting on the end of a 24 mm socket, and gave them a sharpen. Finally, it was back to the barn for a simple oil change. Jonathan really knows his mechanical stuff – he's a natural with spanners and tools. Bit of a shame we can't tempt him into a tractor as a career.

I filled him in on the terrible story of the Deere 5125R tractor. It was finally delivered, months late, just before Christmas 2017, and it was shocking. It had no brakes, the front suspension was one sided, the loader didn't work, my carefully researched and specified tyres had failed to make it onto the machine – it was actually dangerous to use. We struggled with it for a week or so, and then demanded that the dealers come and get it, and return the traded-in Massey 5455 while they sorted the multitude of issues. Luckily, they still had the Massey, so they did just that.

It was also lucky that they hadn't cashed the deposit cheque, so I stopped that, and cancelled the direct debit, and suggested that someone senior from John Deere should come out and tell us why we should even consider taking delivery of the 5125R, if and when all the faults are sorted. A couple of days later, there was indeed an important man from John Deere UK at our kitchen table, who listened to our story, shrugged his shoulders and said, "Yeah, whatever."

The next morning, we formally cancelled the order, and started the hunt for a new loader tractor all over again – but without Deere on the list of possibles. In late summer 2018, we took delivery of the Massey 5713. It hasn't been perfect by any means, but at least it lifts stuff and stops at junctions.

The gale refused to subside, so I took the Santa Fe out for a long drive, and couldn't help thinking how nice it is to drive a machine that works straight out of the box. I left the radio on 'Absolute 80s', one of the many new nostalgia-themed stations that as a rule function without DJs – but, as it was Friday evening, there were two of them, filling in the occasional gaps between songs. Not a brain cell to be found between them. It made me realise how lucky we are to have Wave 105 in our region. Thinking man's radio.

July 4th

There was entertaining news on Noel/Anna and the cattle attack front. The victim has been furiously back-pedalling, and her story has been watered down somewhat. Anna just happened to get some video footage of the victim out walking purposefully, filmed, curiously, the day after being 'hospitalised' in the attack. Smart girl, that Anna.

Still too windy for those crucial late fungicides.

July 5th

Another infuriatingly windy day. I slept in too long and was rewarded with a paracetamol-resistant headache. I battled bravely through it to write up the Mazda (a couple of days late) and also set about the backlog of writing invoices. I hope they'll still pay out for ten-month-old articles. I must get my office system more efficient.

Hazel went off for her now-regular training with Evie up near Andover, and I did bugger all. Neighbour Ashley came in and made a start on mowing the Godwin's pastures and the fallow wheat in Godwin's Park (which he's cutting as whole crop silage), but there was a loud bang at one stage, and that was the end of that.

July 6th

At last, a proper busy Monday. I proofed the next *FonF*, making a few changes here and there, and used the opportunity to make a pitch for a bit more cash for my weekly efforts. We'll see what they think.

Mind you, we had an early alarm call in the shape of a convoy of lorries delivering containers to Blackhouse Farm. The new folk who moved in there a few years ago are starting some massive project, Let's hope construction traffic doesn't clash too much with harvest.

The team digging archaeological trenches in preparation for the new pipeline finally finished, packing up their fences and loading their digger onto a low-loader. All that's left now will be to decide damage and more compensation.

Four copies of Book One sold over the weekend, so I packaged them up, ready for posting, and then, despite the still rather gusty winds, got on with spraying the last fungicides. I finished Rick and Clump, and then did all of Big Field with the first tank, only having to pause a couple of times for walkers on the busy top track. After lunch I did the spring wheat in Blackhouse Road, paused for a cup of tea with Tod, and then did a tank on Kilmeston Road. After more tea and a couple of much needed honey sandwiches, I did the spring barley in Godwin's.

All over the farm, I was dodging foxes, deer and fawns, skylarks, butterflies and hares. And all the while applying nasty horrid chemicals. Funny old world.

The forage gang were back in after yesterday's breakdown, cutting and baling the volunteer wheat in Godwin's Park, and, by the look of it, getting a respectable number of bales to the acre. I knew we should have charged him more.

I came home jolly cheerful but fairly knackered: all the crops have staged miraculous recoveries from the drought. They won't be record-breakers, but they're certainly a huge improvement on the dried-out fields of only a few weeks ago. Tod had said the same thing – and also suggested dropping the fungicide recommendation on the peas. I said I'd see how I got on tomorrow.

July 7th

A stunning morning, and I was spraying the spring barley in the Folly before nine – unheard of for me with my inability to do early starts. At least the Trust walkers hadn't hit Dark Lane at that hour. I cut through the oilseed rape in the Drier (with some difficulty, because it's quite a crop now) to get to BOMS, and finished that last bit of barley.

I got back to the yard just in time meet a courier delivering the box of 30 dust masks I'd managed to source on the internet. They were a bit pricey (£2 each), and I fully expected them to be Chinese tat, built out of waste bog roll and stapled together by slave labour in a re-education camp, but they turned out to be the genuine article. True, they were three years old and the 'expiry date' (for a dust mask?) was 'Q3 2020', but they'll do us for most of harvest, and by the time they run out, supply should be easier at more traditional outlets. We can but hope.

Lunch was early, and then I set off on the long hike to the winter beans in TBHD. On the poor north-facing land they weren't anything special, but up on the top – the best soil on the farm – they looked fantastic for a March sown crop. Good enough to have me slightly worried on the headland turns. Many years ago, I bent the boom struts on my first trailed sprayer when the boom dipped into a monster crop and got forcibly folded back.

Next up were the three small fields of spring beans – or that was the plan, anyway. By the time I'd done Joan's Acre/Dell Close the wind was picking up – again – and from a very inconvenient SE. I paused in the Springshot gateway, and decided that doing the Hangar was out of the question. I went on up to Cheyney, did that one, and called it a day. I was knackered, a loop of pipe had come away from the left-hand boom, and the fungicide in the tank would sit safely for a day or two. Could it be time to head home?

Just as I was leaving Cheyney, the phone rang. It was the delivery driver bringing the new legal fuel bowser I've just ordered, and he was half an hour away. That sorted it. Home time it is. I spent half an hour sorting the loose pipe with zip ties and then supervising Hazel and Jonathan as they pumped up Tigger's tyres ready to go down to North's for a well overdue MOT. God knows what they'll find wrong – it's beginning to creak and sag a bit.

The lorry driver rang again from the bottom of the hill, to check directions and ask if his lorry would make it up the lane. I told him that he'd be fine, and I'd meet him on Godwin's corner. Ten minutes later, a shiny new diesel bowser was being wheeled into the barn, resplendent in bronze green. It's a lot bigger than the old plastic one, but actually holds less – the double skinning makes it so large.

It will be first purpose-built fuel transporter we've ever had. Over the years there have been trailers full of five-gallon drums, tanks on pallets on a trailer, hand pump, electric pumps, exploding pumps, a converted water tank, but now we're fully legal and compliant. Mind you, at four grand, it bloody well should be legal and compliant.

A very long Beer on the Lawn with a full contingent, wrapped up warm against the cold July evening, rounded the day off splendidly. Everyone brought too much beer, and most of it vanished.

July 8th

Not altogether surprisingly, a fairly slow morning. How fortunate we all are being self-employed and working from home. My head hurt.

As usual – from a 'let's jump in the tractor and do a full day's work' point of view – it was still windy, and still drizzly. Luckily, other jobs were available.

For a start, I still hadn't addressed the non-conformances after my ACCS virtual inspection. I'd failed for having an unreadable sign on the chemical store, so I'd ordered a new one. It arrived a couple of days later, and I put it on the table in the spray store and forgot all about it. But harvest is a-rushing upon us, and I need my sacred stickers to say I'm safe to farm. And I won't get my stickers unless I tell the inspectors that I've put the sign on the door.

Putting up the sign was easy; scanning the relevant documents and uploading photos of the sign took the time. But despite a corrupted 'Photos' programme on the computer, a stubborn scanner that sulks most of the time, and the usual snails' pace internet, I got there in the end. Let's hope they're happy and can get the 'harvest stickers' out here before the combine rolls. I'm tempted to whip the new sign off the door as soon as I pass, though; the last thing we need is a big sign on a door saying 'lots of valuable chemicals stored in here!'.

The little bookshop in Alresford rang, with two good bits of news; first, they'd reopened, which is a sign that they're still in business, and, second, they'd sold out of Book One, and could they have half a dozen more? Why, of course, I said. I'd wing them over in the morning. Just the thing to keep the sales ticking over before the massive free plug in next week's *Farmers Weekly*.

Next job: the brand-new bowser. It may be just me, it may be a farming thing, but the first thing I tend to do with a pristine, just-out-of-the-box bit of kit is contemplate adapting it. It's almost as if I want to make my mark on it somehow. Factory fit radios and speakers, for instance, are never good enough, even though they might be. I have to fit my own. My fantastic Ford 7810 I treated myself to in 1991 was nearly wrecked by some cack-handed wiring while I installed the radio.

I walked round the bowser, trying to think what wasn't quite right. The tyres are too thin, for a start. I might get some wider ones – if I can find a set with five 16 mm studs on a PCD of 165 mm. eBay beckons.

To no one's surprise, Tigger failed the MOT test – but not catastrophically.

The front left tyre was out of shape (hence the wheel wobble), the right upper wishbone had a loose nut (hence the severe pulling to the right), and some bushes were knackered. There were a couple of other advisories, but North's said it would be ready tomorrow, after the new bushes had been fitted. Amazing how it limps on from year to year, doing about 2,500 miles, not depreciating too much, and only costing a service and an MOT every pre-harvest lull. The road tax bill came the other day – over £300. A bit harsh for such a low mileage machine.

July 9th

The story of the new bowser – the first time we've ever had a purpose-built diesel delivery system rather than a cobbled-together set-up – made good fodder for *Farmers Weekly*, so I sent that in, along with one of Dad's old slides showing me sitting at the wheel of a Senator in the late Sixties, a row of five-gallon drums lined up in front of it. How we used to do it. The good old days? No.

Tucked away in the barn was an old diesel flowmeter, bought in the days when I was young and enthusiastic, to go onto the terrifying diesel burner in the Alvan Blanch grain drier. I thought it would be interesting to keep track of diesel costs while processing grain. After many hours with big Stillsons and PTFE, I found out that it didn't work; the flow rate was too slow, or something like that. So it has sat in the barn doing nothing ever since. I spent an hour finding it, dusting it off, and doing virtual plumbing in my head, contemplating fixing it somewhere in the back of the new bowser, before deciding it was a project for another day.

Tigger had finally passed the MOT, so we went and picked it up. It was a delight to be able to drive home with the feeling that it wasn't going to leap off the road or head straight into oncoming traffic at last. MOT and a good service – £400. That'll do.

July 10th

Much as I love welcoming Cain the cat onto my bed, he does tend to leave a fair proportion of the farm (and his fur) behind after every day spent snoozing. You don't notice it until Hazel very kindly changes the sheets, and a majestic night's sleep is the result. So, just for a change I was wide awake and ready to go nice and early.

After checking that the 1,100 litres of mixed-up fungicide that had been sitting in the sprayer tank for four or five days was still fluid (mixes have been known to coagulate), I headed out to the Hangar – the last of the three little fields of spring beans that need to be sprayed. In places it's a hell of a crop, but the middle is somewhat less impressive. It's funny to think how reluctant we were to put beans out there thanks to the nearby rook population; in the end, they did no damage at all. The crop that's doing best out there is groundsel, and I trundled back and forth across the field in a cloud of white fluff. Good thing it'll be easy to control in next year's first wheat.

I rang Tod as I was finishing and checked if the peas were still off the list of crops that needed doing. After all, I reasoned, it's a good spraying day, and I'm in the mood, and want to do as much as possible before hitching off and contemplating putting on the hedge trimmer. His suggestion was to go through them with the cheaper fungicide of the mix.

My cheery optimism at the state of the crops was brought crashing down by the state of the peas. It's as if not a single herbicide had worked. I'll admit that conditions weren't the most ideal when I did the pre-emergence application (I think the Isle of Wight got most of it), but it's really disheartening to see wild oats, blackgrass and volunteer spring barley in rude health. And the peas themselves do look horribly thin. I should have held out for more refund from the man from the seed company.

Luckily, the shooting strips cheered me up a bit when I went over them with some 'Shield' that I'd found in the back of the spray store, and with that, all spraying was done for the year. Always a great feeling. I'll get Tosdevine in to do Roundup when needed, so I can hitch onto the hedge trimmer. But probably next week.

And so ends a very odd arable year – or the non-harvest section of it. It didn't really kick off properly until the end of March, and then suddenly is all over. Next job – combining, assuming Luke the Combine Wizard actually comes back and reassembles the New Holland. At the moment, it's in pieces all over the barn.

July 11th

Rather nice to have a Saturday morning with no outstanding farming jobs, so we set about the knackered stable doors to Jonathan's 'gym'. We'd bought new ones some months ago, and I'd been contemplating how to go about it for some days, and, just for once, the mental plans worked. After only a couple of hours in the hot sun, the new doors were up, fitting almost perfectly (a two-inch gap along the top will need filling with a stray bit of wood from somewhere). Very satisfying – and the trusty Makita drill battery died as the very last four screws had been started. How's that for timing? I left Jonathan finishing them off with an old-fashioned screwdriver.

You know you're out of farm jobs when a bit of gardening beckons, and we put the hedge trimming head on the chainsaw-on-a-stick, but Jonathan had to abandon it when oil around the exhaust – from a 2-stroke mix that was too thick – started fuming and threatening to burst into flames. He popped down to the West Meon Hut garage for some Gunk and then gave up for the day. I had a fantastic and surprisingly warm wallow in the pool, and then Gunked the whole engine off and tried five minutes of hedge trimming. No smoke to be seen. I'll get him going with it tomorrow.

July 12th

A nice quiet Sunday. I did get a bit confused as to why Syria had its own Grand Prix this year, and why they'd moved it to Austria – although I decided it was probably something to do with the ongoing civil war there. Downtown Aleppo probably isn't the best place to hold a motor race at the moment. How thoughtful of the Austrians to host it.

It was pointed out that it's the Styrian Grand Prix, and Styria is part of Austria (where my favourite tractor ever was built). Must get new glasses and turn down that highly unlikely job offer as a sports journalist.

July 13th

Not a great day. I had planned to get the sprayer off, the hedge trimmer on, and start the long trundle round the lanes making them a bit safer for harvest. It was interrupted quite early by Tod, ringing for a chat about the complete failure of Falcon to control the grassweeds in the peas. What on earth had gone wrong?

Any number of things, as it happened. The weather might have been too hot, the drought might have been too strong, the water rate too low, the dose rate too low, the growth stage of the peas too late… basically, it was case of 'tough titty'. We'd have absolutely no comeback against the manufacturers. It struck me that we'd completely lost one of the main points of growing a break crop: tidying up the grassweeds.

While I was on the mobile to Tod, the landline rang. I Googled it, and it was the head of the Parish Council of a neighbouring village. This can only mean one thing: someone in the next-door village is having a moan about something, and, once again, this was the case.

We're really lucky in that we have only one shared pasture boundary – i.e. there's only one short length of livestock fence which we share with a pasture the other side. But somehow it's a huge problem. There's a footpath (the Wayfarers' Walk) that goes through both our field and the neighbour's. For years it had a stile, which was capable of handling the walking traffic. But then the Trust added that bit of the footpath to their list of recommended walks for their thousands of visitors, and the stile would collapse on a regular basis.

We'd get complaints about the stile being dangerous, so we'd pop out and give it a patch up – which would be fine for another couple of months. In more recent years, the path became a favourite dog walk, and dogs don't like stiles. The answer? A little pop-open sliding gate. You'd think that would be perfect – but heavy use took its toll on that, too, and dog-sized lambs started to get through.

Rather than repairing the dog gate, someone nailed it shut. No sheep got through, but neither did any dogs. And the walkers were furious, and guess who got the blame again? At this point, the National Trust stepped in with a kind offer: they'd supply all the materials for a super-dooper kissing gate, if we put it up. We needed lots of fencing done, and had booked a team from Monkwood to do it – so it was easy to ask them to do the kissing gate as well. Super job.

The PC Chairman was ringing to say that the shut spring had come off, and the gate wasn't swinging closed properly; could we pop out and put some new screws in? Of course we could, but it was a bit of a shock when we got there to find that every single sign asking people to keep to the footpath and keep their dogs under control had been carefully and methodically smashed to smithereens. We mended the spring, and chatted to a few Trust walkers, and chuckled at our very own version of 'urban fringe' farming.

There were two phone calls in the middle of all this. One was from Garwood's asking if we could pop down to the Drier Yard with a tractor and get the combine header out for Luke to work on. I said we were a bit busy, but we'd do it tomorrow morning. The other was from a highly excited Editor, who had just discovered a new Wednesday evening clay shoot up near Alton, and did I fancy going along to see what it's like? I said I was definitely on for it – if I could find some cartridges. Just the thing to fill the pre-harvest lull.

July 14th

I'd only just dropped off the Massey down at the Drier Yard when Luke the Combine Wizard arrived in his van. Not much of pre-harvest lull for him, of course, trying to get all the machines under his care up and running in time. Hazel picked me up, and I set about finally getting the hedge trimmer on.

It's not the quickest of jobs. There's lots of subframes and lockpins, guards and cables, and, of course, a safety screen to stick to the left-hand door and side window. Another half hour greasing up, and I was ready to go. Well, go all of five yards forward to unbolt the saw blade head, and fit the proper flail head.

The saw blade was a splendid eBay purchase a couple of years ago, when it dawned on me that it had been so long since I'd actually been out with the trimmer that lopping would be easier than flailing. And back in September, before the six-month deluge, I'd had a decent run around Broom Field, cutting some overhanging branches. The fact that I never got up there to put any crop in is neither here nor there.

We can only do roadsides at this time of year – in the name of safety – so the flail head is what is needed. And changing the head is messy, and awkward, and oily, and generally horrible. So once it was all on and assembled, I needed a break from it, and, instead, headed off around Hampshire in pursuit of clay shooting cartridges.

I've got curiously specific about my cartridges as I've got older. They've got to be 21 gram, 7.5 shot, and fibre wad. Hull do a very good one, and I find I can hit most things without hurting a rapidly disintegrating shoulder, and have the bonus of getting to the second bird quicker thanks to less flip and recoil. And they suit my relatively light 1981 Browning B27 Skeet very well.

It's all very well being that specific, but finding them is less easy. The last slab I bought was from Wallers Ash Gun Club while up there shooting, but they wouldn't be open before tomorrow night. I set off in the Skoda to Mole Valley stores in Winchester. Nope, they didn't have any. Mind you, it was the girl checking the computer that assured me of it, and it was sorely tempting to say, "Yes, but can we have a look in the cartridge cupboard to check?"

So it was up the A31 to Alton, and across towards Selbourne, to another country store. Nope, no cartridges at all there. On down into Petersfield, to a store on the industrial estate; plenty of cartridges, but none of that specification. Home for a cup of tea in a deluge. (How lucky that we'd put off spraying Roundup on the oilseed rape this morning.)

I rang the gun shop in Botley and was assured by the girl on the phone that they had thousands, so drove down there – in another downpour. Of course, they didn't have any – only ones with plastic wads. I was getting a bit fed up with driving round Hampshire at this stage, so grabbed a slab of 24 g instead – swallowing earnest assurances that they, too, were easy on the shoulder. We'll see.

It was a lovely drive back along drying roads from Botley, through Bishop's Waltham, up to Corhampton Down, to the tight bends at Lomer, and then down the road to Brockwood, in order to come back via the combine and see what progress Luke was making. There was a time when this drive yielded spectacular views over much of North Hampshire, but the bloody farmers have lined the road with new hedges, so there's nothing to see any more. Anyway, Luke had just finished, and said it was ready to go. Perfect – let's hope for a dry day tomorrow, and we can finally get the Roundup on the oilseed rape.

July 15th

The weather forecast didn't look perfect, grey and a hint of drizzle in the air, but we thought we'd have another go at getting Roundup on the oilseed rape in Drier Field. Graham's huge self-propelled Deere sprayer was in on the dot of nine, and he had the whole lot done by late morning.

That's the harvest clock started – in three weeks' time, we'll be in there with the combine. Mind you, there's every chance that the spring barley will be ready too, and the early winter wheats. Or perhaps the peas. Could be chaos.

So it was nice to see the combine parked up, ready to go. All it will need is a refuel and the OSR sieves installed, and away we go. Not sure about the nightmare of fitting the side knife – the crop isn't tall enough to justify it.

After a couple of hours of hedge trimming in Joan's Acre Road to remind myself of how to do it, I picked up the Editor, and we drove up to Alton for an unusual late afternoon clay shoot. It was just the right side of busy, with the usual cheerful atmosphere, and a reasonably challenging set of stands – although they were a bit limited by the geography of the hillside we were on. I shot well – 33/50, but the Editor shot like a drain – 21/50. And 10/10 of those were on the posh stand, i.e. 'driven grouse'. Shows what sort of game shooting he's used to.

It was lovely to get the gun out again and shatter some clays – still as much of a thrill as when I hit my very first one in about 1974. We were done and dusted and back home in an hour.

The drizzle came on a bit heaver by evening, but late enough – I hope – not to affect this morning's spraying on the oilseed rape. And it's St Swithun's Day. Forty days of drizzle? It wouldn't surprise me, the way this year is going.

July 16th

Sometimes, the *Flindt on Friday* column flows easily, sometimes it doesn't. This morning – the unofficial deadline, although the official one is Wednesday morning – I sat at the computer and couldn't come up with anything. Not a clue. The secret is not to panic – and to beg another day to come up with something. Luckily, the team at *Farmers Weekly* said I could leave it till tomorrow. A huge relief.

Nothing clears the mind like a long session of hedge trimming, although keeping clear of the flood of speed cyclists and non-reversing Audis can demand some quick thinking. Throw in some very soporific Test cricket on the radio, and the afternoon was officially well spent.

After a quick swim in a nicely warming pool, I drove up to Brockwood to watch and heckle the White Hunters during their first evening game of the year. Apart from the occasional 'sanitiser' break, you wouldn't know there was a pandemic crisis. The pitch was stunningly immaculate, the cricket was terrible, the catches were dropped, the umpiring was shocking, and just for a couple of hours, all was well with the world. The only shame was not being able to adjourn to a pub afterwards. But it won't be long.

July 17th

An evening of utter silliness with the White Hunters did the trick: I managed to come up with 600 scintillating and witty words for *Farmers Weekly*. A huge relief – even more so when they accepted them.

Hazel set off to the wilds of Oxfordshire for a long training day with the two brown flatcoats, and I did not very much. My neck was as stiff as hell after yesterday's hedge trimming, so I gave it a rest for the day. Jonathan went into Winchester to meet up with a mate for a beer or two and a much-needed catch up. Social life is returning to normal for him as well.

I managed (I hope) to sort out a new hire company to supply us with a 'rough terrain forklift' – usually a farm spec JCB – for loading lorries at harvest. The local New Holland dealer has helped us out for years, but rang the other day to say he didn't think he'd manage it this year. There's a plant hire company in Winchester who were reluctant at first, saying that field use of JCBs doesn't go well with their engine cooling systems – all that chaff and straw. I pointed out it would only be barn use, and they seemed happier. There's lots of forms and credit checks to be done – but I think I've opened an account at last.

My favourite virus news of the day was that Public Health England appear to have been recording any death as 'due to C-19' even if the deceased had it ages ago and had fully recovered. So it's perfectly possible to get hit by a bus, and be recorded as having died of C-19 only because you had it six months ago. Utterly bizarre.

The *Farmers Weekly* article on 'How to get your Book Published' appeared today – ten copies of Book One were ordered in the afternoon. Excellent. Almost as good as the view of Comet Neowise that we all got after a cursory scan of the north-west sky as it finally got dark. Just about naked-eye visible, and quite spectacular through our cheap'n'cheerful 10 x 50 binoculars. I must ask the Editor if he has a more powerful scope of some sort.

July 18th

Hot and windy, so a quiet Saturday. Hazel went off in Pig to check on the pheasant feeders and drinkers, and I enjoyed packing up sold copies of Book One. We had a session in the band's rehearsal room, clearing up the mountain of empty beer bottles and cans, working on the idea that lockdown restrictions are crumbling so fast that it won't be long before we're back in there on a Monday evening. I even had a go on the trusty Roland – ending what had to be the longest spell in my life I haven't played a keyboard. Quite scary. I was still rubbish.

The poor old shed is looking a bit tired; the ceiling I put up – nothing but sheets of Celotex nailed to some rafters – is getting a bit saggy. In an ideal world, we'd give it a bit of a birthday and put up some plasterboard to sort things out. Maybe a job for wet harvest days.

Jonathan needed a lift to Wetherspoons in Petersfield for the evening, as he was actually planning on having a few beers. Hazel took him, and I agreed (after the requisite bit of complaining) to pick him up at eleven-thirty. He was waiting in the car park when I got there, remarkably sober, and complaining about youngsters he remembers at Churcher's College as being a couple of years junior to him, and now getting blotto in the pub. Honestly – young people today, eh? Shocking.

Mind you, we both sulked like a couple of brats when we found that the Petersfield McDonald's was shut. It was only midnight, for goodness' sake. I was really looking forward to a completely unnecessary burger, chips and strawberry milkshake.

July 19th

The deafening noise coming from Manor Farm was the sound of my Moral High Ground collapsing suddenly and spectacularly. The next noise was the sound of me eating a very large portion of Humble Pie – cold and revolting.

Sasha and I were out for a Sunday walk. As usual, she was trotting alongside perfectly, behaving herself, occasionally stopping for new smells, eating the odd bit of poo, and generally owning the farm.

We'd been through Chalks, up to Clump, down to the Drier, and were walking slowly along Dark Lane at the bottom of the Folly. It was damp, quiet, and I was lost in my own pre-harvest thoughts and contemplations. Suddenly (I'm going deafer and deafer, so everything is 'sudden' these days) two bicycles approached from behind, so I summoned Sasha as quickly as I could, and the two of us stepped off to one side.

It was a local couple with whom relations have been strained for some years. We have never been able to agree on what the rules of Rights of Way are. I'm old school; there are lots of Rights of Way, and everyone should stick to them. This couple are very much of the "hmmm, not sure that actually applies to us – and we're not doing any harm" school of public access. So you can imagine that we're hardly on 'fall on each other's necks and embrace' terms – even in non-virus times.

However, all was polite and smiley; one could even describe the going as 'civilised to friendly'. Sasha picked up the surprisingly warm mood, and did some friendly greeting and nuzzling, and they paused on their bicycles. But all good things must come to an end, and with a cheery "see you later", the lady cyclist put her right foot under her right pedal and reversed it to the ten-past position.

Faster than you could blink, Sasha dived, snake-like, and sunk her teeth into my new friend's calf. It's hard to say what caused it, or what was scarier: the speed of the bite, or the flow of blood that poured down her leg from the neat little punctures. I spent ten minutes on my knees, not just apologising, but also trying to stop the flow with the usual farm coat contents: iffy hanky, wet-wipes (unused, luckily) and empty 12-bore cartridges. Nothing worked – she headed off as quickly as she could to seek treatment, leaving me stunned and mortified in the lane. Sasha was back to calm, and collected, as if nothing had happened. It was all slightly surreal.

Back at the farmhouse, Hazel listened to the whole story, grabbed a bottle of something and jumped in the car to go off and do some weapons-grade grovelling, bless her. She reported back that the welcome was cool, but not unfriendly, and she had to make lots of promises to take action with Sasha; such a thing must not be allowed to happen again. And Hazel being Hazel, and taking dog husbandry very seriously, she bloomin' well will, too.

Meanwhile, I sat indoors, nursing the bruises I'd got falling from lofty moral heights.

July 20th

As I strolled down for an early-ish morning check on the pool, a helicopter was doing loops over the Hurst Down woods. We had the same thing a couple of years ago, when the RPA 'lost' one of our fields from their database. After much emailing and many phone calls, they sent out a chopper to check on the missing field – Dell Close. After only an hour or so's zigzagging, they found it – which was a relief. A few more phone calls and some official letters later, and the farm was back up to full size. Quite a relief, although what the ghosts of the farmhouse would make of the whole affair, I don't know. I wrote it up for *Farmers Weekly*, and even managed to get a screenshot from Flight24 of the helicopter's path backwards and forwards across the Joan's Acre valley. God know what it cost.

I never did work out what this year's chopper was up to.

Yet more hedge trimming beckoned, this time up the no-through-road up to Blackhouse Farm. The only problem is that the new owners have started monster redevelopment work, and all the builders knock off at four. So I ended up dodging more traffic in a half-hour than I have all week. I hope they appreciated that the road is slightly less overgrown than it was. They'll probably go up a gear as a result.

At one stage, I came across a Transit pick-up reversed up into the woods on a track. All my farming alarm bells went off; white Transit, amber lights on top, back full of what looked like gardening clippings – could be trouble. Closer inspection revealed that the 'trimmings' were, in fact, carefully stacked piles of thatching straw, and the jolly couple who emerged from the woods were very apologetic for setting off all my virtual alarms. They were indeed thatchers, and were strolling through the recently coppiced woods, cutting and gathering hazel spars. I enjoyed an informative ten-minute chat with them, and then got back to hedge trimming. Next time I passed that pull-in, they were gone – but it was still a relief to see no huge piles of rubbish left behind.

Best phone call of the week happened as I was finishing. It was from a neighbour, whose wife had been out for a walk, and had heard 'steel drums' going in the woods. Steel drums? I pulled over in the Folly gateway, shut down the tractor and listened for myself. Not a thing. The National Trust get up to some daft things, but I'm sure they'd have told us of a steel band festival in the woods. Or maybe not. 'Twas a mystery. Was it perhaps the 'pinging' of high-speed hedge debris hitting the roller on the flail head? Or my neighbour enjoying some legendary herbal cigarettes? We'll never know.

July 21st

The 'preparation for a harvest that somehow doesn't seem to actually get any closer' continued with a start-up of the combine and a run through the hydraulics. The reel had settled down to a wonky angle since Luke had left, which was odd since the two rams that operated it are on the same circuit, but it squared itself up nicely after a couple of lifts and lowers. I wandered out into the oilseed rape and rubbed some out. It's small, there doesn't seem to be an awful lot of it, and the stems are still green. Will it be the first to be harvested? I've got to decide soon, because there's a lot of sieve-changing to be done, and side knives to be bolted on.

With some splendid procrastination, I decided not to decide, and went hedge trimming instead, finally getting the Joan's Acre Road and Blackhouse Road to something near finished.

Tonight's Beer on the Lawn was different. Neighbour Robert arrived on time (of course), and the Literary Agent and his wife drove the short distance from their idyllic house to join us. I wasn't sure whether he'd accept the invitation, but five minutes later, he and neighbour Robert were new best friends, and the beer was disappearing rapidly. He and his wife didn't stay long, and we were left wondering where the Editor had got to. I texted him that his beer was getting warm, and five minutes later a powder blue Jimny hurtled into the yard – he'd completely forgotten (that was his story, anyway). We eked out the beer we still had, and it was getting proper dark when we all headed our separate ways. I'm going to miss our little beer sessions if we ever go back to the pub.

July 22nd

Another post-beer woozy morning, which foiled any attempts to get the next column written, so I climbed into the hedge trimmer again, and set off to do the stretch of road around Cheyney. I haven't touched that bit of hedge for ages, and it shows. There's hardly room for two walkers to pass, never mind a large tractor and one of the many Trust walkers who enjoy that loop. But after a couple of passes, I'd made a bit more room, and it became easier for the huge tractor and nervous walkers to pass each other – once I let the flail calm down, of course.

Once I'd got that stretch of road under control, I switched jobs completely, and gave the grain trailers a wash off. They're getting on a bit, but have done no other job than cart grain, so come up really well. A quick check of all the tyre pressures, and a run round of all the grease nipples, and all was done. Hold on – I'd forgotten the most important job: record the event in my farm inspection book. Far more important these days than lubricated bogies.

July 23rd

I'm getting serious itchy combine ignition key trigger finger – if that makes any sense. I'd really like to get out there and combine something. The weather forecast isn't good in a couple of days, the combine is ready to go, the trailers are gleaming from yesterday's pressure washing; all we need is something that's fit.

The oilseed rape's out of the question, having only been sprayed nine days ago. The spring barley is still green – so that leaves the early wheats. Were they ready? I drove round them, cutting heads off in the ripest bits, ready to have a home thrashing session (oo-er) and take a bag of grain up to Trinity Grain for testing.

I had hoped to get it done by lunchtime, but my progress round the fields was constantly and delightfully interrupted by inquisitive members of the public, who wanted to know what was going on. It was surprising how many had spotted the selection of wheats in Clump – although the multiple different shades of green make it hard to ignore. One inquisitive family from Four Marks were treated to ten minutes on the technicalities of vernalisation. What a thrill for them.

Even my attempts to get it rubbed out and into a bag were interrupted, but this time by an old friend from Cheriton who'd been asking on Facebook about chicken houses. Hazel offered our old one in the orchard for nothing, if they came and got it. Before you could say hardboiled egg there was a horse box in the back yard being reversed as near as possible to the neglected chicken shed, and within moments, and without even any dismantling, it was gone to its new home. A bag with a bottle of 'thank you' wine was left diplomatically at the gate. Splendid.

Finally, after lunch, I had a bag of reasonably well rubbed out and cleaned Crusoe to take up to Micheldever for analysis. I paused at the West Meon Hut to give Tigger its pre-harvest top-up of diesel, and it was nice to see only a couple of people wearing face nappies, and diesel being still relatively cheap – around £1.20/litre. And I could pay by card with a PIN again. And Tigger is going like a train since the wobbly wheel swap.

There were no combines to be seen working while I drove. A couple of wheat fields – uncut ones – looked far further on than ours, and the meters and measuring kit at Trinity confirmed it: our wheat is not ready to cut yet. Mind you, I wasn't 100% sure that store manager Michael was using all the kit properly. Three young Polish ladies who usually do the testing were sitting in a row chatting nonchalantly and incomprehensibly, not giving Michael much help at all. It was straight out of a Harry Enfield sketch.

The initial harvests reports up there were very mixed. Don't mention oilseed rape, the gravels have dried out horribly in the Thames valley, and most people are sitting indoors waiting for harvest proper to start. Michael said he'd been ringing round trying to find loads for his fleet of drivers to collect. Perhaps I am getting ahead of myself with harvest plans.

The Winnall roundabout confirmed that traffic levels are back to normal, and the idiots are at the wheel again. I had a very close shave with an undertaker (as in using the left-hand lane to pass, not as in someone who buries people) who was veering at random all over the road. I got alongside him as I went down the Spitfire Link, and saw that he probably hadn't passed a test in this country, and he was holding his phone in his left hand for navigation purposes.

Despite harvest being put on hold, we kept going with the preparations.

Hazel and Jonathan blitzed the left-hand lean-to and the main barn, and I fuelled up the combine with the old bowser. Smoke coming off the eBay fuel pump suggested that I'd done the right thing to order a new bowser.

In the evening, the clouds rolled in and a horrible wind got up. My swim was short.

July 24th

Some breakdowns are crucial. The farm has to stop while they are put right. And today's was one of those; the aerial had snapped clean off the top of Hazel's tractor, probably at some time during the numerous tree pruning and flailing operations.

Replacing aerials used to be tricky, but possible. Most of the early tractors with cabs had no radios, so you learnt to install them somewhere where replacement was easy – mud guards, for instance, on the 6600 and 7600s. Then they started coming with radios, and the aerial tended to be up in the roof. With some deft wristwork (and my tiny hands) it was possible to get into the headlining of most tractors, get the nut off the old aerial and remove it, shine up the metal for a better earthing point, and get another one installed. My John Deere has a powered internal one, which doesn't work terribly well, but at least it never breaks off.

With harvest approaching, there's a sense of urgency about getting all the radios up and running properly for those long days in the cab. I grabbed the ladder and climbed up the side of the Massey's cab. It didn't look good. The stalk had snapped clean off, and there was just a stump left. I noted its position and then climbed into the cab itself. There was no way of threading a chunky forearm into the roof lining in this case. I sat and stared at the roof for a couple of minutes, as if some solution would magic its way into my head (sometimes it works, you know), but then headed indoors, and emailed the Massey dealers. "How do I replace the aerial?" I asked.

"It's a 'roof off' job" was the swift but depressing reply. I'm not sure modern tractor designers spend a lot of time on farms. My pre-harvest shopping list had another item added to it: a DAB receiver that plugs into the 'aux' socket on the front of the radio. Sixty quid off eBay.

Another long afternoon beckoned in the hedge trimmer, trying to get the roads a bit safer for harvest, and dodging a seemingly endless stream of cyclists, who sort of proved my point that the roads need to be a bit safer.

I had to pause at one stage to help two walkers who I spotted strolling happily through the peas, having appeared out of Stanmore, and walked the length of the Barracuda strips. They were hard core Londoners (Ladbroke Grove, apparently), absolutely charming, very relieved that I didn't get out of the tractor and shout at them, but genuinely hadn't come across the concept of a 'right of way'. We had a long chat about lots of farming things, and parted the best of friends.

The wind got up again late in the evening, and just as I was dozing off, I thought I could hear a car driving oddly. Or was it the wind? No one would be driving round the fields yet, surely? But then it was certainly a car, and it was heading our way from Kilmeston, very noisily. I watched it go past from the bedroom window, noted the time (11.05pm) and went back to bed.

July 25th

The Facebook posts started early. Hinton Ampner House had been hit by thieves again, with sheds being emptied of gardening equipment. I drove down to Dark Lane to see if a vehicle had emerged from there, but there were no tracks. So I settled down on the sofa for a day listening to the Test match which was going ahead in Manchester despite the forecast of an all-day deluge. We appeared to be getting the rain down here instead.

We had a call from Brad in No. 1, saying that two young lads had knocked on his door, in a right stew because they'd seen a dead sheep in the Hay Field – and that it looked like it had been attacked by dogs. This was odd, not least because the sheep moved out several days ago – and it must have just happened. A dead sheep lying next to the nation's busiest footpath would have meant a flood of calls.

Hazel and I jumped into Tigger and drove out there. There was indeed a large and surprisingly healthy-looking sheep stone dead near the far stile. As we stood and looked at it for a moment or two, the young lads emerged from the trees next to Cheyney, desperate to help. We collared them into assisting us with lifting the slightly whiffy body (maggots and all) into Tigger, and, having thanked them for their help and for telling us about it in the first place, brought it home for the shepherd to dispose of.

We came home via Dark Lane and spotted that the Hinton House thieves had driven along the track from the S-bends, moved a gargantuan tree stump that was blocking the gate into the South Park, cut the chain on the gates, and driven up to the House. We would have stayed longer and hunted for more clues, but the dead sheep was beginning to outstay its welcome in the back of Tigger. We headed home and dropped it on the concrete outside the back barn. I rang the shepherd, who was as baffled as we were. He was mortified that his top-notch record in the 12 months that his sheep have been here had been spoiled. I told him not to worry.

Ian the Policeman was round for a cuppa and to ask if we'd heard anything about the Hinton House burglary. Apparently, there is someone living on site, and there are cameras and security lights, but the thieves still managed to ransack the place. Oh well, it's just my rent money they're stealing.

It dried up just enough in the evening for Jonathan and a friend to head for the Flowerpots garden and enjoy a pint or two. Good lad.

July 26th

A lazy Sunday. The shepherd was up very early for the dead sheep, full of apologies. (The sheep itself was full of maggots.) Hazel knows enough about sheep and their ways to reassure him that it was nothing to worry about. Her theory was that it got a nick during the recent shearing, the cut got nasty, the sheep took to the trees and nettles for a bit, missed the move, and then went down suddenly with toxic shock. It's what sheep do. That and falling into a trough and drowning. The most important thing is that the two lads saw it early and told us about it. If it had been there for days, and the weather had been better, it might have been a different story.

It was a surprisingly good day of sport. The Test Match was a thriller – OK, no live coverage, but the now-infantile Test Match Special was just about bearable, and the wonderful ITV4 finished their week of showing England's games from the 2003 Rugby World Cup by showing the final again. They've been broadcasting the games as if live – start to finish – and it was wonderful to see proper scrums and proper running breaks. 2003 seems only yesterday, not 17 years ago. People still rave about Wilkinson's drop-goal, but it was Dawson's outrageous dummy and break upfield to sneak another ten yards for him that made it possible.

July 27th

Muggy, windy and very wet. Horrible. Funny to think that this time last year we were romping through tinder-dry winter barley, setting records yields and narrowly avoiding setting half of southern England alight with a smouldering engine in the combine. Most of the day was spent doing office stuff and feeling distinctly under par.

The rescheduled launch of the new Defender is imminent, and I'm planning to go, come hell or high water. It's not a launch to be missed. OK, it's no longer a proper two-day event with a luxury sleepover somewhere, but the Defender is still too important a vehicle to be ignored at launch. Unfortunately, we'd all been requested to watch a 'webinar', where we'd all be briefed on the new machines. It's what we would have been subjected to in the hotel, if it had been a proper launch.

It was in three sections: the first was 20 minutes of bollocks about design, the second was 20 minutes of interesting stuff about mechanicals, and the third was all about how the Defender is now a 4WD computer, with 24/7 software updates done automatically. Really? What could go wrong? It being a Land Rover, probably lots.

I had yet another attempt to organise a loader and a bucket just in case harvest ever does start, and we get some stuff in the barn that needs to be loaded onto a lorry. I suppose we will one day; the forecast suggests hot and dry by the end of the week. The loader hire company said they'd only got a monster machine, but we could have it at small machine rates, and my attempts to persuade the New Holland dealer to rent me a grain bucket fell very flat. I might have to buy one instead.

July 28th

A better day. Whatever was bugging me yesterday cleared, and I managed to get the last bits of hedge trimming done, accompanied by some relatively exciting cricket on the radio. I had one more bonus session on the Cheyney roadsides, did the new strip up next to BOMS, and then did the bits outside the farmhouse.

Hazel had met the family who live at the bungalow a few days ago, and asked if they wanted their hedges done, too. Since Grandpa planted them after moving in there in 1997, they've got away a bit, and the present residents haven't managed to keep up with them. So I spent an hour bashing them into some sort of shape. I managed to hit a flat-packed greenhouse which was hidden the other side of one low hedge – and rearranged its shape somewhat. Luckily it was old and manky in the first place.

Tod was back from holidays and did a walkabout. He said the peas could do with their pre-harvest Roundup as soon as possible, but everything else seemed to be on track. I had enough spray in stock, so pencilled that job in for tomorrow.

The Beer on the Lawn was one of the best so far. Neighbour Robert was in first, of course, and we'd just settled down into the first pint when neighbour John strolled across the yard, glass of beer in one hand, bottle in the other, and a look of delight on his face. "Aha!" he cried. "I thought this is what was happening – your manky old Land Rover gives it away every Tuesday night, Robert!" He swiftly settled down on one of the socially distanced chairs.

The Editor and his wife arrived shortly after that, and, despite the chill in the air, we had a very long evening putting away the multiple beer takeouts. John's 'glass and a bottle' supply ran out quite early, but we had enough to keep him going.

Next week, God willing, we should be in a combine, or restrictions will have lifted enough to get down the pub proper. Or not. I'll miss my Beer on the Lawn.

July 29th

Despite last night's beer, I was feeling surprisingly fit. Off came the hedge trimmer, and it was back onto the sprayer; I could have sworn I took it off a few weeks ago with a triumphant feeling of "I won't be needing that for a few months!" Still, Tod's spraying recommendations take priority.

When I got to the peas in White Hill, there were two couples of a certain age sitting on the telegraph poles in the gateway, enjoying their lunch. We exchanged some friendly banter as I drove in, and I thought I'd dropped enough hints about my upcoming spraying to suggest that they moved on – but obviously not. As I unfolded the booms about ten yards away from them, they continued happily munching their sandwiches on the pole, enjoying the hi-tec farm kit demo.

There was only one solution. Stop the tractor, get out and have a nice long chat. As is usual in these circumstances, the questions came thick and fast, and by the time I finally got the Roundup flowing – must have been 20 minutes later – three of the four pensioner picnickers were a lot better informed about farming than they had been when they sat down to their sandwiches. One old dear, however, had spent the 20 minutes some distance away with a lemon-sucking face; not sure why – I'd dissed vegans, organic farming, the National Trust, and she could have been any or all of those I suppose.

The peas looked OK – apart from the forest of grassweeds that have magically survived the expensive grassweed killer. They're standing up, which, as any fule kno, is the single most important things a pea crop can do. The highest yield ratings, the most spectacular resistance to fungi – all useless if the bloody lot goes flat on the floor. Some of the field looked pretty ripe, too, so we could be in here in a week or ten days. Let's pray for no storms between now and then.

When I got back, I found that the next delivery of Roundup hadn't made it, so I collared Jonathan to help me with converting the combine for oilseed rape. We brought down the dedicated lower sieve and the heavy and unbelievably awkward Zurn side knife, and got them both fitted. It was certainly a lot easier with two of us, and once they were in/on, I briefly contemplated a turn or two to start the field. But then went and had a nice warm wallow in the pool instead.

July 30th

First thing, I had yet more attempts to get a lorry loading machine sorted. I rang the people who were due to hire me the loader, and sort of got a thumbs up for next week, and then rang the New Holland dealer to put my name on a big grain bucket to fit it. And then, after doing my *Flindt on Friday* piece (writing up, wisely or unwisely, the complete failure of the grassweed killer in the peas), I decided that I couldn't think of any more excuses not to start harvest, and Jonathan and I got stuck into the oilseed rape in Drier Field.

It was actually quite exciting: what would the crop be like, after 49 weeks in the ground, sown with an accidentally huge seed rate (15 kg/ha) and then a deliberate but not so high 10 kg/ha? Tod and I thought we'd try to feed the beetles to their hearts' content, and then there'd be some left over to grow. It worked in that field, but White Hill, sown at 10 kg/ha by neighbour Raimes with his Kockerling, had vanished within days of growing, so that's our theory up the spout. And then the crop has been on the cusp of being ploughed in multiple times over the season, but made enough of a recovery every time to earn a stay of execution.

It was quickly apparent that the stems were still tough as old boots, and the yield was going to be well below mediocre. Jonathan went home to stand by his phone, ready to be summoned when – if – a trailer got full. I persevered anyway. What else can you do?

The phone rang while I was on my second turn of headland. It was the hire company saying that they didn't have a medium-size loader for me, but they had a ten-metre lift one – the one with stabiliser legs on the front. I pointed out that the barns and the yard were laid out in 1960, and I didn't think that size of machine would be able to handle the tight spaces. And that it would probably push the bloody barns down at the same time. They went away to 'see what they could do'. I quickly rang the New Holland dealer to cancel the grain bucket. And finally got combining again.

After seven very dusty hours of combining, I had filled three trailers, and done about 25 acres. If we optimistically assume eight tonnes to a trailer... oh dear. Better than some I'm hearing about, but still miles off what we used to hope for from the 'black gold' break crop.

I knocked off a bit early, because the headache had started (from a long period of unaccustomed leaning forward) and my shoulders were beginning to hurt as well. The oilseed itself was beginning to shatter in the dry conditions, too, and the buyers don't like yellow in the black. I had a lovely swim, though – the sessions after combining are always the best. And the combine itself went well on day one; always a relief.

July 31st

Not a chance of nipping out to get some dew-laden OSR in this morning. By nine o'clock, a hot air blast started from the east, and by the time I'd hoovered the pool, it was obvious that a quiet indoor day was in order.

I thought we should have yet another go at getting a machine to load lorries sorted out. The New Holland dealer isn't interested any more, the specialist hire company seemed to have lost the plot completely, so I tried one of the Deere dealers. They were interested in helping, and had a Kramer available if we wanted one. Reasonably cheap, but only a little bucket comes with it. Would that suit?

The thing is, I bought a big toe-tip bucket to fit the new Massey tractor last year, with half an eye on not hiring in a machine at all. It's a 1.8 cu.m Quicke bucket, so nothing like as fast at loading a lorry as a proper RTFL with a 2.5 or even 3 cu m bucket, but far cheaper. The hired machine will cost several hundred quid a week, needs to be on the farm insurance, can only be driven by Noel, and can stand expensively idle during a wet harvest week. But in a frantic heavy harvest, it can get three lorries in and loaded in 90 minutes, and harvest can continue apace.

Not sure this harvest will qualify as either 'frantic' or heavy', so I started thinking that using the Massey with the toe-tip was the way forward this year. But we'll need a bigger weight pack on the back. We've got the old front weights off my beloved Ford 7810 – 12 40-kg slabs and a block, so probably about 600 kg. Enough to balance the front nicely, but when I did use it a couple of times last year, everything felt a bit unstable when the bucket was at height. We've got a pile of belly weights off the Case CS150 we had for a few years, which, with a bit of work and some M20 threaded bars, could pack alongside the old Ford weights and add to stability.

Out in the real world, Boris announced that the lockdown easing was on hold, as parts of the community are not obeying the rules, and infection rates are rising. With every passing day, I'm finding it easier and easier to predict government policy using the very simple question; "What would Extinction Rebellion want?"

August 1st

August got off to an early start in reinforcing its reputation as a wet month by sending two small but very heavy showers over Hinton Ampner as I was enjoying a late lazy lunch. Bloomin' infuriating, as, after a good start in Drier Field, I reckoned I only had one trailer's worth of oilseed rape still to be combined.

After a snoozy couple of hours, though, the sun had shone enough for me to pop back out and finish it by the early evening. Not quite six trailers off not quite fifty acres. If I'm optimistic in tons/trailer, that'll be not far off a ton per acre. Too much to finally write off the chances of oilseed rape ever being grown again, but not really enough to rush out and buy the seed for next year's crop.

August 2nd

You can't beat a nice Sunday morning rolling round under a combine, converting it back to standard cereal kit. Even better when you've persuaded your lad out of bed to lend a very strong hand.

After only a couple of hours, the plain round hole sieve was out, the frogmouth cassette was in, and the two 17 mm bolts were firmly in place. Next job was to lift off the side knife (once the safety guard had been taped over the 'sections' – as the triangular blades are mysteriously called) and set all the special equipment onto a pallet, ready for next year. Or will it? Will we bother with oilseed rape again? Just at the moment, the answer is a firm 'no', but never say 'never'.

After an early lunch, I hitched off the sprayer so that Jonathan could use the Deere for corn cart, and we could get the Massey set up with weights and the toe-tip, ready to be used as pusher-up in the main barn. An hour later, we were out in the wheat in Rick/Clump, and it was funny to be rediscovering all the evidence of the horrendous autumn: lumps of soil where the Horsch drill kept bunging up, strange loops in the corn where I had to do a big 360 to try and shed some of the crap that was blocking everything... it was therapeutic to be clearing away all the evidence of that grim autumn, and getting some reasonable wheat at the same time.

More August showers arrived at about four o'clock, just after we'd had a long tea break and a Q&A session with a walker who was baffled by the peas and what they were for. You'd have thought the good Lord would smile on us for doing such good PR work for the farming industry, but no; we had to abandon for the day.

August 3rd

A dry August day! OK, it's only the third day, but...

As a result, we had a good run in the wheat, finishing the early drilled bit of Rick and Clump, and hopping over the hedge into Chalks, which, once you got off the clay at the top, was a serious bit of corn. The old combine had to slow down a bit. By the time evening came, I was quite cheerful – I'll be even happier if it has any quality.

There was a bit of a shuffle in the evening after I parked the combine next to the pool, and Jonathan and Hazel went to get Tigger from New Pond, and then dropped it off at North's ready for another set of post-MOT jobs.

You can't beat having a swim with the cooling combine visible just over the edge of the pool.

August 4th

A proper, full-on, flat-out and successful harvest day – the sort of day that you should file away for recall on one of those dismal mid-November afternoons.

The first two harvest lorries of the season were due, so I had to have a good rummage in the office for passports, red tractor 'stickers' (actually A5 printouts this year – 'cos of the virus), the Hampshire Grain, sorry, Trinity Grain clipboard, lots of membership numbers… and found the whole lot first time.

Noel joined me down at the Drier Yard and we discussed how we'd use the Massey tractor and toe-tip bucket to load the lorries. It has always been a struggle in a tight 1960s-designed yard, especially when the lorries insist on parking on the north side of the yard – as they have done since the 1960s. One of the main reasons we have to hire four-wheel-steer machines is to do the full 180-degree turns.

With the most brilliant flash of inspiration, I asked Noel if he, as a lorry driver, would be able to park his artic at 90 degrees to the barn entrance. He couldn't see why not, and at that moment, the first lorry rumbled down the hill. Noel asked the same question of the driver. He didn't see why not, too.

Ten minutes later, the Massey was shunting in and out of the heap of wheat, executing a quick 90 degrees left, and tipping 1.8 cu m of stuff into the lorry. Quick and as easy as you like. Why the hell we didn't think of that before, I don't know. The big toe-tip bucket has been sitting idle for no good reason. He had two lorries done in well under two hours.

We had a long day combining in Chalks, finishing with 14 trailers off 13 hectares, which would be a very useful statistic if we knew how much is in a trailer.

August 5th

We're well used to one of the four dogs barking unnecessarily at some unearthly hour. Hazel worked out that most of the time it's the pup deciding to torment his mother, so Bella has been shut in the big cage for a week or two, which has given everyone some peace. This morning, though, it was Sasha barking, and she doesn't normally tell tales. All the blackbirds and couple of magpies outside the bedroom window were backing up her warning, so it was safe to assume that Mr Fox was about somewhere. By the time both Hazel and I made it downstairs, though, there was no sign of anything, and all the chickens were untouched, which was a relief.

One thing I did notice as we checked the chooks was that there was a howling gale, and I'd provisionally booked Tosdevine to come in and tidy up the stubbles with Roundup today. I ummed and ahhed about it, then we had a chat. First call was "Let's go for it"; most of the fields are remote, and the sooner the better. Ten minutes later, the wind had strengthened, so I rang back to shelve it. A nuisance for him, I know, but Roundup and a strong wind don't mix. It got even stronger an hour or so later, so it was the right call. The bonus is that the double order of Roundup is due today (Tod pressed the button twice, or something like that), which means that when we do get round to it, we can up the rate to reflect the growing mass of greenery that's out there.

As if the suspicious Mr Fox wasn't enough to get everyone on their toes, Hazel and Julie were nattering out on the road when a black SUV full of a certain type stopped and asked directions for the Eminent Surgeon's house in Kilmeston – full marks to them for getting a word in edgeways. Hazel rang me at once to say they looked as dodgy as hell, so I rang a rather shocked Eminent Surgeon, who said that yes, they were expecting tradesmen in to quote for new guttering. He was very grateful for the call, though. Hazel pointed out that the SUV drivers looked the type who would successfully take down the guttering, and the lead, and the lawnmowers, and the heating oil, and the dogs, and then never be seen again.

Next job was to get the combine fuelled up and greased. North's still hadn't finished with Tigger (waiting for the tyres I ordered), so it was up to Pig to tow the old bowser down to the edge of the tennis court where it was parked. It took a bit of grunting and swearing, but eventually I got there, and the last of the diesel from the old bowser went in. I had a good grease up, too, pausing only to chat with Mac (who had arrived to bale the golden but short wheat straw) and scoff at his predictions of showers tonight.

Two lorries came and went, quicker than ever, and once Hazel and Jonathan had installed the new convex mirror at the exit of the track onto Joan's Acre road, I drove the combine from the tennis court all the way to BLM's, and we cut that in a long afternoon.

Jonathan had his first go at combining, and did well. There's a mountain of info to take in if you've never done it before, but we quickly covered the basics, and he did an hour with me, and then an hour on his own. I was very proud.

A huge bank of cloud came in from the west late in the day, and not long after we'd finished BML's, and I'd driven the combine all the way back to the edge of the tennis court, a steady drizzle started. I must apologise to Mac for scoffing at his weather forecast.

Tigger came home from North's garage with proper round tyres fitted. "Crikey!" said Hazel. "It drives in a straight line!"

August 6th

It was wet first thing, with a steady drizzle. We sent off a couple more lorries, and then a good heavy shower put paid to any combining.

I thought I'd convert to peas anyway, so put the lifters and perforated auger/elevator covers on. The word from the lorry team wasn't great: the oilseed rape was a bit fluffy, and it was all they could do to get a proper load on the first lorry, and after that there was bugger all left. Should they put it on the second lorry? I said they should switch back to the wheat, and we'd have a ponder on the oilseed rape's fate.

The rain cleared to another thirty-something degree afternoon, which probably dried everything to 'combinable' – but we had another splendid Beer on the Lawn instead – rescheduled from Tuesday.

An airliner flew over very late in the evening. It was enough for us all to look up and take notice. Things are crawling back to normal.

August 7th

There was a very odd thing going on during last night's Beer on the Lawn, and it was in my boxer shorts; a sort of itchy tingling feeling. No, it wasn't something lustful. And this morning, the result was plain to see. Certain parts of my anatomy had been viciously attacked by something – probably an ant. I had bites on my hips and upper thighs, and as for my most private possession – it looked very sorry for itself. I normally wouldn't mind it being twice its normal size, but this enlargement came with a certain amount of pain, and the extra bulk came laterally rather than longitudinally. To put it plainly: my todger looked like a sausage roll. Luckily, all the waterworks functions seemed in order.

It all meant a rather tender day, stepping rather carefully, taking it very steady when doing the combine service this morning, once I'd sent in a rather lame *Flindt on Friday* – the trouble when nothing's really going on is that there's nothing to write about. It also gave me another excuse not to join Team Lorry, who, after much debate on the merits of sending the dregs of the oilseed rape up to Micheldever on a tractor and trailer, put the last seven tons onto a lorry. It may not be cheaper, but it's certainly easier than a four-hour round trip. We managed to get two more lorries in (things are still remarkably quiet out there in harvestland), which failed to clear the last of the early sown Crusoe – which is a good thing.

Noel was happy to stand down for a bit, and I set off to start the peas in White Hill. Hazel accompanied me with a tractor and trailer, and then walked home, and I rang Jonathan every couple of hours to get him to pop down and empty a full load.

It all went very smoothly. There weren't many peas out there, although some patches were good. The combine was flying through the nicely standing peas, the turns were long, and I ended up getting three full trailers off 30 acres. Even the totally unforecast storms skipped over us nicely.

My willy still hurt, though. I might write about it next week.

August 8th

No lorries to load, so we all had a quieter Saturday morning. I went and fetched the air filter from the combine and gave it a much-needed blow out; with yet another hottest day EVAH on the cards, the New Holland engine needs all the help it can get. One thing I will say about it: it has never had the cooling problems that the previous TC56 had. I was once driving it up the hill in Big Broom in a serious crop of wheat, and had to turn off the straw chopper and the air con to keep the engine cool enough to avoid the 'automatic overheat stop' feature cutting in. When New Holland designed the model I've got now, at least they gave it radiators to match.

I got going again in the peas just after twelve, and finished the whole field at about seven, just after England had spectacularly beaten Pakistan in the first Test. I'm still listening to the radio on one speaker – the mice ate the other a couple of years ago.

The yield was dismal on the light land, but there were some patches when the cutter bar vanished under the crop. But it was a dead easy crop to combine, and that's what counts with peas. The heaviest crop in Christendom is no use if it's on the floor. After the complete failure of the grassweed killer, I must get it cultivated to try and get as many seeds to strike as possible.

The ghost of Sub-Lt Daly, whose Fairey Barracuda crashed in the far end of White Hill in 1943, and has been known to get in the way of smooth operations in that field, decided to leave me alone and let me get on with the job – unlike when we were sowing it, and the drill control went haywire – twice. I toasted the poor fellow in thanks with the last of my Thermos when I finished.

There are days when Mother Nature can be hideously brutal, and today was one of them. At the far end of White Hill, in the forest of wild oats, a partridge was desperately trying to shield her brood of chicks from the combine. There were more than a dozen of them, nothing more than balls of brown cotton wool. They were scuttling their way through the stalks quite well, but she was struggling; she couldn't desert them by flying off. I paused the combine a couple of times in the hope that they'd get out of the way, but in the end had to get on. Eventually, the standing crop reduced to a tiny strip, and she flew over to the next block of uncut peas.

When I came back up the hill to the same spot, there were rooks and buzzards effortlessly harvesting the crop of tiny partridges. I spotted her again about fifty yards later; she ran alongside the combine for a bit, then flew off, far away, off towards Cheyney. No point in her hanging round here anymore. There's nothing left for her. I wonder if partridges grieve.

August 9th

The first thing I noticed about the new fuel bowser on its first trip out was that it's bloomin' heavy. No surprise really; it's all steel and double skinned, rather than the previous one which was a single plastic skin. I parked the old one, now empty, out of the way in the cattle barn, and heaved the new one into position on Tigger's ball hitch – another sweaty job on another unbelievably hot morning, and started filling it up from the main tank. I gave it three bursts of 250 litres to check the gauge (very accurate) but didn't go the whole way to full. It seemed quite heavy enough as it is.

There was a sticker on the nozzle, insisting that the fuel was recirculated through the system before it was connected, and once that was done, I was ready to go. I set off to White Hill. The next couple of things to notice were that the extra weight sent Tigger straight out of the farm entrance – good things no cars were coming – and that the tall skinny tyres were a tad bouncy. But I got there in the end, and fuelled the combine up.

After lunch, Hazel dropped me off in White Hill, and after a thorough window clean, I drove into the Folly and cut a single length to Drier Field. The barley in the Folly was full of green secondary tillers – a huge problem this year – and I rather hoped BOMS (my final destination) would be better. I paused at the Drier standpipe to give the engine a damned good wash-off, and then drove the short distance along the road at New Pond, and up the track.

Just up the track, a car was parked, in the shade under the trees, and next to it was a man in a deckchair, reading a paper. He looked up at the combine, but seemed remarkably unconcerned. I drove a bit closer and stopped. He rose slowly from his chair, and ambled down the track. "Do you want to get past?" he shouted in slightly irritated fashion.

"Yes, please," I shouted back, trying hard to supress any sarcasm. He stood and pondered this for a moment.

"Are you going to harvest this field?" he asked. I didn't really want to indulge in a long discussion on the relative ripeness of late-January sown Crusoe, or descend into claiming that, no, I just happened to be out for a recreational drive in my combine harvester.

"Well, what do you think?" was the least sarky comment I could muster. Once again, he seemed in no hurry, looking around as if slightly bewildered at the idea of having to get out of the way. "Look," I shouted down from the cab. "I'm very happy to push your car out of the way with this, but it might make a bit of mess of it." Finally, he got the message, and scuttled back up the track. He quickly folded the deckchair, flung it in the boot, and jumped in the car. He didn't bother to reverse back down to the wide bit of the track where he could have passed me, but instead headed backwards into the little copse. I did worry for a moment that an old tree stump was likely to do as much damage to the underside of his Golf as my cutter bar would do to the upperside, but he seemed to get away with it. I could finally head into BOMS and the much better bit of spring barley.

It just showed that if you give the seedbed a bit of work (see March 30ᵗʰ), and up the seed rate (April 1ˢᵗ), you get a better crop. A lesson for the future. We made great progress, with Jonathan running full to the nicely swept Godwin's barn (thanks, Hazel) using the roads, and running back across the fallow in Roe Hill when empty. I had to pause a couple of times and wait for him to get back, but I only lost a couple of minutes all day. Ashley came in with his baler and had the lot round baled by evening. My word, it was hot again.

August 10ᵗʰ

No lorries this Monday morning, so it was quiet. The Toyota Supra arrived for its week of evaluation – a proper old-school low-slung two-seater sporty thing, although, as so often is the way these days, it's an awful lot of BMW underneath. The plan is to take it to the Defender launch on Wednesday – but I might stick with the Octavia; the last thing I need is to put my back out trying to get out at Land Rover HQ.

I parked Tigger in the Drier lean-to, walked over to BOMS to pick up the combine, and headed back through Drier Field to get to Folly East. It was a lot greener that BOMS, but there's little we can do at this stage. I even rang Bill at Trinity Grain to compare notes; he said everyone has it this year. His advice, and it was a bit of a blast from the past, was to let it sit in the barn for a few days, and it somehow evens up in the storage. I can remember Dad doing just that when we stored on-farm here; after a few weeks in the Conder bins, we'd run the whole lot through the little cleaner, and buckets of desiccated 'gramophone needles' would come out.

We had a good run, finishing Folly East and doing the headland of Folly West. And as I dozed off, Ashley could be heard baling what we'd just combined, making sure that if the storms do arrive tonight, there's nothing to get spoiled.

August 11ᵗʰ

Two lorries in, one for peas, one for spring barley, and to everyone's delight, both went for top quality: the barley as Grade 1 Planet, the peas for human consumption. Very good news.

I did a huge grease up, and only just got it all done before the heat sent me back indoors. So it was lucky that we only had a couple of hours left in the Folly to do. When we'd done it, I drove the combine back along the road to the edge of the tennis court and got a lift down to Tigger with Hazel. On the way home, I drove past Godwin's barley, and yes, it was still green as anything. There really is nothing left to combine. Good thing there's rain on the way – and the small matter of the trip to Warwick for the Defender launch tomorrow.

August 12th

My carefully planned early night, followed by plenty of restful sleep followed by springing out of bed at some unearthly hour, ready for a long drive to Land Rover at Warwick, went to pieces very early. For a start, it was unbearably hot and sticky again. Then I was getting myself into the classic 'must get lots of sleep' mode that means sleep is impossible. Then Mr Fox dropped by to shout outside the window for a bit, at 3.30am. At 4.30am, the dogs had their usual waking-up spat, so by five, I was up, but totally unrested.

After a brief but mysteriously unpalatable breakfast, I was on the road by 7am, but only managed to get to Ganderdown before the satnav started flashing up warnings about the A34 being blocked, and suggested a change of route via Basingstoke. Being naturally sceptic about gadgets and gizmos, I decided that it was a glitch, and resolved to ignore it. But at the Winnall roundabout, it started shouting again, this time suggesting the blockage was serious, and insisting that I take the M3 up to the M25, and then getting the M40 up to Fen End.

I don't think so. "M25 at rush hour? Sod off with knobs on," I shouted at the satnav, and set off, like everyone else, on the A34 north.

Even the local radio didn't mention anything about blockages, but I decided that I'd feel mighty stupid if I ignored it, and missed the premier car launch of the year (i.e. only car launch) by getting stuck through bloody-mindedness. So I headed off west toward Andover on the A303, round its ring road, and then up through the countryside and the curiously named villages north-west of the town. The traffic was, of course, a lot slower, and I kept eyeing the 'estimated arrival time' and comparing it to LR's requested arrival time. It was going to be touch and go.

We finally re-joined the A34 just south-east of Newbury, and even as I pulled onto a free-flowing dual carriageway, the nanny voice was still shouting about blocked roads and "no alternative road available!". Mysteriously, she suddenly shut up, and I pushed on towards Oxford.

Just south of Oxford, she was off again – this time, the A34 was apparently blocked just north-west of the city, and I had exactly the same dilemma. Take her advice and get slightly delayed, or ignore her and possibly get stuck? I took her advice – again – and headed round the ring road, then east to pick up the M40. Within moments of re-joining what was my original route, I was overtaking distinctive lorries that I'd overtaken not long ago on the A34. There were obviously no blockages. I was not happy.

Foot to the floor time. Luckily, the M40 was almost empty, save for blacked-out Mercedes coupes with very dodgy and creative number plates, and doing well over the steady 70 mph I was doing. Ahem. The Skoda had a good run, and I arrived at 9.33 – three minutes late. Amazing. I could finally relax.

Except I couldn't. Once I'd been identified – "You must be Charlie!" cried the lovely PR girl from quite a distance; am I that distinctive? Was it the farmers' tan?

The delicate aroma? – I had to stand on an 'X' in the reception building and have my temperature taken by remote heat camera. I had full confidence that I would be asked to bugger off asap and head straight back home. After all, I'd done ten days of the sweatiest harvest ever and was just coming down from an adrenaline-fuelled barrel up the M40. But, no, I passed. I wonder if there's someone making a mint from selling pretend 'heat detector guns', like that bunch of rogues who did so well with 'explosive detectors' a few years ago. I think they got banged up for it in the end.

It was time to get ready. There were about a dozen of us standing in the fierce sun at Fen End, but luckily the briefing was brief. We had cars to ourselves (no awkward small talk or swapping drivers halfway), so we just simply jumped in, fired up the satnav and set off. Off through twee Cotswold villages (now being systematically trashed by new developments), west across the Severn and into the Malvern Hills – a stunning drive on lovely twisting roads.

We drove into the Eastnor Castle estate and had a pee/coffee break, and then had a rather unchallenging run round the 'Land Rover Experience' – rendered a bit tame by the lack of rain. We all put our machines into 'steady trundle' mode, and followed the bone-dry ruts round the woods, as our guide twittered on about how fabulous the machines were over the two-way radios.

After a lunch break in a huge hilltop tepee thing, which would normally have afforded stunning views across the border into Wales, but in this heat meant haze and mist, we had a high-speed motorway run back to Warwick, where we said our goodbyes and headed home.

The MacDonald's Magnet called me in at Sutton Scotney services, and I successfully managed to negotiate the masks, and the distancing, and the touchscreen ordering, and the lack of milkshake, and the swarms of ants sharing my outdoor table – and give the new Defender some thought. It's a fantastic off-roader, maybe a tad less luxurious than its Land Rover stablemates, but you still wouldn't throw a dead sheep in the back. Lots of food for thought, though.

August 13th

Completely and utterly knackered this morning – mind you, I'd done nigh-on 500 miles of driving yesterday, and it was full on in 30+ degrees. And I'd had a burger on the way home. No wonder I felt a bit under par.

Luckily, my head was just about clear enough to come up with the next *Flindt on Friday* – another rant about there being plenty of bugs and insects about, and I have the swollen private parts to prove it.

The weather finally broke in the afternoon, with a selection of heavy showers moving through, accompanied by the most bizarre three-hour thunderclap. The lightning was high and almost continuous, and the world rumbled and rumbled. The good news (apart from there being no ripe crops to be ruined) was that Tim the puppy is not afraid of thunder.

Beer on the Lawn was mooted, but the Editor was working, neighbour Robert sounded knackered, and I felt like going to bed. So that was the end of that idea.

August 14th

It was finally cooler, and we all slept better. It stayed overcast all day, not enough to dry off yesterday's deluge, so apart from loading a couple more lorries with spring barley, trying to write up the Defender and taking the Supra for a long spin round Hampshire, it was a quiet day. It was only when it got dark that I realised I'd missed what could have been a good spraying day. Oh well.

August 15th

August really living up to its reputation as a wet month. There were more showers, and it was a lot cooler. Whatever's bugging me at the moment continued, so I snoozed a lot on the sofa, keeping half an eye on Exeter vs Leicester on the telly. The slight problem was that whoever was in charge of live dubbing of fake crowd noises was really bad at it – and you ended up listening for the terrible surges in volume, and 'oooohs' and 'aaaahs' which seemed to be arriving at random.

The other problem was that, having loved the recent re-run of the World Cup from ages ago, you realise just what a static game it has become, and how much time the referee spends being a cross between an **übernanny** and a social worker.

I did an evening Stockbridge-Andover-Winchester loop in the Supra – that really is some car – and was fit for bed so early that Hazel kindly volunteered to pick up Jonathan from a late pub trip in Winchester, having dropped him off earlier. The town centre was heaving, apparently, and very few masks to be seen. Good.

August 16th

A long morning was spent writing up the Defender. They've kindly given me two pages to fill, but I never know whether to do a long rant about the technical and nerdy details of the multi-link suspension or write it up as 'a travel piece featuring a fancy new 4x4'. I chose the latter. The daft thing is that I could have spun it out for three, even four pages, such was the material I had from the long trip on Wednesday.

Hazel did a long run around all the pheasant feeders, reporting that the Kilmeston end of the farm must have had a deluge a couple of days ago; there was straw and crop residue washed across fields into huge heaps. We certainly didn't get anything that serious up here at the north end.

But it rained on and off for most of the day, and I had to be a bit careful with the Supra as we hustled round the numerous roundabouts on the way to and back from Farnham. And it may be a 50-grand supercar, but the wipers were complete rubbish. The clouds cleared suddenly late in the afternoon and it got nicely warm.

So I hit the pool for an hour, and felt much better for it. The combine sitting at the edge of the tennis court looks a bit forlorn, though.

August 17th

It was dry for a bit, and then another monster storm came in. The man from Toyota came to pick up the Supra – I hope the wipers hold together for his long journey back to the press office.

When the weather is this miserable, you can't beat putting on your wellies, grabbing a sturdy spade, and digging out a few roadside ditches, and the one down at New Pond is desperately in need of a bit of work – the road is about eight inches under water, but the pond itself is dry.

After ten minutes of hacking and digging in the undergrowth, I cleared the last bit of the mud-and-debris 'dam', and then had the intense satisfaction of watching the water pouring off the road, along my newly dug soakaway and noisily into the pond. It's a good thing I'm easily pleased. I leant on my spade, as you do, and pondered 'New Pond'.

Once upon a time, it was just a place where four roads met. The OS map from 1873 shows no buildings, no trees, and no sign that the road running west would one day be the junior partner, becoming (staying?) just a track. Nothing but a 'benchmark' of 285.2. By 1896, someone had dug a pond to the south-west of the junction; perhaps the water that arrived there off the huge catchment area couldn't get away to the west anymore, and a bit of drainage was needed.

Things had changed by 1909. The pond had a few trees around it, a triangle of trees had been planted to the north-west, and a house had been built. It, or perhaps the whole junction, now had an official name: New Pond. Obvious when you think about it.

By the time the Ordnance Survey got their act together after two world wars, it was 1962 (or that's the next one I can find, anyway). (Phil, who comes to hip therapy swim class in Chandler's Ford, worked for OS, and said that all map work ground to a halt around the 1920s, until they realised how good the Germans had been at mapping the UK from the other side of the Channel – during WW2!) By then, two semi-detached cottages had arrived to the north-east (with more trees planted to the north of them), and a barn had arrived to the south. Ken, our old tractor driver, said that barn was put up during his time doing National Service during the Korean War, which would make sense.

Two more L-shaped barns had also arrived some way to the east, along the road to Joan's Acre, but Dad made short work of them when he arrived in 1959. He did add to the barn at New Pond, erecting the grain storage and processing set-up – intake pits round the back, an Alvan Blanch drier, cleaners, and a huge central storage heap that could be ventilated during long-term storage by hessian-covered mesh ducts, all linked to a Typhoon fan and a distribution tunnel.

As the farming boom of the late 1960s continued, alongside the first barn he put up the Conder bins – ten 50-ton boxes bolted together and roofed, with a cleaner and an intake pit at one end, and another Typhoon fan for drying, ventilating and blowing out via angled air vents in the floor. This building features on the 1971 OS map, and by then the two semis had been named New Pond Cottages, and the first cottage was called Keeper's Cottage.

Progress slowed after that. A pole barn was put up as a lean-to in the late 70s on the east side of the Conder bins, and the first barn had its open east side sealed with the sheets of fibre cement that had been its west side, and turned into the 'right-hand lean-to'. A massive upgrade of grain handling kit took place in the early 1980s, with a new 'drive over' intake pit to match the new self-tipping Warwick trailers, a bigger double flow Alvan Blanch drier and a bigger Turner cleaner.

So in 1991, I inherited a pretty good state-of-the-art grain cleaning/drying/storage set-up. It ran pretty well for ten years, by which time, the farming shit had hit the fan, and further investment was out of the question. We'd also changed the logistics of harvest completely. I was now driving the combine, and my long years of being drierman were over. No more obscenely long days in the heat and noise and dust – and thank God for that. We'd started buying storage space at Hampshire Grain, so nothing stayed on the farm for longer than a couple of days. It was dumped from grain trailers onto the floor, and then loaded onto lorries, and waved away. They clean it, they dry it, they market it, they send me a cheque – minus their fees. It suits our system perfectly.

Much of the grain machinery sits down there untouched since the last day it was used. I occasionally get nostalgic and wander over to the massive switchboard and see if I can remember the right order to start it all up. And then memories of the earmuffs, and the dust masks, and the horrors of blocked elevators, shedding drive belts and exploding three-phase motors all come flooding back. What a joy it is to spend long harvest days in a comfy cool combine cab. What a good decision joining Hampshire Grain was.

The keen-eyed observer walking through New Pond might notice one change in the last ten years. Keeper's Cottage once had its name on a plaque, mounted high on the north-west corner. During renovation, the National Trust quietly removed it. I assume someone got triggered. As in offended, not shot. Although if they took offence, they need shooting.

It's a forlorn-looking place now. The two semis stand empty and unloved, on a bleak and grey August day. Where was I? Oh yes, standing in a ditch watching the water flow. All very satisfying.

Every so often we get the pond dredged. Dad used to send Ken in with the old 6610 loader, fully water ballasted and with a concrete-filled boiler on the 3-pt linkage. By the time he'd scraped out the mud with the little earth bucket, driving back and forth for a day or two, the floor was a hard as concrete, and even the smallest water fill would sit for weeks.

We've been lucky recently. There have been several requests from digger operators doing local jobs to use the Drier Yard for loading and unloading their monster machines off the lorries. I'm always delighted to help, on the condition that they spend a day before they go dredging the pond. And it works really well. They park on the rim of the pond and the long reach buckets don't compact the bottom. These days it'll only take a day for the water to vanish down into the chalk.

The rain came on heavier again, and Tigger's wipers promptly popped off their connection to the motor again, so I had come home via the tracks, as visibility was somewhat limited. I set about it in the evening, when the rain cleared and the sun came out again. It was a bit of a job getting the scuttle panel out and popping the key connecting arm back on again, and it popped straight back off when I'd reassembled it. Sounds like a whole new assembly is in order. Or only drive it when it's dry, and I can't see that happening for a few days.

August 18th

A bit drier, but very cool and windy. Woolheads the builder came round to quote for a selection of jobs – all of which are the Trust's responsibility, but I can't raise the Trust's building man for love nor money. Meanwhile, our windows are on the point of falling out. Ah, the joys of being a Trust tenant.

I thought that it was about time the two grain trailers went under cover. I had to tip them up first to drain them, because we'd blocked the drain holes off for oilseed rape. The forecast suggested that Thursday might be fine, too, and there was a pile of urgent Roundup-ing to be done. If I got the trailers hitched off and stored away, the Deere could, once again, go back onto the sprayer.

It was a scary trip to the drier. I met picker-up Julie on the bend below the house, then a Zafira full of a holiday family coming down Roe Hill like a lunatic. It was a relief to have resisted the temptation to disconnect the brakes on the trailers to make dropping off easier. I got both trailers parked in the left-hand lean-to, came back and hitched onto the sprayer.

The evening threatened to be cool, but the wind was supposed to drop, so Hazel decided that Beer on the Lawn would go better with some heat. She set off with the wheelbarrow and Johnny Muscles, and came back with three hollow blocks and a huge wheel rim. It's one that has been hanging round the farm forever, and was rumoured to be an ex-MOD WW2 relic. It weighs a ton, and in my youth, it served two roles. When you got home in the terrible 6610 loader tractor, you had to drop the concrete filled boiler (on the 3-pt linkage as ballast) onto something to take the weight off the hydraulics. That old rim was just the job.

It was also useful when Ken was renovating the combine knife, chiselling off all the rivets and replacing the knife sections. It was a sturdy, if slightly low-level workbench. That job is slightly easier now, with bolts instead of rivets.

The rim hasn't served any purpose since then, but now it was sitting in the middle of the lawn, on three hollow blocks, stacked with the driest of beechwood. A couple of bits of newspaper later, it was flaming nicely, and by the time neighbour Robert chugged his way into the yard, it was a very satisfying heap of glowing embers. It got dark not long after Mr and Mrs Editor arrived, but the old wheel rim made all the difference to what was by now a chilly August evening.

It got dark enough for a bit of star watching and satellite spotting in the crystal-clear skies (what Granny Flindt would have called a 'weathermaker'), but by the time we all went our separate ways, it was only 9.30. I hate the end of summer.

August 19th

Grey and wet again. Tod came round for an extensive redrawing of next year's cropping plan – now that oilseed rape has definitely been ditched – and I went for a long, wet, sticky walk. Bugger all else.

August 20th

Another rowdy autumn night (odd, for mid-August). I was up at some unearthly hour shutting windows and wedging old paracetamol boxes into the sash gaps. I hope the crops stay up – luckily, they are not exactly top heavy.

Despite the lack of sleep, I got the next *Flindt on Friday* away reasonably early. It was interrupted by an email from the Editor, saying that, after 29 years, he would no longer be the Editor. There was then an hour of phone calls to discuss it and congratulate him. He, and Mrs Editor (now Mrs ex-Editor), both seemed delighted with the news, so I can only assume that the retirement package is satisfactory. Gosh, I wish everyone would stop retiring.

I drove round and rather optimistically checked some crops, but they were all sodden. The bottom corner of Big Field would combine now if it were dry enough, but round the top and the west side, it's still pretty green. In the afternoon, there was a miraculous window of calm weather, so I leapt in the sprayer and invaded France. Hold on, that's not right – that's June '44; I went out to Big Field with 2 1/ ha of Roundup, and did the remains of Rick/Clump – including the grass patch that is what's left of the unvernalised wheat.

Much of Big Field looked a remarkably good crop, and also like it didn't really need the Roundup. Halfway across I thought I should stop spraying that bit, and only do the outsides – and use the rest of the tank of Roundup elsewhere, perhaps on the stubbles that have been crying out for glyphosate for weeks. In the end, for the sake of consistency, I did the whole block, assuming that at some stage, surely, we'll get another batch of spraying weather – i.e. less than 35 degrees and/or a force nine gale.

It will mean waiting for a week before we can go in with the combine (the 'harvest interval'), so that will mean combining somewhere else for a bit. Luckily, all the Godwin's spring barley is ready, and I dare say the spring wheat in Blackhouse Road would go, too.

The odd little window of calm finished by ten o'clock – but by then I was indoors, fed and watered, and in bed. I'd already had to shut all the windows again as the wind got up.

August 21st

My word, the wind did blow. The house shook, the tiles on the south end rattled, and debris hit the windows like rain – but it stayed dry. In fact, the forecast was quite optimistic: a chance of showers today, and then dry and windy for Saturday, Sunday and Monday. Time to start thinking about starting that combine again.

We thought we'd do a job that's been on the 'to do' list for ages: dismantle the last of the upright grain walls in the big Godwin's barn. When neighbour Robert was the tenant over there, he stored a huge pile of grain behind three sections of sleepers held in place by metal uprights. We took two sections down when we started using the barn as a tip'n'go store, but never got round to the third. Now that we're loading lorries with the slightly unwieldy tractor rather than the nimble 4WS loader, the time has come to improve access. Ten minutes with the loader and Johnny Muscles, and the job was done – perfect for the big rush tomorrow.

The howling gale meant no more spraying was likely, so I took off the sprayer (again), and rather than hitch on a trailer, spent an hour blowing out the multiple radiators that lurk in front of the Deere's engine. It's amazing how efficient the plastic mesh screens are at trapping dust and dirt, but they do mean that high-speed corn cart can get the engine quite hot. Jonathan had noted it on the gauge – what a good lad. Mind you, he was doing corn cart last summer in Godwin's when neighbour Robert had dropped in with the on-trial new combine, so things were pretty hectic and hot. I was away delivering the first copies of Book One to a wholesaler in Sussex (and test driving a Range Rover at the same time). Looking back, it was a funny sort of day.

Anyway, at some stage, Jonathan, driving the Massey that day, and hauling a full trailer as fast as he could up the steep slope of Middle Broom, managed to set off all the overheating warning lights. The Oakes Bros mechanic, in the field to supervise the test New Holland combine, very kindly dug out his compressor and blew out the radiators. No damage done, and a good lesson for Jonathan.

While in the 'harvest restart is imminent' mood, I grabbed the step ladder and the grease gun and strolled down to the combine, still parked next to the old tennis court. I paused at the pool to give the poor pump a clean out of all the leaves that had blown in, and then set about the most awkward job on the New Holland: greasing up the UJ in the unloading arm. Luckily, the evening was drawing in, and a shaft of light shone very conveniently in through the little hatch (held on with straw-coloured wingnuts, so, whatever you do, don't drop them in the, er, straw.)

When that was done, I whizzed round the rest of the grease points getting ready for the weekend. To put my mind at rest, I strolled out into the spring barley in Godwin's, and did a tooth-based moisture check; much drier than this morning, and if the forecast hadn't been so confidently good, I might have had a few trailers off tonight. But I didn't.

And when the Editor rang, keen to have a trip to the pub to mark his imminent ex-Editorship, I declined his invitation; I needed all my wits about me for an early start tomorrow. How very responsible of me.

August 22nd

The rain started just as I was setting off to get a grain trailer: a sharp storm that lasted for about twenty minutes, and left everything saturated. It also had the magical effect of changing the BBC's short-term forecast from 'dry all day' to 'showers'. Bastards. I sent an expletive-filled text to the Editor saying I could have come down the pub after all. He rang back to gloat, and to point out that in reality I hadn't missed much. The pub they went to (not our favourite local) was dreary, dull and unwelcoming. He said he doubted they'd darken that particular hostelry's door again. Mind you, given the way country pubs are going – even before the government/XR's criminalisation of fun – I doubt that that pub will be there for long.

So it was a quiet – and rather sulky – Saturday. Luckily, Mac called in to discuss baling plans for the rest of harvest. Well, that was the theory, anyway; in practice we had a really good and therapeutic moan about the rain – now promised to continue for the foreseeable – and an even better gossiping session. There was much talk of him helping out the new owners of Blackhouse Farm, who are spending billions of squillions on restoration and renovation. Mac's landed the job of turning some fairly dull and unloved pastures into nectar-rich flower meadows. I said he was welcome to use any of our cultivation kit – we've got a really chunky rotavator which might be best at working up a tilth after the glyphosate he applied a few days ago has done its job. Anything would be better than the faff of ploughing it.

And then there was the unbelievably specific mix of fancy grasses and plants that have to be planted at a very specific – but low – rate, and then mollycoddled for months; I said he was very welcome to that job, too. At least the ground up there will be a bit softer now.

Anthony had some time off from work in London, so popped down on an empty train to Petersfield, where Jonathan picked him up. They got a vast pile of MacDonald's finest on the way home, and we had a lovely late but slightly cold burger-fest, listening to his tales from town, and his plans. There's talk of moving out of a rented room in the tumbledown villa in Cricklewood, and renting a whole flat with a schoolfriend in Camden. He is also approaching 'exams' at his present job, and if he does well, there should be opportunities to finally get off the bottom rung of the ladder at that company. He's got a bit of a case of itchy feet, though, and beginning to wonder about staying there at all. We said he should do the exam and see what the company might offer him. The wave of unemployment that's due to break on Furlough Beach might persuade him to cherish what he's got.

The post-Big Mac farts were the stuff of legends.

August 23ʳᵈ

Full marks to Cain, who despite the delicate burger odours wafting up through the duvet, was determined to yowl his way in and settle down on the bed. Bless him.

It was damp again, but the radar suggested that we might get away with a dry day – most of the heavy stuff was brewing up just after it had passed us. We had an early lunch, and then I walked down to the combine and drove it the length of Chalks, through Rick/Clump, and down to New Pond, where I did a run up/run down of the drum and the fan to spread the grease. Hazel was there with the loader to move the telegraph pole, and Jonathan arrived to pick up a trailer and do corn cart. Also arriving was a flood of traffic; the council are resurfacing (aka 'gluing a few chippings down') the A272 through Bramdean and have closed the road.

So we had to tip-toe our way along the short bit of road at New Pond (narrowly avoiding a phalanx of cheery cyclists), and then do a sharpish turn into Blackhouse Road. All very neatly executed.

Twenty minutes later, the heavens opened, and we were forced to abandon. Jonathan had one tankful onboard, so we left that ready to top up later. But even in that 20 minutes' work, I noticed that the spring wheat was better than I had thought it would be. All we needed was some dry weather. By teatime, the wind had done its job, and we went out and did another three-hour session, finishing just before eight. The 'trailer rate' suggested I was getting eight-ish tons off 3.5 acres-ish. That'll do. It looked good, too; I must book a lorry first thing to see if it has any quality. I was out for the count nice and early.

August 24ᵗʰ

Groundhog August continues. You can waste hours looking at many different forecasts and rainfall radar maps, and out of the window, but still be none the wiser. I decided we might as well just get on with it; if it rains again, it rains.

I fuelled up the combine in quite bright sunshine, and kicked myself for not getting going late morning. Instead we had a reasonably good spell after lunch before the rain swept in again. It coincided with the arrival (finally) of the 2 o'clock lorry at 3.30pm. When Team Shovel got back from the yard, they reported that it had already dried off as if the rain had never happened, so Hazel and I went out and got another two loads off – enough to ensure that we'd have a full lorry tomorrow.

Just as the combine was approaching the end of one long turn in Blackhouse Road, there was a bang from the chopper. Always a worry, but everything seemed to continue OK – no flashing lights or vibration. But when I approached the same spot, there was something metal stuck in the soft ground. My first thought was that it was something someone had stuck in the ground in the standing crop, and I'd combined it – hence the bang.

But that in itself seemed very odd – so I climbed out to have a closer look. It was a piece of metal, about eight inches long, and pretty mangled. And I quickly recognised it as being part of the 'frogmouth' sieves that are an integral part of the combine.

What do you do when you realise that a vital part of your combine has been ejected out of the back? Everything felt fine – the sample seemed as good as ever, and nothing felt wrong. I did the last couple of turns rather nervously, and then headed for the New Pond corner and shut down.

A quick glance inside revealed that one of the five long sections of the self-levelling upper sieves had lost a couple of these little plates, and others were lying flat. Something had done some damage, or it might just have been wear and tear. One plate must have fallen *through* the disintegrating sieve, over the bottom sieve, up the returns elevator, through the drums, over the straw walkers and – bang – through the chopper. No wonder it looked a bit sorry for itself.

Anyway, that was for tomorrow. Tonight, at Anthony's insistence, we were going out for a meal, and he'd booked us into a pub in a local town. It was an utter delight. The boys changed out of T-shirts and looked right smart, there were no masks, the place was buzzing – the only indication of the virus was the £10/person lopped off the bill as the Chancellor's incentive to get us all to eat out. It worked. We were all supposed to fill in our names on our individual menus, but only Jonathan did that.

I had a simple tomato/basil soup, a 6 oz fillet steak, and sticky toffee pudding. And it was fantastic. I sought out the man in change and told him the steak was superb – and that we were beef farmers. (Only a slightly white lie – we'll be back in beef again one day.) His fraught expression changed briefly to a broad smile, so it was worth telling him. Both boys were on top form, and it was almost as if all was well with the world again. So much so, that I didn't mind when the text came through late, showing that the first load of spring wheat had gone as feed, or remotely bothered that my precious combine appeared to be disintegrating.

August 25th

If you're going to be slightly overslept after too much food and drink, AND have a combine in pieces, you need some weather than means a lie-in is acceptable – and Hurricane Killer-storm We're All Going To Die Francis duly obliged. (I think it was only Storm Francis, but it's fun to join in with the Met Office's doom-laden attitude.)

Luckily, I was up in time to catch Garwood's just after opening, and get my name down for Luke the Combine Wizard's first outing. He had some vital indoor jobs to do first, but they promised he'd be out just after lunch.

The gales and rain were proving to be quite scary, and the lights flickered once or twice. It was lucky that we didn't have a lorry booked for the morning – Noel was taking sheep to Salisbury – so we could all have a quiet morning.

It got busier after lunch. Jonathan took his big brother back to the station, the second lorry came and went, and Luke arrived to take a long hard look at the combine. It was a first for him, too, seeing the self-levelling sieves disintegrating like that. We spent a lot of time poring over the parts book – although it was quite hard to read; Cain had found the open pages overnight, and slept on them. He was very wet.

Luke and I decided that we'd go for a bit of a patch-up job rather than the time-consuming option of taking out the whole frame and rebuilding or replacing. We'll save that for the winter overhaul. He reckoned he should be able to get parts sorted overnight, and we might be up and running again by... let's not tempt fate by setting a deadline.

Bill from Hampshire Grain rang to ask if we had any more corn to go. I said we hadn't but wanted to know how come the second load of spring wheat was first-rate quality (the result had just come through by text), when yesterday's was shite. He said he'd go and check the figures. As I drove into the yard, he rang back; it had been a typo, and both loads were Group 2 Grade 1. Hurrah. Not sure it'll pay for the combine repairs, but there we go.

Mac was in the yard shortly after that, cruising in silently in his Fendt, looking to take away and try the rotavator for his grass replanting job. A long cup of tea was, of course, compulsory before anything productive could be done. Having said that, he did ask if we had any spares for the Shakearator he borrowed a couple of years ago, and, after a moment's thought, I remembered that we had; some heavy points and a shin, somewhere in the barn. On his way round to hitch onto the rotavator, I loaded him up with nine assorted points and the shin, and even the old soft-headed mallet that came with the Shakearator when we ordered it in the mid-80s. It was the machine of the day, a subsoiler with an eccentric weight that was designed to help shake up and crack the subsoil. All it really did was shake the tractor cab's mountings to pieces. Some people still use them and swear by them (without using the weight), but I haven't missed it at all. A good dry spell opens up this clay ground much more cheaply and efficiently. A 'dry spell'. Fat chance.

Late in the afternoon, there was a slightly familiar face at the back door, looking somewhat bedraggled. It was one of our excellent local policemen, in civvies, and therefore – for some reason – unrecognisable. He said he comes across that phenomenon all the time. Anyway, he wanted to know if it was OK to park a minibus outside the silver gates; he's organising a Police Cadet yomp across the countryside, and was running a check-in point. I said that was fine. He returned a couple of minutes later with another almost-familiar face; it was the Inspector – someone I've met and talked to dozens of times, but once again, not a clue who she was in tracksuits. Funny that.

The gale got up again in the evening, with more showers. No combining for a bit. Luckily.

August 26th

A busy morning on the phones. Luke rang to say that the holes on the sieve frames were elongated beyond repair, and the common-sense move would be to install a whole new one – which would also save a fortune on time spent disassembling and reassembling the old one. The new one would just need slotting in. He reckoned about £600–700 for a whole new unit, and they've tracked one down in Germany. I agreed that that's the sensible thing to do, and told him to go for it. Combine ownership is usually all about taking a whack every few years, but mine has done very well in avoiding big bills until now.

Next up was diesel, running a bit short, and there's a fine bank holiday on the way. So I rang round the usual trio of suppliers, got the usual drivel – "Has yourself had any quotes so far supplied to yourself at all, my lovely?" – and got the best quote from the usual one. I placed the order if they promised a delivery before the weekend.

Once upon a time you had a loader tractor, or a forklift, and you checked it was OK every so often. But now, you have to have a certificate to say it's OK. The Massey dealers at Chichester haven't got their inspector anymore, but their branch at Wilton does have one, and the former put the latter in touch with me to get it sorted.

By now, the gale had, at last, dropped a bit, and I reckoned I had time for one, or maybe two, tanks of long-overdue Roundup. I did the fallow in Godwin's Park – the one Ashley took a crop of wholecrop wheat/weeds off a few weeks ago – and Roe Hill, which had turned into a forest of thistles, charlock and died-off groundsel. Luckily, a combination of good guesswork and my trusty T-Jet 23.5-metre line finder meant that I found all the tramlines. At least, I hope so.

The forecast suggested we might have another fine morning tomorrow, so I booked Tosdevine to get as many beans sprayed with pre-harvest Roundup as possible, which would mean I could keep going on the fallows. He said he'd be in nice and early.

We might, of course, be reassembling the combine tomorrow. I was so excited at the prospect that I had an early finish. Stanmore is under water – according to Hazel, who did a huge pheasant feeder round in Pig. So another day's draining won't go amiss.

August 27th

No sign of the new bits for the combine, so we had a frantic 'beat the rain' spraying session. Tosdevine's chap came in to put pre-harvest Roundup on the beans, and I did a tank on Pipeline and Broom Field. By about 11.30, the radar suggested that both of us stopping after one tank would be wise; heavy showers, and more, were on the way again.

They arrived just after lunch – at first not too heavy, so I think the Roundup should have been on long enough to do its job. But by the time I drove to APM to get more grease and a new yard brush – and get out of the house/tractor/ combine for a bit – the showers were getting heavier. And by five o'clock, a scimitar of purple/white (on the radar, anyway) rain clipped us, with thunder. Just north of it, it was a lot heavier. If it's going to rain, we might as well have a non-functioning combine to make the most of it.

I took Sasha and Evie out for a loop to Clump and back, pausing on the way up the farm hill behind the cattle barn to watch a Churcher's College van driving slowly through to Kilmeston. I thought it so out of place that it would be worth emailing the College to ask if one of their vans should actually be out here at eight o'clock on a wet Thursday.

The van I really want to see is the one bringing my self-levelling sieve from Germany.

August 28th

Lots of hideous rain, lots of scary wind, and a veritable lack of combine sieve. Garwood's were very apologetic, and almost as cross as me about it. No one seemed to know why it hadn't made its way over the Channel – I was sure someone was going to say 'Brexit' or 'the virus', but instead we all blamed the French (who still had it, apparently) for being useless. Some things never change. The workshops manager claimed that it had been put on a dedicated van and would be arriving late tonight. Fantastic back-up plan if true, but if not – who knows? Let's just all keep calm and be grateful that the weather still rules out any harvest work.

The nice people at Churcher's College were very grateful and somewhat tickled that I'd been doing the Neighbourhood Watch routine on one of their vans, and, yes, it was supposed to be on the road between Hinton Ampner and Kilmeston. A new member of staff was using it to move house. So that's alright then.

We decided to put the Aga out of its misery, and flicked the switch to turn it off. That'll be nearly five months since the last service, which isn't too bad. Another burst of rain late in the evening meant I'd probably have the morning free tomorrow – even if the sieve does arrive.

August 29th

There was a text late last night – late enough for me to miss it – from Garwood's. The new sieve had arrived. Some poor soul had been given the job of hanging around after hours to sign for it – and it looked as though it turned up at 10.30pm. Luke (said the text) would be out asap today. Being an old cynic, I refrained from cheering wildly – I've had enough examples over the years of the wrong bit being delivered.

I got stuck into the Aga service, and had it up and running within an hour. Funnily enough, I had all the wicks and brass elbows in stock, which is unusually efficient for me. And in a fit of maintenance enthusiasm, I checked out the pool, which is now sitting slightly lonely and unused, as cold wind and rain sweeps in. It seemed hardly worth giving it a big hoover to get the multitude of leaves off the floor; will we be getting back in it? The autumn is rushing in so fast, and the nights are cooling horribly. But I know that if I pull out the bungs, we'll have three weeks of blistering September heat.

Luke was doing well when I finally plucked up the courage to check on his progress. He reckoned he had half an hour left, and everything seemed to have slotted back in correctly. I left him to it, and came back via the Crusoe and the spring barley in Godwin's, trying to decide where we'd go when we restart. Stay where we are in Blackhouse Road – a thin crop but should dry out quicker? Switch to the Crusoe in Big Field, and hope the Hagberg has been saved by the Roundup? Get the spring barley in before it all germinates in the ear? We're hoping to bale both the Crusoe and the barley, so we need a dry few days, as well as a balerman who will be in promptly. Do we trust the weather forecast enough to leave everything to dry for a couple more days?

There was certainly nothing to be done this afternoon, so I had a snooze in front of a one-sided Sale vs Bristol rugby match on Channel 4. Luke left a message to say everything had tested OK, and by the evening the Aga seemed to be chatting away happily, so it was a slightly more productive day. I was feeling relatively cheerful until an unforecast band of rain came in from the north-west late in the evening. Yes, it was light rain, but, in the words of the White Hunter cricket captain when yet another catch gets dropped: oh, for goodness' sake.

August 30th

A damp August Sunday bank holiday morning, but I reckoned we'd have a go after an early lunch. In the meantime, I'd relax with some papers and enjoy – finally – some BTCC racing. That plan all went to pieces when neighbour Teddy arrived on his electric UTV complete with toddler, and there was an outbreak of coffee and winding up small people. And that's far more fun than sitting in a combine, or watching crash-bang-wallop racing at Knockhill.

The highlight of what turned into a lengthy chat and catch-up was Sasha deciding that she must adopt this small human, and the small human returned the compliment by gently stroking her ears and singing gently to her. I've never seen my ruffty-tough Mali/GSD cross look so content. She'll be demanding it every day now.

By the time we finally got out to Blackhouse Road, it was gone one o'clock. And I then lost another half hour reattaching the drive belt from the end of the engine to the hydraulic chopper clutch. Thank goodness for all the warning lights and buzzers that went off when I was just about to get stuck into some wheat – I hadn't done a pre-start inspection. Luke must have disconnected it as a safety feature when testing after installing the new sieves. I'll give him some stick for that. Twenty minutes was lost with a 19 mm spanner loosening the tensioner pulley to get the belt back on, and then retightening the pulley.

By the time we called it a day not long after seven o'clock, we'd knocked off another 30 acres, and refilled the left-hand lean-to to the brim. And the last couple of loads felt a lot drier. And nothing fell out of the back of the combine.

August 31st

At last – a morning that feels summery: bright, calm, but pretty cool. Much easier to leap out of bed early on a morning like this, and get the *Flindt on Friday* proof done. Mind you, it's a bank holiday, so I wasn't sure who might be at the end of the email line when I sent it.

Tosdevine's sprayer arrived just after eight to finish off the pre-harvest Roundup on the spring beans in Cheyney and the Hangar. I asked him to do Long Field while he was here, although we spent half an hour in the yard working out how to do 14 ha at 3 l/ha (Long Field) and then 14 ha at 4 l/ha (the beans) all on the same tank – it seemed daft to come all the way back to refill halfway. We decided that if he filled up as if he were off to do all 28 ha at 3 l/ha, and then put the last 20 litre can in when he'd finished Long Field, that should do it.

The combine needed a big grease up and a refuel for what I'd hoped would be a long day, and then I thought I'd better check up on the lorries that were due to clear some room in the left-hand lean-to. Still on their way, according to Bill at Trinity Grain.

I texted Luke to tell him off for leaving that drive belt off when he'd finished the repair. His reply was very swift: he most certainly did not leave that belt off. In fact he'd done a full run-up to check everything was working before he left. I felt a bit guilty for questioning his professionalism, and baffled as to how such a vital and sturdy belt had somehow leapt off its pulleys yesterday. A bit unnerving.

Another 'where are my lorries?' call revealed that they'd been put back to mid-afternoon. I told Bill to shelve them, and decided we'd switch to the late-drilled Crusoe in Rick/Clump and Big. There were only a few acres to be done in Rick and Clump (during which I gave a lift to a couple of ramblers who'd been intently watching the combine in action – it made their day) and then we got stuck into Big Field. Some of it was good, some dismal, and I'm not sure that the man who's bought the straw will be happy with the deal. We may have to diplomatically lower the price.

In places it yielded quite well, and was certainly weighing well; it was one of the hardest day's combining I've done for years. The ground is soft, the crop is hanging right down, the stones were never rolled in, and there's a lot of sideland ground. I was lucky to get away with no broken sections. By seven, I was knackered, and called it a night. We'd done another good 30 acres, though.

Another month done. There's silence on Brexit – apart from tiny snippets of news about accusations from both sides of the other side refusing to budge on negotiations. Fishing is still the totemic issue. The virus has effectively stopped killing people, but not infecting them – but the authorities are still obsessed with stopping us from… well, doing anything. And they make five Twitter-driven U-turns per week. And riots across America in the name of BLM still rumble on. Thank goodness for the relative sanity of our little patch of English countryside.

September 1st

A lovely quiet morning was soon ruined when, with much beeping, the lorry arrived to empty the cess pit. We found the rusting lids in the nettles, and dragged them off to reveal the old Victorian chamber looking pretty full. Without the numerous teenagers in the house, it has been 18 months since we had it emptied.

I half expected the chambers to be a hideous mess of poo, with blocked soakaways and overflowing access pits, but it was a simple job. He poked his huge pipe down through the crust, added lots of sections to connect it to the lorry, and set it to 'suck'. An hour later, he was on his way.

The driver was as cheery as ever, and commented that he'd had a very busy lockdown, what with everyone spending more time at home. It's an ill – and pongy – wind, as they say.

There was a time, of course, when Dad would slip the driver a tenner, and the lorry would drive out onto the pastures somewhere and get rid of the lot. No one noticed, no one minded, and everything was cheap and easy. I remember doing my lunchtime dog walk with Jess, our first dog, and having to give the Bottom of Englands a wide berth for a day or two.

Two more grain lorries went (again, both good quality), and Jonathan and I got stuck into the rest of Big Field. It was not the most enjoyable bit of combining; the stones were more numerous than yesterday's, for some reason. I had two jammed tables (cue the vomit button) and one broken crop finger on the main auger. And when we set about mending that, we noticed that the inspection plate had a couple of stone-caused cracks in it. I phoned Luke, who promised one ready tomorrow.

I had hoped to finish Big Field, get the odd bits and pieces at the top of Clump done, and then swing into Blackhouse Road and get that finished. But by the time we'd fought with massive flints, and dismantled stone-damaged front augers, it was getting dark when we finished Clump. Blackhouse Road will have to wait till tomorrow.

We were all a too knackered to have a Beer on the Lawn. Neighbour Robert rang for a chat, saying that they were into their beans, which were proving a bit of a low-level challenge. We've got that job to come, but not for a bit yet.

September 2nd

In anticipation of a proper long day, I had a fuel up and a grease up. The new-ish Deer Control Man arrived for a chat and a bit of a moan. Actually, it was a lot of a moan. He couldn't get anyone at the Trust to renew the culling licence – and it is much needed. I sympathised – we've got major building and repair work that is long overdue, but can't get anyone at the Trust to act. Mind you, if the rumour mill is true, they've all effectively been laid off and made to apply for their jobs again. Madness. I told him that I'd drop an email to our latest Agent and see if I could get things going by pleading for some deer control.

It was quite a relief to get combining at last. I did the last little sliver of wheat up on top of Clump, which finished a long and varied arable season in that field. And not a very jolly one, either. We then shuttled across to Blackhouse Road and finished that one, too. The master plan to open up the spring barley in Godwin's was scuttled when heavy drizzle started just as we were finishing Blackhouse Road. So we shrugged our shoulders and went home – a feature of this year's harvest.

Garwood's had texted to say that the bits for the table auger were in, so I drove up to Alton and fetched them. It made the day feel slightly less frustrating.

September 3rd

Everything was still soggy from last night's rain, and a muggy wind meant nothing dried at all, so I sat indoors and wrote next week's *FonF*. Two more lorries went, and both of them, again, achieved good quality. Small mercies.

A band of rain lurked just north of us for most of the day, and then arrived mid-afternoon. I was fitting the new bits to the header auger at the time, and had to make a sharpish dash home before the rain got too heavy; Tigger's wipers still don't work.

Beer on the Lawn (the Thursday Mix) was moved indoors because of the rain, which annoyed Jonathan, who had specially given the grass a mow in the drizzle. We spaced ourselves round the huge shoot table, and drank far too much. I know I did.

September 4th

Either I'm getting pathetically light-headed, or the beer was much stronger last night. I'd had a 3am loo visit that nearly turned messy, and I wasn't feeling much better by the time my alarm went off.

So it was fortunate that it was a very odd weather day. No rain, but nothing dried at all. It was dull and muggy, and generally not very nice.

September 5th

A sad day. It should have been Alresford Show day, but all the time Extinction Rebellion are running Boris via Carrie, such harmless and fun events will be banned.

But it turned into a bizarre day. Shortly before nine, I had a phone call from the local butcher. "Hi, this is the butcher. Have you got Joe Smith's phone number?" (Joe Smith – not the name he actually used, of course.)

I told him that I thought he had the wrong number – I had never heard of this fellow. "Are you not Mr Flindt?" he asked. I said I was, but why was he ringing me? "Oh, my boss said you'd know this chap's number." I suppose it's a huge compliment to be considered to be the local Yellow Pages. (Look it up, kids.)

The next landline call (two in one hour – very rare) was Murph from next door, saying that there had been some astonishing fly-tipping through his lanes, and he thought we ought to check ours. I jumped in Tigger, and sure enough, someone had driven along the minor road from the bottom of our hill, down to New Pond and along Brockwood Bottom, methodically throwing waste out of the back of their vehicle. There was builders' waste, domestic waste, glass, chairs – all sorts. I could only just get through safely, and came back via the fields.

The local Facebook pages were buzzing with reports of the tipping, and it seemed to have gone on for miles: from us to Marldell, across the A272 to Bramdean Common, both sides of the Beauworth crossroads. Astonishing.

I got hold of Policeman Ian just as he was starting his shift, so he popped out for a look, and then used his hotline to the council to extract from them a promise of 'urgent action'. Can't see it happening, myself. Saturday, furlough, lazy sods, etc. etc.

The rest of the day was spent making a good start in the Godwin's block – which, luckily, needed no road work for corn cart. We did all of Middle Broom, and the top square of Child's Broom, and Mac was in baling quite close behind, although he didn't get it finished.

It was quite hard to concentrate, though. I kept trying to get my head round the fly-tipping. How was it done? A slow drive along the lanes in the dead of night, with a monkey in the back slowly throwing out the waste? Why not the 'traditional' way, in a lay-by or a yard? And bearing in mind how close they drove to our Drier Yard, open and unguarded, I realised how lucky we were. We must invest in some blocks, or huge gates, or something. Fortress Countryside is coming.

September 6th

We're not getting on very fast with this harvest business. I drove out to Childs' Broom in Godwin's to grease up and refit a freshly blown out air filter, and then sat on the top of the combine and listened to the roar of Sunday morning traffic on the A272. It's easy to see why those who live on the very edge of it are driven to distraction by the noise. The wind was a cool NW, so you could hear the bikes coming from miles away. Time to count your blessings for living just over the hill – in relative peace.

I did the headland of the tiny field right alongside the main road, which finished it, and then drove over to Big Broom. The spring barley and its straw was good in places, but I doubt it'll be malting quality after all this time. I managed to get hold of Bill at Hampshire Grain, who booked two lorries to go tomorrow.

Just after we'd had tea at four, there was ten minutes of heavy drizzle, which stopped things. I fell asleep in front of the curious crowd-free T20. We'll have another go tomorrow. The forecast is good. Again.

September 7th

A proper autumn day's harvesting. The first big fog of the year meant everything was very damp, but very beautiful. We were just thinking of getting going when Mac drove into the yard at some pace in his pick-up. There was a bit of a crisis: his tractor was losing water, his back-up baler man was about to leave the country, and man No. 3 had a puncture. It was all frightfully serious, not to mention confusing.

So we put the kettle on. And half an hour later, all was well with the world. We'd had a laugh, put the world to rights, discussed the merits of retirement, and agreed that who baled which fields didn't matter in the end. They just had to be baled.

Sure enough, just as we finally set off to finish the spring barley, Kevin arrived with his baler, promising to get the whole block done today.

Big Broom took longer than I thought it would – somehow, fields always do – and I set off to Kilmeston Road, pausing to finish the odd little strips of spring barley in BOMS and Folly I'd left as being unripe weeks ago.

There was then a massive shuffle of grain trailers and combine headers. We took the header off the combine in the corner of the Folly (first time we've had to do that this season – it has been an 'inside-out' harvesting year), headed across Springshot and hitched on again. Hazel arrived with trailer No. 2, and tea, so we paused for ten minutes, and then got stuck into Kilmeston Road's spring wheat. It wasn't brilliant, but there were good patches. That field got severely rooked during the spring, so it was nice to see anything out there at all.

Heavy cloud meant it was getting dark by six, so we called it a day. Given a decent run tomorrow, we should get through it.

The early finish was nothing to do with the fact that The Thomas Lord Old Gits had decided enough was enough, and a rehearsal was in order – no, really it wasn't. Shed 3b was a bit manky, but pretty well just as we'd left it. Hazel had sneaked in and done a bottle clear out, and half-filled the scrap skip with tins, but everything else looked the same. And once we'd covered the greetings and health issues – Ian the drummer had been hospitalised by a spider bite at some stage – Tod took one look at the song book, said "Right, where were we?" and we set off into Proud Mary as if we'd not played for a week, rather than six months. Just what we all needed.

September 8th

My shoulders and arms were mighty sore after a long evening hammering my Roland piano last night, so it was a bit of a late start. We got two more lorries away – the spring barley went as 'Planet feed' which I assume is a notch above plain feed rather than something in a nearby galaxy, and the spring wheat from Kilmeston Road had lost Hagberg, and went as Grade 2. Still better than feed.

We had a long afternoon in Kilmeston Road, finishing all the cereals. After many hours of romping through lightweight crops at 5–6 kph, I reached the old thrashing yard near the exit onto the road to Kilmeston, and suddenly had to wind right back.

Lights thrashing, drum whomping, a great yellow swath of straw coming out the back; just imagine what the yield would be like if the whole field – or farm – had been like that.

Ashley had bought the straw, and he arrived to start baling just as we finished. I doubt he'll get the whole lot done tonight; the evenings aren't as long as they were.

We put the header on the trailer and did a bit of conversion to beans (slotted auger cover, opening up sieves), but bravely resisted the temptation to do a couple of turns in the spring beans in the Hangar as it got dark, and headed home for an early bed. Clean sheets, too; out for the count in moments.

September 9th

One day we'll make all gateways wide enough to get through without taking the front of the combine off. Until then, it'll be complicated. I drove down to Springshot with a tractor and grain trailer, dropped the trailer near the Hangar gate, and hitched onto the header trailer, c/w header already loaded onto it. I drove out into the beans and parked on nice level ground, ready for the combine.

Then it was back to the Kilmeston Road gate to fetch the combine, getting my shoes soaked in the heavy dew, and, after some final setting of the sieves, drive it into the beans and got the header back on.

I did two turns of headland to make space for the grain trailers, and was thrilled to find I'd almost got a tankful. Mind you, I'd double drilled the headland back in the spring to get rid of excess seed, and that seems to be the only way to get any yield. The landwork looked a bit poorer. There was now a tractor and empty header trailer in the way, so I drove it onto the cut headland, dropped off the trailer, and brought the two grain trailers over and dropped them there, too. At last – ready to crack on.

Back at base, Team Lorry Load had sent away another load of malting barley from the Godwin's barn, and were into the good stuff at the back. It passed as Grade 1. Unfortunately, there was a little heap left.

What do you do with a little heap? You could load it into a grain trailer, try to make the trailer legal (hit the lights until they come on), pump up the tyres so they're less likely – or is it more likely? – to give up halfway to Micheldever, and ask Noel to spend four hours driving up and back.

The other option is to summon Trevor and his lorry back, load him with the piddling little heap, and take the 'cap' fee for underloading a lorry. And that's what we did.

Luckily, I missed all the shovelling, being out in the Hangar doing 90 miles an hour. The beans were coming off better than expected, and the rolling in the spring meant that I could get the cutter bar really low to get as many as possible. The dewy pods weren't shattering either, which helped. By the time I summoned Jonathan to help with yet another decouple and move, I'd got two-and-a-half trailers off the 20 acres. This year, that's a result.

After another huge logistical operation, we started on Cheyney. Two unpleasant surprises greeted us: the yield seemed to be well down on the Hangar's, and yet another heap of fly-tipping had been done just inside the entrance. Just a little heap of gardening waste; I suppose we should be grateful that it's not been dumped along the road.

After doing five turns of headland and a bit of landwork, it became hard to see the ground with the low sun on dirty cab glass, so we called it a day.

September 10th

No Noel today, so no lorries. I finished the beans in Cheyney, and we did another disconnect and long hike through the farm to JA/DC, and I made a good start there.

The race is now on to get all the beans – and harvest – finished before the heatwave next week. Bizarre.

PC Ian called in for a cuppa to talk through the fly-tipping. Luckily, he was a farm manager in a previous life, so is well used to trying to get any sense out of a sweaty, grumpy, dirty combine driver at seven in the evening. He said he'd done his best with the fly-tipping, but the Council were just monumentally useless. They're not worth much in normal times, let alone these mad days.

September 11th

Ninety-nine-point-nine per cent of the population would just love to be woken by a deer barking outside their bedroom window. I'm in the 0.1%. "Ukk!" long pause. "Ukk!" Long pause. It barged its way into my weird dream and got me out of bed. But what do you do? My first thought was that it was the fox, and a trip downstairs for the rifle would be in order – but the chaos of getting past/through the dogs ruled that out, even if it had been a fox.

All I could think of was to flash my phone's torch at it. This 'torch' has a habit of coming on spontaneously during phone calls (which one day will be my undoing while I'm trying to stalk and report night-time hare coursers), but being impossible to find when actually needed. After a couple of minutes of stabbing at the screen I had a light, and I proceeded to 'flash' it out the window by running my hand back and forward in front of it. There was no sign of anything scampering away, but it went quiet. Success.

Unfortunately, the dogs decided that 'wuff o'clock' would today be at four o'clock, and so we were all woken up while they tumbled, argued and barked for absolutely no reason. Not a good night's rest – and harvest is beginning to catch up.

And I was a day late with *FonF*, but wrote up a 'duffers' guide to pulses', which they seemed to like when I sent it. It was a neat summary of all the aspects of pea and bean growing that neighbour Robert and I laugh about, and you never read in the official 'how to' guides.

I was a bit woozy while finishing off the spring beans in Joan's Acre and Dell Close. I got a reasonably full third trailer off, so might have done a ton to the acre. Before heading home for lunch, I opened up a block of the winter beans in TBHD. These, too, were sown in the spring, and there are horror stories circulating of winter beans being total failures, so I was pleased to get the best part of a combine tank after a couple of circuits.

On the way home, I tipped my trailer in Godwin's barn. There's now a respectable heap – although we'll be saving a chunk of it for next year's seed.

Trinity Gain sent another lorry, and I had a long lunch to make sure I didn't clash with that one. Team Lorryload came back with news that there was another part lorry load left, which suggests that the spring wheat did do better than I'd dared to hope.

I headed back out to the winter beans, and had a three-hour stint watching the pods get a bit brittle, and the combine header take a pummelling as I kept pushing it lower and lower to get as many in as possible. A shut-down inspection revealed several knife sections in need of replacement, and some very sorry-looking skid plates under the header. I can't wait to get onto the Top of Hurst Down, where the ground is level and smooth, free of huge stones, and has a better-looking crop of beans, too.

Two texts from Trinity Grain said that the spring wheat were the best quality loads of the year, which cheered me up. And Policeman Ian sent a late-night text to say he'd got nowhere with the fly-tippers. Which would have been better had it not woken me up. And I'd had to wait for ten thousand cars from a local rally club to finish heel-and-toeing their way through Hinton Ampner until I could go to bed. I might book a few nights in central London to get some sleep.

September 12th

This is a dangerous stage of harvest. The forecast is good, and there's only a long day's worth of combining left to do. The temptation is to take it easy, and spin it out to two leisurely days – or three lazy days. The next thing you know, the weather breaks, and it's a couple of soggy September weeks before you finally finish.

It's also tempting to not bother with that grease up; after all, there's only a day or two to go. It'll last that, surely? This time, it'll be something on the combine that breaks for lack of inspection/grease, and finish is once again delayed.

So I spent much of the morning doing a really good grease up and checkover – even emptying the stone trap, convinced that it would be full after the last few days spent with the table on the floor. Curiously, there was nothing but dust. And while I was in the maintenance mood, I replaced seven knife sections and a pair of knife fingers.

Once upon a time, replacing knife sections was a nightmare. They were rivetted on, and in-field repairs meant a club hammer and a sharp chisel to get rid of the old rivets, and then the immense skill (which I never mastered) of holding the new section steadily in place while whacking the new rivets (holding another hammer firmly against the bottom) until it 'mushroomed'. A hideous job, and all done with the ever-present danger from the razor-sharp sections. Towards the end of the 'rivet' years, I bought a G-clamp that had been adapted as a rivet squasher – but I think the old boys preferred the hammer technique.

These days, it's simply a case of removing a domed 10 mm nut from cleverly fixed screw bolts, and replacing the section. Occasionally the fingers have to come off to get access, but it's so much easier, and safer.

Finally, by about eleven, the combine was ready. Did I crack on into the last bit of beans? No. Sister-in-law Heather and her husband Keith were due for a pillaging session in the orchard. This means, as it has for 35 years now, lots of gossiping, lots of cake, lots of tea and coffee, and – once the ladies are away in the orchard, stuffing their carrier bags to their limits – lots of gun talk with Keith. He's yet another one who has retired, and has a gun-sized cheque burning a hole in his pocket. Luckily, the cheque remains intact; demand and short supply means his quest for a Beretta 694 is fruitless – unlike the orchard, which is heaving this year. I feel an article coming on.

Not long after their car groaned its way out of the yard, almost on its axles, Anthony arrived, down from London in a work van, looking for stuff to furnish his new – and first – flat. He and an old school friend have moved into one in Camden, and I've never seen him so enthusiastic. After years of terrible student flats and surprisingly nice rooms found on 'spareroom dot com', he's moving on in life. Off went a large sofa, assorted tables and lights, and there was a humdinger of a row about which boy owned the huge TV in the playroom. Hazel had to step in and say "neither of you!". Jonathan jumped in the van, too, and they headed off to London. I suspect getting that huge sofa up some stairs and into a tiny flat in London will be slightly harder than getting it out of a huge old English farmhouse.

The combine beckoned, and once I'd got off the last of the almost-bare sideland ground in the Bottom of Hurst Down, the job became a lot better. The beans were taller, the ground was flatter, and I was able to push on to about 7 kph. The beans themselves were better, too, so I'll make sure I save a last trailer load from up there as seed for next year. 'Next year'! Good God. Already thinking that far ahead. Let's get harvest finished first.

I stopped just after six, with about fifteen acres left. Keep fingers crossed.

September 13th

'Lazy Sunday' or 'finish harvest day'? It was very tempting to have a day off and get everything finished tomorrow, but wisdom prevailed (after I'd spotted that the BTCC wasn't until next week) and I set off to Hurst Down with a tractor and trailer.

Of course, it was never going to be simple. Once combining, I filled up the new trailer, topped up the part-filled one that had been out there overnight, and did some mental sums. Could I get the remaining acreage into the combine tank, and so not have to drive a trailer down to the barn, empty it and come back up? I thought I'd give it a go.

Trouble is (and it's actually no trouble at all – it's a very good thing), the southern end of Hurst Down was the best bit of beans, and the combine filled up pretty quickly. I was going to have to stop, shut down, jump in the Deere and do the long slow slog down across Bottom of Hurst Down, across JA/DC, along the road and into the main barn, and then drive all the way back. (Worth pointing out that my support team weren't available today. Hazel was taking Tim the puppy to his first training session, and Jonathan was still in London with his brother.)

About an hour later, I could empty the combine tank into the fresh trailer, and get on with the last couple of acres of Harvest 2020. I did try to make a witty and amusing video of the finish, but even that went wrong.

Finally, harvest is done. No one to celebrate with, or hug, or cheer with. There was no great feeling of satisfaction or relief. We've had a really easy ten days, which makes it feel as though it has actually been a doddle – a farming memory deletes the difficult bits all too readily. Otherwise we wouldn't do the job.

I shut the little combine down, patted it on the wheel, and congratulated it on another good season, apart from the disintegrating sieve episode. The last half trailer was tipped in the barn (leaving one very full and untipped, to be used as seed), and I headed home, slowly, thoughtfully. I had to thread my way through a large family outside the tractor barn who were picking chestnuts. "Can you do me a favour?" I asked them as I sauntered over to lock the gates.

"Of course!" one said – looking slight worried, as if I was about to launch into grumpy 'get orff moi graaaas' farmer routine.

"Could you all say 'well done, Charlie!'?" They looked a bit baffled. "It's just that I've just finished harvest, and I've got no one to celebrate with." I did indeed get a huge cry of "Well done, Charlie!" and a bonus long round of applause. Lovely, really lovely.

Once again, temptation beckons. Put my feet up, watch telly, have a Sunday snooze; but no, there are little jobs to do, and the quicker the better. Hazel was back from dog training with a shattered Tim, so she gave me a lift out to Hurst Down in the tractor, and I brought the combine down to the New Pond junction, and she brought the last trailer in before it started overflowing with acorns. (It was parked under one of the overladen oak trees.)

Before hitching off the header onto its trailer, I gave it a good coating of wax – a job always worth doing while the metalwork is shiny, or 'slightly shiny' after the beans have left a layer of pasty stuff on it, and then made a right pig's ear of hitching it off. It took ten minutes with a bit of heavyweight angle iron to lever the now detached header correctly into its cradle. But finally, everything was where it should be. Hazel had a session putting the telegraph poles back across assorted gateways now that hare coursing season is officially 'on' again, and then we could call it a day. Thank God for that.

September 14th

As usual, it takes ages to wind down after harvest – especially when we're already getting itchy feet about the next arable year. The problem is that we're all still sore from last year, when the rain started on the autumn equinox and didn't stop till the spring one. I've got clear fields, seed left over from last year...

Tod rang for a long chat and a catch-up, and we agreed that if the Good Lord had offered us that harvest on March 20th, we'd have bitten His hand off. I had a drive round trying to come up with some plans for where we go first, and decided that the Stanmore block would need a bit of work before we went anywhere near it. So I rang neighbour Robert Jnr to see if his Kockerling was available. He reckoned it would be by the end of the week. That would be perfect.

The last ten tons of spring wheat went, although we kept a few tons for the pheasants. It continued the run of top-quality wheat – never seen such high Hagbergs. I dropped off the empty grain trailer and reversed up to the hedge trimmer; I thought the best way to avoid drilling is to do something else constructive. I couldn't actually see the hedge trimmer through the harvest-dusted windows, so a long session with a hosepipe, a bucket of warm soapy water and a brush beckoned. Then the trimmer went on easily. The hard bit – swapping heads to saw blades – would have to wait until tomorrow. I had a pool to test.

It was just about warm, and worth all the effort of keeping it clean this long. Lovely.

September 15th

It was another stunning, cool and misty September morning, so I made the most of it to get the heads swapped on the hedge trimmer. It was the usual frenzy of 24 mm spanners, tyre levers and splashes of stinky oil, but I got it done in under two hours. By then the unusual heat had kicked off again, so I was glad I'd started early. I could have done with a shower, though.

Policeman Ian was on the phone, with a very odd request: could he and his new sergeant pop over and use one of our empty fields to practise flying their new drone? I've heard a lot about this new toy, and how far it can see (day or night), and how cheap it is to operate compared to the other aerial option – a helicopter – and how useful it will be. I said I was delighted for them to have a go, and we agreed that Drier Field would be perfect – no one else about, and no precious pheasants to disturb.

About an hour later, they were in the yard. Did we have another field they could use? There was no wi-fi in Drier Field. Perhaps the drone isn't quite the magic crimefighting tool we all thought it was – yet. I sent them off into the Back Meadow.

I did an afternoon on Roe Hill, next to the road, trying out the saw blade. It just loves low-hanging branches, and deals with them far more effectively than overgrown hedges. It did strike me that the field will be left relatively undefended against poachers. Still, we can call on the drone if they do arrive – subject to wi-fi coverage, of course.

It was warm enough to have another Beer on the Lawn. There was much talk of harvest results, and how, in the end, we were grateful for what we'd got. We lit the lorry wheel brazier to keep things pleasant, and it was well past ten o'clock when we said our goodnights.

September 16th

Tod had ordered a huge pallet of Roundup for the autumn's stubble spraying, and I was expecting it early, so got the loader tractor set up with pallet forks. Inevitably, the lorry got held up, and it was past nine o'clock before he arrived. He was very grateful for the tractor doing all the unloading – 32 20-litre drums of glyphosate and 16 20-litre drums of ammonium sulphate take a bit of shifting and stacking. Mind you, it did leave me with the job of getting them off the pallet and into the spray store. I would have booked the Muscle to do it, but he was off with Hazel in Tigger buying a lovely leather armchair she'd spotted on a local Facebook page – once they'd cleared Tigger of all the harvest paraphernalia, of course; grease guns, broken sections, old rags, the stepladder. In theory, there was now room for a chunky armchair.

A long afternoon in the Stanmore block with the saw blade left the edges of the field littered with branches and boughs. Very satisfying, and occasionally quite unnerving, as I set the blade to 'up as high as I dare, and certainly out of sight from the cab', and crept along, flinching as another limb came crashing down, often with a freak hailstorm of acorns.

Luckily, there was one of the last bits of cricket to listen to on Radio 4LW, and, as it has been for much of the late summer, it was a joy. Huge credit should go to the organisers who have managed to bring us lots of live cricket – test matches, T20s and 50-over games. They dub some crowd noise on it – the stands are empty, of course – and you can almost imagine the summer is a normal one. Almost.

The Colonel rang from Scotland to say he'd be down next week to pick up the Subaru. How dare he? I've got my name on that. Mind you, it's been here for ten months, and I haven't been out of the drive in it. Anyway, his African Odyssey is effectively cancelled, so he'd like it back on the road. Fair enough. He said he'd drive his mother's Golf down, get it to her in Wiltshire somehow, and drive back in the Scooby. He'd booked North's to pick it up and give it an MOT and a service, and they'd be picking it up tomorrow. Was that OK with us? Of course, I said. I'd put it on charge overnight.

For that, I'd need one of the 50-metre extension cables that have powered the pool pumps over the summer, so I sadly disconnected them, rolled up the cable, wired up the charger, and connected it to a flat-as-a-pancake battery. All the alarms went off – I was effectively reconnecting a battery, and the alarm doesn't like that. I had to do what I should have done in the first place: disconnect the battery. I'd dig out the correct procedure for silencing the alarm later.

One last swim in the pool was in order, and it was heaven. We must make a comprehensive list of bits and piece that are needed for it for next year. We got away with duct tape and zip ties this year, but I don't think we'd get away with it next year.

The armchair just fitted in Tigger, and looked lovely in the hall, facing the log burner. It was too wide for just one person, but not wide enough for two. However, one person and three flatcoats fitted perfectly. One Mali could fill the whole thing perfectly. Just wait until the Editor tried to settle down in it.

September 17th

Graham the Sprayerman was in early for a big 200-acre session Roundup-ing the stubbles. I gave him a map with White Hill, Drier Field, BOMS, Chalks and Godwin's Park coloured in, and sent him on his way. Luckily Hazel nipped out and moved the telegraph poles and the old cultivator that would otherwise stop his enormous self-propelled sprayer from getting to most of these fields.

The Subaru started (after several combinations of reconnect battery/turn key/press 'lock-unlock' button), and I drove it round the yard for a bit to get the rust off the brakes and get it warmed up. I'll miss it, even though I've never actually 'owned' it. North's arrived to take it away for its big TLC session.

Having saved a green trailer of winter beans for seed, we sent away the rest, and it wasn't anything like as much as I thought. There was a very odd first lorry, which needed 30 buckets to fill it, which had us all baffled – and normally it needs 23 or 24 of good weighing (i.e.77 kg/hl) produce. But the weight came back as 30 tonnes, with a hectolitre weight of 78. It made no sense. But there's nothing to be done. Very odd. The second lorry was half-full, so it looks like a final yield of 15 cwt/acre. Ho hum.

I tried a late swim to cheer me up, but somehow the pool had chilled dramatically since yesterday, and I managed about ten minutes before calling it a day. And what a thoroughly 'meh' post-harvest day it has been.

A late-night car hurtling up the hill and stopping suddenly and noisily outside the gate was enough to get me out of bed, into my dressing gown and out across the yard to check what had happened. Your first chilling thought is that there will be a flat cat on the road – but all I found was a young badger scurrying back and forth. They are digging up the roadsides all around the farm; I suspect the fields are getting a bit hard in this heat.

September 18th

Even though I saw the badger last night, it was still a relief to have both cats in, as noisy and demanding as ever. After a brief breakfast, they headed to their daytime positions – Cain on my bed, Abel on the sofa. That's their day done.

The Colonel rang early with an update on his travel plans. The elderly Golf had had a flat battery, and then refused to leave 'park' on the automatic gearbox. The AA were going to bring him and the Golf from Perth to Hampshire. He'd optimistically nominated North's as his garage of choice, and, unbelievably, they'd accepted it. A long day in car transporters beckoned for him.

All matters related to harvest finally finished as the spring beans got loaded onto lorries, and this time there were more than expected – a lorry and a half, when we'd anticipated just over the one. And we'd saved a green trailer and the little blue trailer full for seed, so that cheered things up a bit. The barns are empty, the toe-tip bucket has done its bit, saving us a fortune in hiring big kit for six weeks, and we thanked Noel for his time. I was tempted to go and put the combine away in the now-empty barn – which would have really *really* meant the end of harvest, but started greasing up the Horsch instead.

As if by magic, neighbour Robert Jnr arrived in the yard. I'd rung him after tree lopping in the heavy fallow lands up at Stanmore, asking if he fancied working the ground down for us. He'd been up and had a look – the only thing that would get through/down into that soil was the Solo disk/deep leg combo. If that's what's needed, that's what's needed. He said he'd be out in a day or two. I'd better get on with greasing the drill.

The Colonel was on the phone yet again, with an exciting update on his travel plans. The AA had abandoned their mission to get him to Hampshire in one day, and had booked him a hire car so he could go on ahead. The Golf would then be delivered to North's tomorrow. Blimey – makes his trip round the west coast of Africa seem simple.

He arrived through the back door just after nine. The catch-up and gossip took us until midnight.

September 19ᵗʰ

The best way to get your mind off farming for the day? Do stuff with cars. Mind you, we had to get them all where they were supposed to be. So the Colonel went off in the hire car to meet the AA at North's, where they were dropping off the broken Golf after its long drive south. Then he went into Winchester to drop the hire car off at the station – once he'd found the impossible-to-find 'return' car park. Hazel tracked him down (having been into Tesco), brought him back to North's where he picked up the serviced and MOT-ed Subaru, and he drove it here. Invading Russia would have been simpler. I missed most of it, sitting indoors drinking tea.

We set about it with sponges, brushes and a bucket of warm shampoo, which made it look a lot more loved, and then did a Formula 1-style tyre change, only slightly slower. All of the summer tyres were hideously perished, so the Colonel vanished into his container – still parked in the yard – and emerged, slowly, with winter tyres. An hour later it was reshod, an inch higher (the winter wheels are slightly larger than the summer ones) and ready to go.

And I didn't watch the weather forecast once.

September 20ᵗʰ

Bloody typical. I'd finally reached the 'Sunday with no harvest so lie in' state of mind, when the phone rang at just after seven. It was a neighbour whose wife had spotted a Transit parked on the entrance to Kilmeston Road, and its inhabitants could be seen enjoying a leisurely 'walk' across the stubbles.

By the time I'd got dressed, got my keys, got Sasha (after persuading Tim he wasn't needed) and got out there, there was no sign of them. But the 'season' has started.

The Colonel played with the Subaru all day, Hazel went dog training with Tim, Jonathan set off, with only a few misty-eyed hugs, for his second year at Newcastle Uni. He's taken the Hyundai i20, having insured it himself. I couldn't blame him; I tried uni without a car and hated it, and was thrilled when I got my first Polo GLS; freedom! No buses or bicycles! Parking tickets! (Granny Flindt used to pop tenners in the post with "this is not to pay for your parking ticket!" written firmly but unconvincingly in the letter, just after I'd casually dropped into a phone conversation that I'd got another parking ticket.) Jonathan has earned well over the summer, so can just afford the insurance (just under a grand with a black box driving tracker fitted), and the quicker he gets on the no claims bonus ladder, the better.

Meanwhile I lay on the sofa watching rugby and the BTCC. Hazel complained that she'd been training just the other side of the A303 from the Touring Cars, and she and her team could hardly hear themselves think. I apologised on their behalf.

A proper Sunday – although we're just beginning to keep our eyes on the forecast to see if another endless set of rain is imminent.

September 21st

I'm getting itchy drilling fingers. No sign of neighbour Robert Jnr with the Solo cultivator, so I had a seed sort-out down at the grain store. The right-hand lean-to is full of all the seed we didn't get in the ground last autumn, so I approached it with some trepidation. Most of the 500 kg bags were OK, but some had holes and rips, some old, some new. I got all the winter barley bags over to the left-hand lean-to, put eight bags of Zulu winter wheat on the old bale trailer, and popped it back in the barn. I brought one iffy bag up the road, slowly, for calibrating the drill.

A lorry was due sometime this afternoon with seven tonnes of fresh Zulu, so I thought it best not to venture too far away with the hedge trimmer, and did a couple of hours of very unsatisfactory work on BOMS. Those saw blades do not like soft material. As I got home, I noticed that both rear tyres on the Deere were going soft, so I parked it next to the barn ready to set about it with the compressor in the morning.

The lorry arrived at 5.50, which in the old days would have meant asking a man to work overtime, but nowadays it's routine to hang around for a bit. I'm paying my own wages, after all. The lorry was vast – I'm sure they've got longer in the last couple of years. The turning area we carefully put in five years ago is now only just big enough.

And with great sadness, I started draining the pool. Summer is done. Although it was still warm enough to be tempted to do one final dip, I resisted it.

September 22nd

A worrying sign: there was a small puddle of oil under the Deere. Once upon a time, tractor oil leaks seemed to be compulsory. Our set of seven Fords that filled the barn in the mid-1980s only seemed to stop dripping oil when it ran out. But nowadays a leak is a bad sign, especially after days of driving over recently sawn-off branches and boughs.

Rolling underneath, I saw it was coming from one of the hydraulic filters. It's tucked up deep in the chassis, and has a very handy half-inch recess for a socket drive. It was with huge satisfaction that I found the filter had worked its way three-quarters of a turn loose. How it came loose was still a bit of a puzzle, but I was just grateful that it hadn't gone further, and hadn't dumped the whole oily contents of the back axle in the middle of a field during drilling. Small mercies.

Both back tyres had indeed dropped to just over 10 psi, which is another worry. They must just be getting old, and more porous. Even though there's probably a dry autumn's tread still on them I rang Micheldever Tyres to get a quote for two new ones. Peter in their agricultural department promised to email some quotes.

I really couldn't face any more hedge trimming for a bit; I've done the early wheat ground and the barley ground, and if we get those done and onto the bean stubbles, I'll be delighted that we've got that far that fast. Chances are that there'll be more hedge trimming opportunities to come. And my neck bloody hurt this morning. So I took the trimmer off, and hitched onto the Horsch, ready for the worst job of the year: checking the row of packer tyres on the back.

You need a compressor, and grease gun and years of yoga under your belt. Two out of three ain't bad, I suppose. Many of them were flat, but they all turned easily on their bearings – so I pumped them all up to see how many would be flat in the morning. Slow punctures I can cope with, but getting in there to sort out bigger holes is a nightmare job, and one I should have done during the quiet spells in harvest. But back then, drilling is always a hundred years away.

The biggest excitement of the day was when my email resigning from the NFU finally got through. I'd sent it after finding a leaflet for something called 'farmvention.com' fell out of my NFU membership magazine. It was a flyer that we were supposed to hand on to our primary schools, and it could have been written by Greenpeace, all about getting five-year-olds to help farmers fight 'climate change'. I emailed the organisers and asked if my £1,300 membership fee paid for this green indoctrination. "Oh yes," they replied, merrily. I cancelled my subs.

This cancellation worked its way round the organisation, and just after tea, an odd mobile number rang mine. It turned out to be the NFU's Regional Director, asking why we weren't at the Pots; he knew (thanks to the *FW* column) that I was always in the Pots on a Tuesday night with Neighbour Robert, and so had made a beeline for the pub to intercept me for a little chat. Great thinking – if we weren't now doing Beer on the Lawn until things return to normal. I suggested he come round for a cuppa on another day.

Despite this odd episode, we managed a post-equinox boozy evening, but only just. The 'lorry wheel brazier' earned its keep as the four of us sat round it. The Colonel was still here, Neighbour Robert joined us, but the ex-Editor and Mrs ex-Editor couldn't make it. I thought we'd only manage an hour outside, but when we pulled stumps it was ten-thirty.

September 23rd

Finally, the house is empty. The Colonel set off to pick up his wife from Bristol airport, and Hazel and I are on our own again. He made a very welcome guest, covering the shock of Jonathan going back to uni after his six-month visit. The yard is somewhat emptier, too. Jonathan took the little white i20 with him, and the Colonel took his beloved Subaru. Luckily, we were too busy to notice.

Neighbour Robert Jnr's chap arrived with the Solo discs, and started work in Broom Field, doing a fantastic job – until heavy rain put a stop to that. I played with the Horsch a bit more, getting the dodgy wiring sorted. Then the heavy rain put a stop to that, too.

What we're all afraid to mention is that the rain started this time last year, and didn't stop for six months. So I won't mention it.

September 24th

The inspiration for the next *Flindt on Friday* had finally decided to show up, and I was just getting stuck into another 600 finely crafted words (in truth, it was just another daft piece about the joys of the last days of harvest, but there we go) when the lorry driver who was due this afternoon with a massive load of Crusoe seed rang from Sutton Scotney services to say he'd be here just after nine.

There's not a lot you can do under these circumstances. There's no point saying, "But your transport manager rang yesterday and promised you'd be here this afternoon!" It's hardly worth ringing the transport manager herself and having a moan, because there'll be lots of half-hearted apologies and the same will happen next year.

Nope, what you do is shrug your shoulders, save the half-finished article, and get out there. It took five minutes to get the loader sorted out (weights on the back, bag lifters on the front), and ten minutes restacking the Zulu that arrived the other day so there's room in the barn for today's delivery. I only had time for a couple of minutes leaning against the door pillar (the traditional 'waiting' pose, but one which needs a cigarette for maximum effect) when the lorry turned up.

For a third of a century I've been lifting seed off lorries and stacking it in the barn, but it's still a challenge. You know damn well that a moment's loss of concentration means a ripped bag or a damaged lorry, but all went well. I had to pause for a phone call from Robert Jnr to say they wouldn't be in cultivating with the Solo today – it was too wet. Fair enough.

It didn't get any drier. Not long after the lorry had trundled off, a band of rain, hail and thunder came up from the south-west – all very dramatic. I kept playing with the Horsch in between downpours, and realised that I still had three flat tyres on the rear packer: one on each of the folding wings, and one slap bang in the middle. I decided I'd leave the middle one and sort out the outside ones.

Tucked away in the back of the old calf pens is a DIY tyre repair stand, which is designed to break the bead and then lever the tyre off the rim. But what it does need is a firm fix into a concrete floor to give the operator something to push against. This meant a trip into Winnall for some 10 mm anchor bolts and a decent 16 mm masonry bit. And shopping these days is slightly bizarre. I had to use the horrible mask in the Skoda, and keep two metres apart, but apart from that, it felt normal. I had a classic 'old man' moment as I walked across the car park, not knowing I was shedding bolts from an unsealed bag. I obviously have no high frequency hearing left at all. There was one left when I reached the car. Luckily, retracing my steps rescued the rest, scattered across the car park. Man, we're all going downhill so fast.

Ten minutes with the masonry bit in my Makita cordless drill made it obvious that a bigger machine was needed. I hardly made a mark on the block of farm concrete. There's only one person you ring in these circumstances; Tod the Agronomist, who – of course – had just the thing: a heavy-duty hammer drill he'd spotted for sale in, of all places, Lidl, at an astonishing price. So, Tod being Tod, he'd bought it. And he was amazed at how often it had been handy. He promised to drop it off tomorrow.

I thought it wise to make alternative plans, just in case that old concrete remains undefeated, and realised the simplest thing would be to cannibalise the old CO3 drill, still parked up in the back barn; that was, after all, one of the reasons I'd kept it. So I went round and loosened a couple of wheels. But that would be a job for tomorrow. It was getting dark, and suddenly really cold.

How cold? Well, I spent half an hour before bedtime chasing Cain round the house, from bedroom to bedroom, into the alcove at the top of the stairs, into the bathroom; he was not going out. I finally got him into the old larder and fed him – but turned my back for a second. He was upstairs again, and we did it all again. That's how cold it was.

September 25th

By the time I'd got two of the three flat tyres on the Horsch packer roller replaced, I noticed that both tractor rear tyres were soft again. They're obviously beginning to get too porous for practical use; the last thing I need is to be at the far end of Pipeline when one of them decides to go down a bit more quickly. It was time to dig out Micheldever Tyre's quote for some new 18.4R38s.

Their ag tyres man had quoted six different makes, ranging from £600 to £900 each, so I chose the cheapest big name that they said they had in stock now – Kleber, for £700. I asked what the chances were of getting it done soon. "Be with you by one o'clock!" was the answer.

I've never put new tyres on the Deere, and it has done nearly 4,000 hours. We don't burn crops or power harrow the soil anymore, so the flints are uncracked theses day, and we rarely run a tyre in a ploughing furrow, which used to cut the sides to bits. Mine had a few splits and cracks, and may have had another dry season of work in them, but were obviously simply beginning to perish. Of course, in the old days, tractors were usually replaced on a three-year cycle, often with less than a thousand hours on them. It was a very tax efficient thing, apparently. New tyres were rarely needed.

The man from Micheldever was done by two o'clock, and after a brief and good-natured row about taking the old ones away, he was off to his next job. All finished – order to delivery – in under three hours. Amazing.

Neighbour Robert Jnr's man had returned with the Solo, and I guessed he should have finished Broom Field by now, so got the drill calibrated and set off to join him in the remote lands of Stanmore. There was a slight problem when I got there; he hadn't done the headland of Broom, but instead had gone and done all of Pipeline, and was just starting on Long Field. As soon as he saw me and my drill, he was back into Broom – the headland had been far too wet earlier.

I chose to drill at an angle across the Solo's work and had a fairly rough day. As good as that big cultivator is at biffing the slumped land into some sort of seedbed, it leaves considerable lumps and ridges, and I was feeling pretty sore by the time the setting sun was right in my eyes. I made a mental note to check the pressure of the brand-new tyres – the fitter probably pumped them up far too hard.

There was a curious moment as I was about halfway across the field: I glimpsed the roof of a car through the trees, in Rough Field. I at once assumed it was Neighbour Robert Snr popping out for a visit and inspection, and fully expected to see him eventually find the right way into the field. But no vehicle arrived. And then, on the way home, I noticed fresh hare coursing wheel marks in the pea stubble. The buggers had been out in broad daylight, and while there were two of us in the next-door field. And the roof I had seen was them driving off the field and into the Barracuda game strip at the top of Rough Field. If they're that brazen and that early, it's going to be a long winter.

Still, we'd made a good start on sowing, and the weather forecast says dry and windy for a few days. Perfect. Mind you, everything hurt. Shoulder, hips, lower back, and, bizarrely, a hamstring in my right leg. It was a big 'hello' to my friends Mr Voltarol and his chum Mr Ibuprofen at bedtime.

September 26th

It was a great surprise to find that all limbs and joints appeared to be working this morning, so I set off to Broom Field for an early Saturday start. The Solo man was up there even earlier, of course, and he finished Long Field just as I finished Broom. I filled up the drill again, and headed off to Pipeline, which looked a treat in the September sunshine. I did a few turns of headland until I was empty again, walked back to the loader and trailer, and headed home for lunch.

After lunch, I topped up the seed trailer at the Drier Yard, and drove through the wood to where the drill was parked, and then had an uneventful but productive day finishing the headland and all the long work. Not very exciting, but we've had quite enough drama and cock-ups up there over the decades. Dull is good.

September 27th

The dullness was never destined to last. I loaded up a few more seed bags and headed off, again, to Pipeline, and finished it. The short work was very 'peaked', as Dad used to call it, so the last bit didn't take too long – each turn was a lot shorter than the last.

Next up: Long Field. I had room for another bag in the hopper, and nipped across the Pipeline shooting strip, full of determination to make a decent start – maybe get the headland done and then roll Pipeline this afternoon. The first bit

– the very short headland at the southern end – was fine, but then I hit the first of the soggy patches that the Solo couldn't get through. Foolishly, I thought I'd force the Horsch through them, and within a few yards was dragging heaps of hideous wireweed with me. There was a lot of reversing, and lifting and lowering, and eventually getting on the bits that had been cultivated. Twit. I should have just gone around them.

As I reached the north-east corner of Long Field, the next issue presented itself: in the huge easterly gusts of wind that shook the house last night, an ash tree had blown over, out into the field. Much of it had shattered, but the last thing I needed was to put my back out, so I went round it, deciding that we'd move it tomorrow and I'd redrill that little square.

After four turns of headland, I thought I'd check the seed level and stretch my legs. Everything sounded very odd. The hydraulic fan was emitting a Vulcanesque howl. Closer inspection showed that, somehow, the bottom seed flap had opened – perhaps one of the lumps of weed had caught the little handle. The airflow to the distributor mushroom had dropped, the seed had failed to make it up the three feet of vertical pipe, everything had backed up and was now solid with seed. Seed was emerging, but through the ventilator grille and out of the bottom flap. I'd been sowing a single thick green strip of corn, four metres from the last one, for some time.

First job was to undo the huge Jubilee clips to get the flexible hose off and 'drain' the seed out of it. Then I had to give the metal vertical pipe a minute or two of thumping to free the blockage. I then reconnected everything, but took the lid off the distributor mushroom. I slid the spool lever into 'drive', the fan started, and a very satisfying burst of seed shot skywards.

Two more jobs remained. First, put the lid back on, and second – most importantly – do something about the pile of seed that had accumulated. I moved the drill forward, and spend some time kicking the seed outwards as far as I could. After a couple of 'drive throughs' with the drill (with the seed flow switched 'off'), you wouldn't have known anything had happened.

I was mighty grumpy by now, so it was a relief when the seed ran out as I'd hoped, at the north-west corner of Long Field, where I'd planned to do all the filling tomorrow. I locked up and walked back to Pipeline to pick up the loader and the seed trailer, and went home for lunch.

Hazel got back from dog training, having picked up Diana from Winchester station on the way home. Reports from her journey down were interesting; lots of empty carriages and cities. She's back in the office in Cambridge, but that, too, is almost deserted. The job – writing video games – is going well, though. A good career choice in these mad times. She did look as though a couple of days of farm living and intensive multi-flatcoat therapy wouldn't go amiss.

I was a bit fed up with drilling, so switched to rolling, and, once I'd got the terrible hydraulic coupling on the Massey sorted, did the whole of Pipeline in a long afternoon. It looked fantastic in the sunshine. I tried the new Pure DAB kit for the first time, and tuned into Absolute 80s, who were doing a chart rundown from September 1980. Where was I then? Probably doing corn cart in this very field, having just finished A levels and left school. Funny old world. I'm sure it was the dust that made my eyes water.

September 28th

After an early diesel run up to Long Field (pausing to take lots of lovely pictures on the way) I rang the Tenants Farmers Association. One of the downsides of leaving the NFU will be the loss of my business insurance, which covers me for things like arguments with the landlord, VAT inspections, tax investigations and so on. The TFA do a similar scheme, so I thought it would be wise to make sure we're covered when our NFU membership expires at the end of October. As usual with the TFA, it resulted in a long chat and a gossip. The whole organisation is slightly slimmer and more intimate than the NFU.

We spent the rest of the day in Stanmore. I finished drilling Long Field, and had enough seed to redrill the dodgy headland and still have a bag left over for White Hill and Cheyney – if we ever get there. The forecast from tomorrow onwards is terrible. Hazel rolled Broom Field and made a good start on Long, but didn't manage to finish it. We'd do that in the morning.

September 29th

Michaelmas Day, which is the start of the new farming year – or the end of the old one. I can never remember. So it's either the start of our thirtieth year of farming, or the end of the twenty-ninth. Either way it didn't get off to a great start, with the 'light drizzle' that was forecast overnight turning out to be a very heavy shower. We'd got off lightly, judging by the reaction of the 'Drill Operators UK' Facebook page. An awful lot of land had been left prepared for drilling today, and had had a big soak. You'd think we'd all know not to trust the weather muppets by now.

Tosdevine was due to come in and do the pre-emergence weedkiller on the Stanmore block, so I rang him and put it off till the afternoon, in the hope that the rain would dry off in the emerging sun. Which, luckily, it did.

The next test car – a Subaru XV Hybrid – arrived, and by the time I'd given the driver a lift to Petersfield station, it was warm and sunny again. Hazel set off to Stanmore to finish the rolling, and I cadged a lift with her and brought the Deere and the drill back. It'll need some TLC before we start on the next crop, whenever that happens.

After Tod had been round for long chat and a check on drilling plans, I put the three-metre disc/deep leg combo on the Deere and started giving Roe Hill a good cultivate. It started well, in the short work at the far end, and I had plans of getting the whole field done today, maybe only get a light shower tomorrow, and then drill it on the promised dry day on Thursday. But then I got into the dried-out charlock plants – and they simply refused to go through the machine. I had hoped that they'd be so brittle that they'd just disintegrate. Not a chance; we're going to have to get out there with the topper. Plans, eh?

The huge sprayer arrived in the yard at five – I pointed out that he'd be working in the dark, but he seemed relaxed about it; with all the gadgets and gizmos, he can go in the dark – and there are no telegraph poles up there.

Having had our last 'Beer on the Lawn' last week (and the week before, and the week before), somehow it felt warm and calm enough to have one more. I fired up the brazier/lorry wheel yet again with a mountain of beechwood, and we started in the dusk. I didn't reckon we'd last long, but it was past ten-thirty when we admitted defeat. One of the longest and loudest evenings yet. When Diana came out and joined us for a beer or two, we had to pause and check if we were still legal, but luckily no one knew the rules. A bit like Boris.

Just as I was about to head off to Stanmore and see if the sprayerman was OK, he came home. It had been pitch-black for two hours, so I hope he was in the right fields up there. Time alone will tell.

Bedtime was delayed for half an hour while we enjoyed a slightly tiddly game of 'Hoover the daddy-long-legs'; hordes of them had come through the open back door in pursuit of the light, and although it felt slightly cruel, it was hugely satisfying as each one disappeared up the Hoover pipe with a little 'pop'. We must get out more. What an odd way to start the new farming year. Or end the old one. One day I'll work it out.

September 30th

The new farming year (or was it?) started calm and dry – almost kind enough to make me think that the sprayerman could have left last night's late job until today. But the wind got up by mid-morning, and then blew a gale, and the promised deluge duly arrived. Just the thing to make us feel pleased we'd got out of Stanmore. Assuming, of course, that it stops raining at some stage.

The NFU pensions advisor arrived for a much-delayed review of finances. Our pension pot is reasonably impressive – not quangocrat level, of course, but given a few more years of inputs, it will yield something quite useful.

I drove the test XV up to Micheldever Tyres to pick up the two Horsch packer wheels that they'd taken away to be mended after they'd put the new tractor tyres on. It was unusually empty, so I was in and out, with an unusual quota of 'Bud' and 'Boss' being used. Do I look somehow more authoritative in a face nappy? The same applied at the Horsch dealer, just down the Roman road, where I was 'Mr Flindt'. Mind you, they're proper polite innit. I bought some more following harrow tines, and discussed the economics of replacing the whole rear frame on the Sprinter ST4, which had broken and been welded up rather shoddily by the previous owner. It could be over two grand, but as an overhaul, it would give the drill a good few more years. The XV Hybrid turned out to be rather fun – although the way I was driving it meant that the mpg was a somewhat non-green 32.

Grim news from London. One of Anthony's work colleagues has tested positive for the virus, and they'd been sharing vehicles for a couple of days. Poor Anthony has to self-isolate for a fortnight in his new flat, with no flatmate and no internet. Luckily, he still has phone contact, so we were able to send him sympathetic messages. Must make sure we keep in touch.

The month ends, the farming year ends (somewhere round here); where are we? It's virus chaos, but we seem mostly unaffected, except for poor Anthony. Boris and his green advisors are busy stopping everything we enjoy using the virus as a cloak. Meanwhile Brexit seems to go nowhere, with snippets of sniping from both sides. 'Good faith' this', legal instrument' that. Meanwhile, the farm finances look like they'll be OK if we put all the harvest produce into the 'long pool' for next year's selling. We won't get the cash injection that we usually get at this time of year from selling stuff in the 'off the combine' pool, but we'll benefit from the prices that are going berserk as news of stock worldwide turns slightly less positive. Funny old world.

October 1st

Another wet start, so I wrote the next *Flindt on Friday*. It was the one I've been meaning to write for ages, about the National Trust's trawling through the history of their houses to establish slavery links. Poor little Hinton Ampner has fallen foul of the Woke Police, who discovered plantation links from around 1770. I find it absurd – how far back do you go? – and tried to fashion that sentiment into a column that wouldn't get me evicted. We'll see.

By lunchtime, it had dried, so Hazel and I took the XV out across the stubble to measure the holes left by the archaeology gang who'd been digging up the route of the pipeline, looking for stuff that might be of historic value – some real historical investigation. They found nothing, but left a dozen or so cropless patches, usually about 25 m by 8 m, with tracks between them. Not a lot of crop loss, but something to add to the very generous payments we've already received for disturbance and allowing access. It seemed a bit ironic to be using a 'green' Subaru to check on progress of a new aviation fuel pipeline. After a couple of hours of highly technical tape-measure waving, we had a clipboard full of figures, ready to be processed and sent off to the land agents who are in charge of the whole thing.

The afternoon dried up even more, so I thought I'd put the new harrow tines on the drill. I was interrupted by a family leaning over the silver gates, looking into the yard. They looked rather guilty, explaining that the farmhouse looked so pretty, they wanted a closer look. I invited them down to the main entrance and gave them a potted history – the Georgian bit, the Victorian bit, the mathematical tiles, and all that stuff. They were lovely to talk to, and in simpler times you'd have got them indoors for a cuppa. But not these days.

Sasha and I went for a walk, doing the loop to Clump. Not usually a remarkable thing, but I realised I hadn't stepped out of the farmhouse for a walk in weeks. All that harvesting, hedge trimming and drilling; all very worthy farm work, but hardly putting one foot in front of the other for an hour or so. It showed by the time we got to Clump – I was feeling very unfit. Luckily, there was someone in the edge of the bushes, picking blackberries, so I stopped for a chat.

She was another of the cosmopolitan residents of Brockwood Park School, famous for its alternative approach to education: exams bad, vegetarianism good. She was charming, though, and we chatted for some time. She said she was originally from southern Russia, and I told her the story of how, all my farming career, I've been warned that the great deep soil plains of that part of the world will soon put mediocre farmers like me out of business. "No chance," she laughed. "They're incapable of doing a day's work!" That cheered me up enormously.

October 2nd

More rain. Big Rain. Serious rain. One of the trailing arms of Storm Alex got stuck over us for most of the day. It was all hands to the drains as water started pouring through the back door, and my drive to my new dentist in Alresford was a bit hairy; I was quite pleased to be in a four-wheel drive.

After twenty years or more of using the same dentist in Winchester, I decided to change. Getting into town and parking was never easy – the city authorities seem determined to drive traffic away – and Alresford is much easier. The dentist (a farmer's wife) who'd been poking around in my mouth for years had retired, and the practice itself had morphed into a really creepy cosmetic surgery centre. The dentistry had been banished to the back rooms. I hadn't been to see anyone for what must be 18 months, so chose this new one in Alresford. Hazel had already been once, and came back with good reports.

But here's the funny things about dentists. When, back in the 1960s, I was dragged crying and screaming to see Mr Edwards, in the St Cross Road in Winchester, I was treated pretty well as a grown-up (once I'd finished crying and screaming). I was asked to sit down, shut up, open up and put up with the pain. He did once apologise to me; after I'd cried every night for what seemed like a year (I can still smell the oil of cloves), he reluctantly pulled a painful tooth. It had a large abscess on it. He said I'd been right all along. Mind you, it didn't make my farts go 'Honda'.

These days, you have to arrive in a face nappy, have your temperature taken, and then are guided to a chair by a girl with a voice so squeaky and enthusiastic that it's just inside your hearing range. Everything is 'PARFECT!!!' Oh, and fill in another form.

The form is relatively mundane – I couldn't remember all the details of multiple inhalers and pills that have become part of my daily routine, so I generalised a bit. It asked what gender I identify as. I crossed that out and put 'sex', then 'male'.

Finally, I was seen by a dentist. All seemed well; no fillings needed, gums were good, lymph glands were fine (why do dentists check these?). She took some X-rays (ker-ching) and some photos, and then gave me a lecture on how I was grinding my teeth. This is odd, because I don't.

In fact, measures to combat 'grinding teeth' have become the dentistry equivalent of 'new shock absorbers' when you visit a fast fit car service centre. In the days before I really got stuck into car DIY, I used to visit these places quite a lot. I'd point out that the steering was a bit woolly. "New shock absorbers, mate!" was the answer. No window wash left? "New shock absorbers!" A howling from the nearside front wheel when Hazel's first lime green Fiat 127's steering was at about ten degrees left? "Definitely new shock absorbers." And that last one is a true story.

Hazel had been recommended some night-time gumshields (ker-ching) but declined. I had the same offer (ker-ching) and a demo of how to clean my teeth with an electric toothbrush. She highly recommended the model I didn't have (ker-ching). Luckily I managed to get away (literally) without buying any of these, but I couldn't get away without an appointment with the hygienist. I've yet to meet one of these who treats anyone as an adult, but I'll go along with it.

One thing I did do was make an appointment to see someone about some implants. Finances suggest that a few grand could be well spent on a slightly less graveyard-style smile. Let's hope they treat me as a grown-up. Otherwise I'll sulk.

The afternoon could have been a lot more serious and grown up; the Regional Director of the NFU was coming round to try and persuade us to change our minds about leaving his organisation. We drank a lot of tea, failed to eat any Hobnobs – the rotter didn't bring any – and actually had a very long and good-natured row about the way the NFU is becoming indistinguishable from Extinction Rebellion with its green policies, and is still not a happy place for Brexiteers like me to be. I was glad that we were still friends when he left, despite having failed to change our minds, and him not bringing any Hobnobs.

October 3rd

Another wet day. Really wet. No decent sport on the telly. I couldn't even get enough enthusiasm to start the year-end accounts. I scooped 42 litres of water out the wheelbarrow, divided that by the area of the top, and reckoned we'd had 3.2" of rain. Well, we needed it. And we're out of Stanmore. So we don't care.

October 4th

A lazy – and wet – Sunday. Hazel took puppy Tim off for more gundog training, in the hope that Carrie will let us have pheasant shoots sometime in the future. Tod and his son Dan called round to borrow the old MIG welder that has been sitting in the diesel barn for decades, unused. I bought it off a chap who worked here briefly back in the terrible 1990s, but he had to go when I realised he was not terribly discretely turning that barn into a car servicing workshop. He went, the welder stayed.

Ever since I've had no employees, it hasn't been plugged in once. Yes, I've broken stuff, but owner-operators tend to be more careful. Most welding jobs I need are small enough to pop in the truck and be taken to Rod's.

Tod and Dan lugged the welder and its cylinder of argon into his truck, and then had a tour of the old barn. It's not tidy, it's not pretty, but most real farm barns are like that. We did manage to find a programme for a ploughing match in 1975, and an instruction book from 1970 for a County 4WD tractor. One for eBay. We then took shelter from the wind and rain in the farmhouse and got all nostalgic. And Dan's not even very old.

The Literary Agent has been fretting that he has never returned the invite for the Beer on the Lawn he came to a few weeks ago. Far be it from me to tell him that such gatherings for beer'n'peanuts are far from formal, and nobody keeps count – so when he suggested Hazel and I pop down to his gorgeous Arts and Crafts house down the valley, we accepted.

Trouble is, I accepted by text, which didn't get there. Luckily, because it was nothing more than beer'n'crisps (no peanuts), it didn't matter, and even though we turned up 'unannounced', we had a very jolly couple of hours of gossip. Highlight of the evening was me telling one of the nation's best-connected literary agents about Talking Pictures, the little Freeview channel that has had a wonderful lockdown showing discarded and forgotten films from the last 80 years – and gathering a huge cult following at the same time. He'd never heard of it.

October 5th

It was nice and sunny Monday - for a bit. I finished the *FonF* proof, and gave it the thumbs-up, still not completely convinced that the National Trust would take it the right way. There was then a series of slightly arm's length emails with the new editor at *The Field*; decisions about the future of the magazine – and those who write for it – are still up in the air. On the assumption that *The Field* will need copy for their December issue, I took the Subaru XV out for the Winchester–Stockbridge–Andover–Winchester loop in yet another deluge. And I got stuck behind Mr Sensible up the Test Valley road. A shame, because it's a great testing road. We pootled up it at 32 mph.

Not a great day was finished off as Tod texted that he couldn't raise enough for a band rehearsal.

October 6th

I'm in the middle of a run of lying in and having terrifyingly vivid dreams – is it the 'long COVID' that we hear so much about still bugging me after whatever I had in Jan/Feb? This time, I was in the Drier Yard, and the back end of an artic lorry came crashing down out of the woods. It was something to so with the Trust tidying up the old pheasant pens – and must relate to the fact that the beaters' wagon in the old days was a converted train carriage. In the dream, it was a curtainside, and it came rattling down the Blackhouse Road, crashing into a tractor at the entrance of the Drier Yard. Out of the field opposite came children from Cheriton School, all dressed up in camo as if either shooting or doing some absurd 'Earth Day' nonsense. Because it was a dream, it had to be the former.

The next dream was really bad. I was back in the dentists' chair while someone was poking and prodding my mouth to see if it was good enough to have implants done. There was a battle with 'cheek spreaders' to get a full view of the teeth. I was not in a good mood anyway, having had to wait nearly half an hour for my appointment, and sitting in a hideous plastic chair, not finding breathing through a face nappy terribly easy, while multiple members of staff scurried round with antibacterial wipes. And I'd used the loo and couldn't operate the sink – what's wrong with an old-fashioned set of taps and a plug, for goodness sake? And listening to the camp receptionist tell all his workers loudly that he was a vegetarian – which is unusual for a vegetarian. And then the final estimate for a couple of new implants came to a quid under £13,000.

Actually, that last one wasn't a dream; it was how I spent my morning.

I spent much of the afternoon in a state of shock – and car shopping on the internet. Thirteen grand will buy you a very nice Mazda6 Estate – my latest object of desire.

The Subaru XV went, and I was sad to see it go. I sat in it for half an hour, making notes for the review. It's something I don't always do, but I regret it if I don't. I'll miss it, not least because Tigger's wipers haven't been fixed, and it's still raining.

October 7th

The rain passed for a bit, so Hazel and I went up to the Hay Field to try and patch up the kissing gates. They get a monumental amount of use, and, once again, the screws for the self-shutting springs have come out. Murph's sheep have arrived back on the lush grass in Springshot, and will be heading for the Hay Field soon, so we ought to try and make the gates sheep-proof.

Half an hour with the cordless Makita yielded nothing but the conclusion that traditional gate-closing springs are not designed for heavy farm gates suspended six inches away from their posts. But we did the best we could and resolved to find something better on the internet.

We took Tigger across White Hill and up to the Stanmore fields to see how it looked after all this rain. There were some shoots of Zulu just peeking through, but in places the clay had run together quite nastily. It's lucky that we piled the wheat seed in quite thick. Probably best to leave it a week before coming back to inspect it again.

Hazel did a long drive round the shooting strips checking pheasant feeders, and Sasha and I did the Clump loop. And, back indoors, just as I found a gate-closing sprung lever on the internet, the heavens opened again.

October 8th

A low-key birthday. There were calls and messages, plenty of parcels and cards. One card was anonymous, signed only as from 'Hawick fellow farmer', and saying nice things about Book One. Can't decide if that's creepy or lovely.

Much of the morning was spent watching the last two British Airways 747s leaving Heathrow in tandem. I wasn't actually there, of course, but there was a livestream on YouTube from some wonderful nerdy plane-spotter who runs 'bigjet.tv', and I watched the planes as they moved, using the equally wonderful 'flightradar24', zooming in on the north runway.

The weather up there was equally foul, so plans for all sorts of parallel take-offs and fly-bys were abandoned, and in the end just the one of them did a loop over the M25 and a low-ish fly past in the murk.

Fifty years or so ago, such online viewing was out of the question. Dad piled us into his Rover 3.5 Coupe, drove up to Heathrow and parked up on top of one of the multistorey car parks, and all with the aim of seeing one of the very first jumbo jets arrive.

Mind you, he was a bit of an aviation nut himself. In the attic are photo albums full of black-and-white pictures of Croydon Aerodrome, which was only a couple of miles from his childhood home in Sutton. His slides from more recently were full of pictures of the Farnborough Air Show, with Concorde doing low-level fly pasts astonishingly close to the crowds. One year in the mid-1970s, he headed up there having forgotten to lift two boxes of Eley Grand Prix out of the boot of the Volvo 264GL. (By then, the legendary car salesman Alan Robbins had prised him away from Rover.) The entrance to the show was crawling with sniffer dogs (this being the IRA's most active time) who descended on Dad's boot as if it were full of raw steaks. To this day I don't know how he managed to blag his was out of that mess – but he did.

I got the next *Flindt on Friday* done – telling the tale of the Russian lady who was picking blackberries. Not a very exciting story, but should be good enough.

We had huge steaks and birthday cake in the evening. All very lovely, but I do miss having children around for it. It was still jolly wet.

October 9th

It was nice for a bit, so after a lengthy office session, I thought I'd pop out and do some winter barley seed sorting – stack a few on the old bale trailer, bring a bag back up ready for calibrating the Horsch, all that sort of stuff.

It promptly rained hard for a couple of hours. You can go off farming, you know.

October 10th

Sasha and I went and kicked the mud in BOMS, and decided, possibly a bit optimistically, that it would drill. So I calibrated the Horsch, had a bit of a tyre pump-up and grease session, and headed out after lunch.

I marked out the north, east and south headlands, and then started drilling with the road. It didn't go very well; there was an awful lot of weed growth clogging up the drill. But just as I was about to give up and come up with an alternative plan (aka, sulk), the weeds stopped, and the drilling went a lot better. Not perfect by any means, but I got through it, and that's what counts. And by the end of the day, as I finished the field, I was quite cheerful.

It dawned on me that the horrible weedy zone was where Mac had spread our diminutive muckheap a few years ago. It needed to be spread, for legal reasons, and the only field that was dry enough to take the work was BOMS. The trouble was that the little heap was never going to cover the whole field, so Mac did a strip next to the road. And that was where, some years later, it was almost undrillable. Funny old world.

I parked the Deere and the Horsch under the trees at the bottom of BOMS, and had an immediate flashback to the horror days of last autumn, when it sat there for three months. Not again, surely?

October 11th

A perfect farming day, even though it was Sunday: dry, calm, sunny – just right for a bit of spraying, or rolling, or even to get stuck into Chalks with the drill and get a few more precious acres sown. But somehow, none of these appealed to me. I didn't feel 100% – very dizzy and off colour, and, more importantly, the BTCC had reached Croft, and that's one you don't miss.

So while Hazel took Tim for another gundog training day up near Thruxton, I sprawled on the sofa, drank too much tea and ate too many biscuits. But the motor racing was top notch.

It wasn't a totally wasted day; Tigger's wipers needed mending, so I had a session removing rubber trim and that funny plastic plate that sits at the bottom of the screen, to get to the rods and linkages. I popped the curious little sprung socket back onto its ball joint; it seemed to click back on firmly, so there was no obvious reason why it had jumped off – twice. There was, of course, only one solution; silage bag tie. I found the point where two rods (including the wandering one) ran pretty well equidistant through the wiping cycle, and fastened them to each other. Sorted – I hope. That should guarantee dry weather for the next three weeks. Not.

October 12th

That was a bad decision yesterday. The rain that was supposed to get here early today was delayed, and it turned out that I/we could have got Chalks in and rolled. Shoulda coulda, and all that. Hazel rolled BOMS, although it didn't seem to make a world of difference to the seedbed, but it looked slightly better from a distance.

I drove down to New Pond and brought the Deere back via Rick/Clump and Chalks, and headed indoors. Hazel brought the rollers back, hitched them off, and between us we put on the huge flail mower, with a view to sorting out the stuff in Roe Hill that wouldn't go through the discs when I was cultivating it the other day.

The mower is a heavyweight Major machine, with huge hammer flails, bought in the days of compulsory set-aside, when large areas of 'fallow' regrowth need mowing. It takes some power and takes no prisoners. The dried-out stalks and mini-bushes in Roe Hill didn't stand a chance. I did most of the lower west end, and it was as smooth as a baby's bottom when I finished, and the rain started – again – and went on all night.

October 13ᵗʰ

Whisper it gently, but it was almost a normal Tuesday. Hazel and Bella set off early to Barrow Hill for their first picking-up day of the year. I had an office morning, finally getting two more press cars booked for the pre-Christmas deadlines, and then had another session down at the grain store shuffling seed bags. I needed to get the big green trailer full of winter beans up to home ready for the seed cleaning gang who are due to process it tomorrow. It was blocked in, in the left-hand lean-to, by lots of bags of winter barley seed, so they all needed shifting. It's lucky that our bags haven't started to disintegrate like some I've heard of. There are scary stories of loops giving way at unexpected moments, and bearing in mind how much we spend leaning under them to open them... Mine seem – so far – to have held up OK. It about time the bloody stuff was in the ground rather than in bags, but there we go.

The little Massey struggled a bit coming up the hill to the farm, and on the way up I noticed the engine temperature gauge was reading nice and warm. This was only a relevant observation because the cab was still freezing. The heater obviously isn't working. Yet another niggle to have a shout at the dealer about. Two of the six quick-fit hydraulic connectors have also given up – a very common but expensive problem.

But I've got to be a bit diplomatic. After the episode of the bent steering wheel, the AGCO PR girl got in touch on Facebook and said they'd pay for it. "Thank you very much!" I said. Since then I've heard nothing, and the bill came for the 500-hour service – including the new steering wheel – a few weeks ago. We held back from paying it, hoping for a credit note for the wheel, but nothing came. So, we paid it, and I sent a mock-grumpy message to the AGCO girl. Ten minutes later, an email arrived from the Massey dealer, with a credit note for the whole – quite substantial – service. Very generous of them. I will have to be less grumpy when it comes to pointing out the latest failures. Luckily, 'less grumpy' is part of my nature.

Hazel came back from the shoot in very good spirits. Most of it had been 'normal'. True, there was lots of 'social distancing', no vehicles were used, and the legendary slap-up meal in East Meon was off the menu, but there had at least been a shoot, lots of laughs, and plenty of retrieves for Bella, who had slotted straight back into the groove brilliantly. Everyone had seemed relieved to be doing something together for the first time in ages. How long Carrie will let things go on, who knows.

And, to round off the day, after Sasha and I had had a stunning walk among the showers and rainbows, Neighbour Robert and I went to the Flowerpots. It was the all-new Flowerpots, which has been blitzed in the lockdown. There are new bars, a new colour scheme (looked a bit 'operating theatre' to me), and new staff. And all that before you include the virus-related changes: wear a face nappy to come in, ring a bell to be shown to a table, table service only, staff in masks and clear cropspraying visors. It was the Flowerpots all right, but not as we knew it. But the crucial thing was that Robert and I sat down, had a couple of beers and a couple of packets of unnecessary peanuts, and went home mostly happy. And that's what counts.

The Octavia Scout was making odd rattly noises as I parked up in the garage. Not sure what that might be – I fear it's the dreaded DMF death rattle. It's been faultless so far in 18 months and goodness knows how many miles. Ironic that one of the cars I booked this morning for testing was one of the new Octavias, having raved to the Skoda press office about how bulletproof they are.

October 14th

Hazel was off again picking-up, this time at Hill's on Cheesefoot Head. Picker-up Julie is a regular there, and kindly asked if Hazel would like to come along with Evie, and let her sit and watch her first ever shoot. Hazel, of course, said yes, she'd pop along for the morning

It's easy to forget, when you've got a puppy (Tim), that Evie is still a baby, too. She's only 16 months old. But she had a good morning, apparently. She insisted on meeting and greeting everyone, and wasn't very good at concentrating on the job; she's a true 'valley girl', all kooky and ditzy. But towards the end of it, something clicked, and she got the message, and even did a couple of retrieves. There is hope.

I faffed about for the morning, and had an odd run of orders for Book One. One order was for two via 'Farm Marketplace', but from the same person, and only moments apart. I took the unusual step of ringing the orderer, who sounded like a sweet old thing in the New Forest, and she confirmed that her computer has 'gone all funny', and she'd pressed the button twice. I said I'd only send one; she mentioned it was for a birthday present, so I managed to get a name off her and write a daft message inside the cover.

We took the Octavia down to North's for them to have a listen to the rattle. Two minutes' research on the internet suggested it was an early sign of 'dual mass flywheel' failure, but with a warm engine, there was very little rattle at all. North's agreed that it sounded a bit iffy, but no panic yet. Sometimes these dreaded DMFs go one for another 50,000 miles. Our old Octavia reached 120,000 without a problem – then again, it was a single mass flywheel.

A trip to Stanmore on the way back revealed some very iffy looking wheat. It really suffered from that freak rainstorm (3.2", according to the wheelbarrow), and has panned together horribly. The newly emerging plants have been hit by the herbicide, too. It's probably best to leave it for a few weeks and then look again.

To get to Stanmore, I had to cross White Hill, and once again, we'd been visited by the hare coursers. There were fresh wheel marks sweeping all over it. But where had they got in? The gates were untouched, and there was no sign of the numerous telegraph poles having been moved. A drive slowly round the outside revealed that they'd driven in over a steep bank – one that we'd not bothered to block, thinking it was impenetrable.

And just as I paused to inspect the new gap, I realised that I wasn't alone. Just the other side of the bank, parked on the road, was a dodgy white van. Two very likely lads had got out and were also checking the bank. The fact that their dodgy Peugeot was towing a horse trailer, out of which stuck the two long shafts of a pony trap, did little to keep my hackles down.

There was then the now-familiar routine of them pretending that they were nothing to do with the violent hare-coursing 'community', and me pretending that I believed them. They'd stopped (they said) because, on the way up the hill, the long shafts of the pony trap had clipped a low branch. Luckily, all seemed fine now, so they'd be on their way. "Any more low branches this way, Boss?" asked the revolting fat one. I assured him he'd be fine, trying to memorise the number of the van.

Back home, I put the number into the DVLA website: no tax, not MOT. I rang Policeman Ian with the details, just for the record.

We'd been meaning to saw up a huge limb that fell off one the beech trees near White Hill gate months ago, and that was our cue to get on with it. We grabbed the battery-powered chainsaw (fantastic toy) and cut off as much brushwood as we could, and Hazel used the loader to stuff it in the 'new' access gap. Another hole plugged.

October 15th

On our little rough shoot, the first drive has always been a problem. We set off from the garden and go east, along the top edge of Chalks. It's always better if someone is in the Back Meadow, but, if we do put someone in there at the start of the drive, it's a flipping nuisance for them to retrace their steps to the yard entrance when it's over. So, this morning, we did what we've been meaning to do for ages, and cut a small farmers' gate out of the Back Meadow, just beyond where the drive usually finishes. Not a big job: just a couple of posts and some wire snipping, but I still managed to shred my forearms and end up dripping blood. Well, it wouldn't be a fencing job without it.

By afternoon, it felt dry enough to have a go in Chalks with more winter barley, and it went really well – for a bit. The control box started beeping, with a 'COMMS ERROR SPEED' message. I jumped out and cleaned off the vital radar, checked connections, and tried everything else I could think of. Nothing solved it. That's the problem with these fancy electronics, tucked away in sealed boxes: all well and good when they're behaving themselves, but impossible to mend when they don't.

When the BIN 1 message started flashing as well, and the whole box seemed to go into meltdown, I decided to call it a day, and ring the Horsch dealers. They'd have someone out in the morning, they said. I'm not getting very far with this drilling.

October 16th

Two lads from the Horsch dealer were at the back gates on the dot of nine. I gave them direction to the drill, and went back to catching up with some writing. I did the next *Flindt on Friday*, and proofed the Toyota piece for *The Field*. I then skipped merrily down to where the drill was parked next to the old tennis court, ready to jump in and start drilling.

Unfortunately, it wasn't the radar causing the problem. And three hours later, they were still scratching their heads. That's the bloody trouble with fancy solid state electronics – there's absolutely no clue as to what's gone wrong. There was an outbreak of parts swapping from my old CO3, but still nothing.

I shuffled back and forth from the tennis court to the house, trying to keep calm and not get into a stew. Eventually, I dug out the mobile number for the Horsch area manager, who has always been helpful in the past. "No speed reading," I said. "Swap the radar adapter," he said. "That'll sort it." I took the old one off the CO3, strolled down to the ST4. "Try this," I said, trying not to sound as though I was at my wits' end. It took about ten seconds to unplug the old one, and plug in the new one. It worked. It was all slightly embarrassing, after all that head scratching. I thanked them for their time, left them to put everything back where it should be, and had an early lunch.

It was a huge relief to find that everything had been sorted. The trouble is, we'd changed the main cable from the cab at the same time, so we couldn't be sure it was the 'radar adapter'. Although there was a little note on the tractor seat when I got in – "The old radar adapter had lost its earth wire – this was probably the real cause!" Nice to know. Anyway, I cracked on.

The ground had dried beautifully, and by the time sunset burst out from below a blanket of cloud that had crept in during the afternoon, I'd finished Chalks, and marked out and made a start on Roe Hill. Fantastic. A long day tomorrow with fine weather and a fully functioning drill would do wonders for the soul.

October 17th

There's nothing like a successful afternoon and a good plan for the next day to ensure a good night's sleep. I was up well before my alarm would have gone off if it hadn't been Saturday. I thought I was particularly early, based on how dark it was. Thank goodness the clocks change soon.

The darkness turned out to be nothing to do with the early hour. It was dark because it was pissing down with rain, and had been for some time. This came as a bit of a shock after the hundred weather forecasts I'd watched in the past 48 hours. I stood at the open back door and let loose some flowery language.

It was very tempting to head back to bed in a sulk, but you can't sulk if Cain the cat comes purring up to see you in bed. So I stayed up and joined in with the coffee-and-chocolate bread frenzy when picker-up Suzie arrived for a flatcoat yomp. And when the ex-Editor and his boy turned up for another coffee on their way to shoot some pigeons over the bean stubbles in Hurst Down, I was cheerful again. Probably all that coffee.

It didn't last. After lunch I headed back out to Roe Hill and tried some more winter barley drilling. It was only just dry enough, but I reached the bits I hadn't bothered to mow the other day with the big topper. Sure enough, every 50 yards I was bunging up. I gave up after ten acres, and came home – in a sulk – and put the topper on the Massey again.

Hazel took the enormous hint, and while I enjoyed the top-notch rugby final, went out and mowed the last bits of Roe Hill. And then the ex-Editor texted to say that he hadn't seen a single bloomin' pigeon. Now, he was sulking. Which cheered me up.

October 18th

Hazel took puppy Tim off for another session training, and I cracked on with the winter barley. Yesterday's mowing had done exactly what was wanted, and I flew through the rest of Roe Hill with the Horsch. The was not a lot of dust to be seen – although it did seem to have dried out a bit – but the seed was going into the ground, and this year that's what counts.

Tim and Hazel got back from training just as I started the swap to Godwin's Park. Tim had had a good training session, passing his initial assessment with flying colours, and Hazel had been approached by the organisers of the highly respected training centre, who wanted to know if she'd be up for joining the training team. High praise. I soon brought her back down to earth by suggesting she go out and roll Chalks.

Meanwhile, I got the rest of the barley seed loaded, and set about Godwin's Park. Once again, it was sticky but passable. I marked out a headland and got all the long work done before it got too dark. A good productive day.

October 19th

A drive up to Stanmore to check the September-drilled Zulu didn't cheer me up much. I don't know why I'm expecting some sort of miraculous recovery from 'bloody mess' into 'neatly mown lawn'; it went into knobbly clay that had been heavily cultivated, and then had 3.2" of rain. I should be grateful that there's anything at all up there.

Hazel's attempt to roll Chalks was stumped by the very heavy dew – the rollers started bunging up, so she gave that up for a bit.

I cheered myself up by ordering some more central heating oil. The cheapest quote was just over 30p/litre – an astonishing drop from the 42p/litre for the order just before lockdown. They promised delivery before the end of the week, so I hope ours doesn't run out before then.

By now, the wind had got up, and once Hazel had helped me trickle two bags of barley into the drill through an old combine sieve (to keep back any unwelcome lumps after 13 months of storage), everything was dry again. Godwin's Park finished beautifully, with the last of last year's seed running out about three-quarters of the way round the sixth and last turn of headland, so I was quite smug as I folded up and brought the drill back to the farmyard. Hazel finished Chalks and started on Roe Hill – from a distance, I thought I saw a bit of dust. Then again, I had barley dressing in my eyes, so it could have been anything.

Over lunchtime, I grabbed the loader tractor, put a tonne of Crusoe in the drill, and did a calibration. It was a significant moment, finally getting stuck into the pile of new seed after clearing all the old stock of Zulu and Tower, and I set off down the hill and across Folly in quite a cheery mood. From the Folly, I crossed Dark Lane into Drier Field, made a 20 metre-ish mark around the whole headland, unfolded the wings, put the end harrows on and got going.

By the time it got dark, I was well out of the short 'peak' work nearest the Folly, and well past the Drier buildings, but – inevitably in this shittiest of shitty years – there was a problem. The wonderful front suspension on the Deere started playing up. I'd thought it wasn't running 100% in Godwin's Park, when the hydraulic pump could be heard occasionally struggling, and the drill would do a 'low fan speed' warning bleep, suggesting that the oil flow had temporarily been cut off. Just when I was 'relaxing into confidence' in Drier Field, there was a loud alarm and an amber warning light on the dashboard, both warning that the front suspension – the 'TLS' – had packed up. Luckily, Drier Field is smooth, I wasn't going flat out, and I only planned to stay out there for another hour or two, so I decided to press on and ignore it. I'd ring Hunt's in the morning.

Hazel finished the rolling in Godwin's, brought the Massey and rollers home, walked back out there to pick up Tigger, drove it down to New Pond, where I jumped in it and drove home, leaving the Deere and the drill in Drier Field. And Hazel walked home with a pack of dogs. At least, I think that's what happened. In the end, we all ended up where we should have been.

October 20th

Last night's rain was a lot heavier than we'd expected, so there was no chance of keeping going with the drilling this morning. I rang the Deere dealer instead, to get someone out to look at the tractor's suspension. They promised someone would be out late morning to check it over.

It's a funny stage in the farming cycle. We've just finished congratulating ourselves on paying off a whole bunch of loans, and there's suddenly a whole bunch of breakdowns: the combine sieves during harvest, the drill last week, and now the trusty tractor. Somewhere in the attic is a file full of lecture notes, and somewhere in it is a graph showing how as depreciation drops, repair costs start to rise. And to think I used to dismiss all that age-old wisdom as nonsense.

I did some seed cart, just in case the world suddenly dries up. I loaded up the old bale trailer with nine more bags of Crusoe and took them down to the Drier Yard. Drier Field was almost dry enough, but not quite. It was sorely tempting to load up a couple of bags and bash in another ten or twelve acres – especially as the Deere repair boys had gone, texting me that a simple sensor was at fault. If they're right, that's a relief.

The first shoot of the season in on Thursday, so I thought I'd start on the jobs that need doing beforehand. The wonderful sheep trailer that is towed behind Pig with a garden bench zip tied into it has a flat tyre, so I whipped that off, pumped it up, and spent ten minutes looking – in vain – for air bubbles when I dunked it in a trough. If it's that hard to find the puncture, it'll stay hard for a day.

Neighbour Robert and I decided to try the Flowerpots again, and stumbled across the ex-Editor and a chum, so we joined them. No idea if that was legal but we did it anyway. The Editor's chum turned out to be a neighbour, who has lived in Hinton Ampner for ages, but, as often happens in this hamlet, I hadn't actually met. Still, we were new best friends after a couple of pints.

October 21st

Wet, really wet. I didn't sleep at all well; beer and peanuts sitting a bit heavy, left hip hurting like hell (another new hip soon?) and a strange painful left hand that crept into my surreal dream about auditioning for the role of Bottom in Midsummer Night's Dream that was being staged in the new theatre that appeared to have been built in the bottom of Chalks. More of 'long COVID at work? All I know is that my audition was to read page 41 of the script. And I was late. And I opened the script to find it was the spare parts book for the combine. All the usual stuff in dreamland.

We did lots of shoot preparation instead. Hazel cooked and cleaned, wine got delivered, virus safety messages were printed off and laminated, Pig got refuelled, the tyre went back on the little trailer (still hard), and plans for the day were generally hatched. The forecast for tomorrow looks slightly better, too.

Another load of heating/Aga oil arrived – another 2,000 litres. We're running at almost exactly 4,000 litres per year. Call it 11 litres a day, or £3.50 per day to pay for a big hot brick in the kitchen and the central heating. Not too bad, although the hot water still comes via an immersion heater in the bathroom. I miss the Rayburn Nouvelle we had in the bungalow when we lived there. It did all three. Mind you, it broke down every six months.

October 22nd

The first day of the season on our little rough shoot. Things have progressed nicely since we took it on five or six years ago, and we like to think that it's now a well-oiled machine. This season, though, we've got a whole set of virus-related issues to contend with, of course. So there was a lot of printing off of warning notices, and forms for signatures, and putting extra sanitiser and wipes in Pig. I was actually quite nervous about doing everything possible to keep everyone happy – and legal.

But once all eight (four with guns, four dog team members) of us had gathered – no hugs or kisses – and set out across Chalks, just as yet another monster shower petered out and fantastic sunshine emerged, all was well with the world.

My other big worry, based on what I'd seen round the farm in the last few months, was Trust visitors, who I feared would be dead keen to snoop on a rough shoot, and take further action if we were seen not wearing face nappies or keeping socially distant. But, like the weather, everything turned out fine.

We did the four home drives in the 'S', had elevenses at the Drier Yard, and then did the long drive at Big Field. With a bag of 27 by then, we decided to just do George's, which yielded three more (all mine, thank you very much). At that point, although it was still light, and we could have squelched our way up to Stanmore, the Keeper called it a day, and we went home for a long lunch.

Luckily, two of the eight volunteered to go home, and make sure that we kept to the Rule of Six – but for the life of me, I can't remember which two they were. Curious.

October 23rd

It should have been a nice quiet post-shoot clear up day, but it didn't get off to a very quiet start. Hazel met up with a chum for an early dog walk (she obviously hadn't got enough exercise yesterday), and headed off round the farm from the Drier Yard – straight into some early morning hare coursing.

But it wasn't the usual longdog/white van coursing. This was a pair of designer crossbreeds, hurtling across Drier Field in full voice in pursuit of a hare. No point ringing the police with the special 'coursing' codeword for this lot.

Hazel and her walking companion then met the owners of the loose dogs (now in the rough vicinity of their owners) in the woods – but things didn't get any better. The 'guest dogs' promptly attacked the little dog belonging to Hazel's companion, and a terrifying tussle ensued to separate them. There was shouting, screaming, swearing, injuries, blood – and an urgent visit to the vet.

The rest of the day was spent trying to track down the other walkers – no names or addresses had been exchanged at the scene, of course – but after a few phone calls and a bit of internet research based on a hint that one of them was a half-familiar face, they were found. Locals they were not. They'd come some way to let their dogs loose in National Trust-owned woodland. Emails were sent, apologies were forthcoming – as was an offer to pay any vet's bills. All profoundly depressing, but it's the English countryside in 2020.

My day wasn't much better. There were battalions of slugs in Drier Field, too, and the evening rugby was dismal. I got the next *Flindt on Friday* done, though.

October 24th

It was relatively dry for a bit. Not anything like dry enough to do any field work, but I was able to get into the tractor and rescue old spraying recommendations without getting too drenched. I'd decided to make a start on the accounts, and the first and most horrible chore is the valuations of the crops 'in store', and for that you need details of every penny spent on them. Also in the tractor was the bible of fertiliser applications, so I rescued that, too. I printed off a list of the fields and what was in them at harvest, and then photocopied 15 'field record sheets', ready to start work.

But then I got bored, so went and cut some firewood, ready for a Saturday watching rugby. Unfortunately, Ireland vs Italy was another complete non-event, and the France vs Wales friendly was wrecked by the clueless ITV commentary team, who still think that Alan Partridge is a role model.

My mood wasn't involved when the lights started flickering in the gale that had got up, and at one stage the rain was louder than the wind. No drilling tomorrow.

October 25th

A walk across Chalks was only just possible thanks to last night's rain – and Chalks is as its name suggests: chalky. At least there were no slugs to be seen, and the winter barley was just beginning to show. Last year's wheat is making a very strong showing, though, which is a bit of a nuisance. The ST4 only shuts off one spout per wheel for tramlines, and a lot of corn gets rolled down, out of the combine's reach, late in the arable year. Much of that corn had just decided to grow, damn it. Luckily, Tower is a feed variety, so a bit of wheat in the mix isn't a problem.

Sasha vanished as I was heading back towards home, and once I caught up with her in the kitchen, it was obviously why she needed to hurry home: the ex-Editor was sitting at the kitchen table tucking into coffee, and already having a debrief on Thursday's shoot with Hazel. Sasha, of course, had her head in his lap. It was agreed that the shoot had gone very well, and that we were lucky to get a fine day in among all the deluges.

Once I'd lit a fire, tuned into the BTCC and settled down on the sofa, yet more ferocious showers came through, with the odd rumble of thunder. Luckily, the racing was fantastic.

October 26th

Hazel did a pre-rain pheasant feeding round   and came back with mixed news. The pheasants were still out there in huge numbers, but the wheat plants in

Stanmore weren't. She thought I should have a look for myself. I tore myself away from procrastinating about the accounts, grabbed Sasha and Tigger's keys, and set off across a just-driveable White Hill. I parked on the top of the ridge next to Barracuda dell, took a deep beath and walked into Broom Field.

It was not a pretty sight. Half of it just wasn't there, having rotted away – I assume – in the incessant wet weather this month. Bits of the field were green, but it took a lot of imagination to think that there would be a good crop out there come harvest. Another huge oak tree had toppled onto the northern headland, just to add to the desolate scene. Long Field and Pipeline weren't any better. I guessed the area lost was once again about half. The notorious wet spots in Long Field were unwalkable, with great pools of water lying.

It's a far cry from that warm Tuesday September evening, as we drank our beer on the lawn, enjoying the warmth of the lorry wheel brazier, and feeling particularly smug that we'd got those three fields cultivated, sown, rolled and sprayed by the end of the month. Four tons to the acre was guaranteed next harvest. But now I was on the phone to Tod to discuss redrilling options. Ho hum. That's farming.

Hazel went off to do some accountancy at the stables, and I faffed about with bits of paper, trying to commit myself to the accounts, and actually did quite well, sourcing seed costs from the multiple files in the office, and gathering up the last of the spray recommendation sheets. The forecast suggests that there are plenty of wet days ahead to keep the job going.

The first of the weekday short evenings meant that both fires were lit and all the curtains drawn by five-thirty – luckily, there was a band rehearsal. Tod had managed to get us all together for a fantastic session in Shed 3b, and bearing in mind we still have no gigs lined up, that was quite an achievement. Although we still like to just get together and play.

October 27th

I'm not very happy with United Airlines Flight 47. At 4.23am, it flew over Kilmeston – admittedly at over 40,000 feet, but its roar was enough to set off all the pheasants, which set off all the flatcoats, which woke me up. I turned on Classic FM and drowsed my way through yet more bizarre and vivid dreams.

It was wet all day – again – and Hazel got thoroughly wet picking-up at Barrow Hill, and I did some more accounts. Not a lot, because somehow I ended up going through the old stack of photographs in the cupboard, and once you start that…

It's funny how the digital era meant the sudden end of paper photos, and now there must be getting on for ten to fifteen years' worth of family snaps hidden away on the hard drive, just waiting to be wiped out by a lightning strike. Sad, in a way.

By the time Hazel got back (and the sun decided to make a spectacular appearance) I hadn't actually done very much in the way of accounts, and done far too much in the way of tearful nostalgia.

Still, there's always a cheery trip to the Pots to bring a smile to even the grumpiest farmer's face. Alas, not this time. They're doing a fantastic job of keeping open under Carrie's War on the World, but the stress levels involved are obviously pretty high. Wander round one of the new bars without a mask, and you risk a stern telling off. Try to pay with cash, and the reaction is even worse. I'm afraid I went off on one, pointing out that there was more danger from a falling meteorite than my humble 20-quid note. It all got a bit sweary and unpleasant as neighbour Robert and I left, and that's a first in 35 years.

October 28th

We had another attempt to make the kissing gate on the southern boundary of the Hay Field stock-proof. It's a lovely new gate, perfectly balanced, which means it won't 'shut' to one side or the other. We've tried fitting coil springs to make it shut, but they've proved less than successful; something to do with the fact that the spring needs to be fitted as near vertical as possible, and that's hard with a gate that's several inches away from its hanging post.

My new purchase was a spring-loaded rod that sat in a runner on the gate, and after a couple of false starts, and many good-natured exchanges with the many walkers doing the Trust's walk to Kilmeston, we got it fitted successfully. Open the gate, walk through, and it returned with just the right amount of emphasis to the small post. The big test will be to see if it survives the intense traffic that goes through it on a daily basis.

Just as we finished, the heavens opened yet again, and the rain continued for the rest of the day. So I did more accounts, and drank far too much tea.

October 29th

A curious internet-related morning. Once I'd finished the next *FonF*, I emailed it to *Farmers Weekly*, and all seemed fine. There was a reply, thanking me as usual, but saying that they'd had a furious phone call from someone who runs a company that is related to health and safety issues. This person was spitting teeth about something I'd said about them on a *Farmers Weekly* 'members only' Facebook page.

Well, this left me scratching my head a bit. What had I said? The posts had all been taken down, so I had to rely on my memory. They'd put up an advert for their services, linking it to the NFU. I think I'd put up a light-hearted comment about the NFU's cosy links with some companies that occasionally make my teeth grind. Then this company had put up at least another half a dozen adverts, and I'd suggested that the Facebook page – designed for jollity, assorted comments and, ahem, bants – was not the place for endless adverts. The adverts duly disappeared.

Apparently, monumental offence had been taken at this, and the owner had been making furious phone calls to *Farmers Weekly*. I decided that there's only one way to sooth troubled waters: pick up the phone myself and have a chat. I traced the company without any difficulty, rang the contact number and put on my best conciliatory/charming voice.

It didn't work, I'm afraid. I was treated to ten minutes of expletive-laden abuse, followed by an abrupt hanging up. Nothing further to be done on that front, I think.

The 'Zoom' call with the bank manager was somewhat more polite and friendly. It was little more than a chat about how things are going. I did have to spent ten minutes frantically pressing buttons to get the whole thing to start, and spent the whole 'meeting' feeling slightly ill-at-ease with talking to a screen, and with my picture up at the top of the screen. I never realised how bad my repeat lockdown buzzcut looks. It's either been done a lot shorter than the one we did back in the spring, or I have gone a lot balder in six months. Luckily, the manager was too diplomatic to laugh at it, and seemed convinced with my message that things are trundling along OK at the moment. The prices of all the stuff we've got 'in store' up at Hampshire Grain have rocketed, and if the Single Farm Payment comes in on time in December, and at the healthy rate that the weak pound has suggested (or is it still linked to the sterling/euro rate?), we'll be fine with the overdraft we've got. "Will you need the same overdraft this time next year, or can we talk about reducing it?" she asked. As if I knew.

A drive round the farm revealed a group of teenagers struggling along the path at the top of Big Field, heading into the wind and rain. They were doing the Duke of Edinburgh Scheme Silver Award, and were heading for the Back Meadow, where we'd said they could pause and cook a meal. I'd met the supervisors a couple of weeks ago, walking up and down the footpath, looking lost. When they told me what they were up to, I offered the meadow. They were amazingly grateful. It was just a joy to see a bunch of lads laden with rucksacks, cheerfully striding out in the foulest of weathers.

I caught up with the supervisors who were by now waiting in the yard, and offered the back barn as respite from the weather. Not needed, I was told. It's all about being stuck outdoors. Poor sods. What's sad is that the virus means that setting up a camp and spending the night is now forbidden. They'll miss the joy of sharing a tent while doing Corps Camp in 1979 with a fellow called Barrington Orr, who would light his first Marlboro at 0530. Wonder what he's doing now? Probably lighting another.

Then it was back to the accounts – and the last lap. Every input to every field has been laboriously recorded, and now they just need to be costed, so the 'cost of production' can be established, ready for the final valuation. Luckily, Tod dropped in for an old man's whinge (and to say he didn't think the Stanmore block was as terminal as I had thought), so that put a stop to that. Sasha and I did the Clump loop, avoided the cattle barn hordes of pheasants on the way home, and lit a big fire for yet another dark wet evening.

October 30th

Bugger all. Hazel went for a ludicrously long walk, checking the gates on the way, and I sat indoor and did the accounts.

October 31st

It was almost a normal autumn Saturday. I sat down with the accounts – again – to finish the final *final* push, but kept being distracted. I had to wave Hazel and Nessa off to Murph's shoot next door without giggling too much at the forecast – several hours of severe gales and horizontal rain. Then neighbour Robert rumbled his way into the yard in his aged Land Rover, and that meant more tea. By the time I'd overindulged at lunchtime (not sure I really needed that whole chocolate bar), the last day of the 2020 Six Nations Rugby was about to start. So I gathered a few more logs, lit the sitting room fire and settled down for the afternoon.

The rugby wasn't thrilling, although the stream of obscenities flowing through the pitch-side microphones was, and in the end, England wrapped up the Championship. The afternoon was enlivened by the ex-Editor dropping in to watch the England game, and Hazel coming back from picking-up having had a great day watching stratospheric pheasants doing Mach 2 over young and inexperienced Guns. She got very wet to start with, but the sun came out in the end, and she and Bella had had a busy day.

The day should have ended with a slightly over-heating pile of people and wet dogs, slumbering on assorted sofas and armchairs, celebrating an England triumph. But Boris, as instructed by his World Economic Forum overlords, popped up on our screens to tell us that thanks to the stunning success of the previous lockdown and all the determined wearing of face-nappies, the nation was going to have to go into lockdown again from Thursday. Will that wreck our little walkabout shoot, due on Thursday? That'll teach me to tease Hazel this morning.

November 1st

Now that Hazel has been asked to join the staff at the world-famous dog-training school near Andover, she and Tim were off ludicrously early. For me, it was a busy morning on the phones, trying to work out what Lockdown2 means for our little shoot. That's the trouble with farming: our social lives are often limited to shoots in the winter months, when – in theory – there's nothing else going on. Take that away from us, and we'll be cross. I know it's nothing compared to those who will be losing businesses, or the ability to hug relatives, but I'm still fuming.

Hazel got back from Mullenscote saying that the atmosphere up there was pretty bleak, too. Their courses would have to stop, and bearing in mind the nation's obsession with buying puppies during lockdown, the last thing we need is less dog training.

We decided to work on the assumption that our shoot on Thursday would be off, and got on the phone and Facebook to try and bring it forward a day. Hazel's beating team took very little persuasion; she had the team of four within moments. The ex-Editor couldn't do Wednesday, but I got two neighbouring farmers and brother-in-law Keith lined up pretty quickly. We'll have a shoot, we'll bloody well enjoy it, and we'll curse Boris and his leftie academic advisors at tea.

And it rained a lot.

November 2nd

It rained all through the night, and the gale shook the house. Not a lot of sleep to be had.

My motoring column for *The Field* was a day late, so I dug out the copious notes I'd made about the Subaru XV (always worth making copious notes) and had the piece finished quite quickly. I then logged onto the complicated 'freelance hub' that the new owners of the magazine have set up for us to use, and submitted the Word document. At least I think I did, and proudly emailed the new 'content editor' to say what a good boy I was.

She emailed back to say what a git I was; there's no need to email copy to the new 'hub' – I simply had to email it to her. I apologised and did so. The really good news was that the new editor emailed to say I'd soon be getting commissions for January and February next year. This was a huge relief, as there's no guarantee that the new regime will have anything to do with the old regime's highly respected contributors (aka drinking/shooting mates).

This did mean, of course, I'd need some test cars, and Boris' Lockdown2 didn't bode well for getting them out here. I emailed Skoda and Mercedes – who were due to send out cars in the next couple of weeks. Mercedes said, "Not sure yet", and Skoda said, "All as normal here." So I've got one sorted, anyway.

Hazel did a big pick-up of stuff from Tesco and set about the Big Shoot Cook (sounds like another idea for Channel 5), so Sasha and I did a yomp round most of the pheasant feeders to check them out. The good news was that most of them were approaching empty, the bad news was finding hare coursing wheel marks all over the Folly. They were fresh, too – I reckon from some time over the weekend, probably when the wind was nice and noisy.

No band rehearsal, so I signed up to something called 'Preparing for zero-carbon farming' – a webinar being organised by the AHDB. Now, the idea of producing carbon-based life forms for a living, and (in the case of my crops) feeding them using carbon-based gases in the atmosphere without using any carbon is a bit of an interesting concept, so I was looking forward to the details. I dug out a proper headset, pressed all the right buttons, and tuned in at seven o'clock.

I was none the wiser a couple of hours later – just a lot more confused. The concept of 'zero carbon' is still bollocks as far as I could tell, and my question – 'can I check that carbon dioxide is still plant food?' – was as welcome as a carbon-based fart in a lift.

November 3rd
Another long and wet day of shoot preparation. On top of all the usual stuff, there was much research into the new virus-based logistics: what we could and couldn't do, what we should and shouldn't do, and all with the grim feeling that this might be the last time we do our little rough shoot for a very long time. Still, Carrie and her XR chums will take that as a job well done.

November 4th
Flipping heck, that was cold last night. I hadn't slept well – still, after all these years, I lie awake fretting about a day's shooting – and realised, as I fitfully snoozed, that I was freezing. Luckily, I needed a pee, and spread my dressing gown over the space-rocket duvet when I returned. Classic FM soothed the rest of the early hours away.

The frost was indeed hard – and Tigger's wipers have given up again. It needed a couple of jugs of warm water to start the de-icing, and then 20 minutes in the low but warm sun. I used that 20 minutes to go onto eBay and finally order a new wiper linkage. Not cheap – but it should work better than silage bag ties.

Then it was time to get our head round the day's shooting. Hazel was warming up soup and sausages, and I did paperwork – COVID briefing forms, a sheet for assorted signatures and so on. I took Tigger (smelling nicely of warm sausages) down to the Drier Yard, got a lift back in the Skoda, and then started the wonderful shoot morning hunt for kit. The paper case cartridges (Purdey, by the way – on special offer from Just Cartridges a couple of years ago), earmuffs, radios, cartridge belt – all the paraphernalia. In my cricketing days, I had a simple 'shoes, socks, trousers, box, shirt, sweater, two pairs of gloves' line to make sure I'd remembered everything. I haven't got a similar thing for shooting yet.

The sunshine was fantastic as we strolled round the farm, although the wind was a bit light. Still, it's better than being drenched. The whole world was out doing hastily organised pre-lockdown shoots, and shots could be heard in the distance all the time we were out. A very curious day.

November 5th

As is traditional, I was knackered after the shoot. And, as is traditional, Hazel was up and raring to go early, and so went off walking with a chum at some unearthly hour. Feeling a bit sorry for myself, I completely failed to write the next *FonF*. I wasn't in the best state of mind to get stuck into another AHDB zoom call either – this time about 'regenerative farming'. I've yet to get my head around this mysterious magic form of farming when my faculties are running ninety-nine to the dozen, so sitting through a screenful of its disciples promising to save the planet using 'quarry farming' (as we old hands call it) was never going to work. I asked my now-traditional question about the wonderful crop-feeding properties of carbon dioxide, and got the traditional sour lemon faces of disapproval. Greta says reasons – and that's all you need to know. God save us.

Enough eco-fascism. I drove the Deere back down to the Drier Yard and hitched it onto the drill, still parked up down there after many weeks of idleness. Sure enough – dare I say 'as is traditional'? – the feed rotor was blocked solid with growing corn. But just as I was about to throw a monster tantrum, the ex-Editor arrived in the yard, looking for a catch-up and a natter. We headed home for tea and cake (unless it was illegal, in which case we didn't) and to make plans to keep the shooting going under the new rules. And that cheered me up no end.

November 6th

The weather finally looked like it was going to be kind for a few days, and that's enough incentive to get on and finish *Flindt on Friday* – already a day late. Luckily, I'd started it last night, and come up with the closing section while in bed. I sent it off nice and early. Still a relief when it does come together – and they accept it.

Then it was off down the Drier Yard (once the hard frost had lifted) to get the blocked rotor freed up on the Horsch. I had a couple of big white buckets and some old feed bags, and decided pretty quickly that the only way to do the job properly would be to empty the hopper. There wasn't a great deal in there, but I'd look daft doing half a job and then sowing all day with bits bunged up, and the seed rate all wrong.

An hour later, I had dismantled the roller and the motor, emptied about 60 kg of Crusoe seed, given the hopper a good clean out, lifted the lumps from the seed, and put it back in a reassembled hopper. Best of all, the frost had lifted, the sun was low but warm, and a really handy drying wind was picking up from the south-east.

I had an early lunch, and then cracked on, and very well it went, too. The packer wheels were still running muddy, but the seedbed looked good, and the ground had dried after I'd been back to the headland and refilled – usually a warm October phenomenon. By the time it got dark – far too early – I'd done all the landwork, and the first turn of headland. But it was only five o'clock. November days are short days.

November 7th

A bit of a shock to have two good drilling days in a row in November. Hazel popped out early to move all the telegraph poles across all the gateways on my route from Drier Field to TBHD, and once I'd finished the Drier Field headland, I folded up and trundled up the Joan's Acre valley.

I started drilling with the contours, which means about forty-five degrees to last year's tramlines, and almost perpendicular to those from the year before – so it wasn't the smoothest of afternoons. It took some time to get out of the short work right next to Brockwood Bottom, and it was pretty tough and soggy in places, but as it got dark, I reached the flat land on the Top of Hurst Down.

Best of all, something happened which I'm sure hasn't happened in any of the thirty or so times I've sown that field. There's a huge dell near the south-west boundary, and no matter which way you sow the field, there's always an annoying bit of 'short' landwork the other side of it. The routine is this: you drill the landwork until you're quite near to the dell. Then you do six turns around it. Then you keep drilling the now-curtailed landwork, ignoring the little bit the other side of the dell, until it's possible to do a long pass to the far hedge again. The last job is to fill in the little bit of landwork on the far side of the dell. And today, for the first time ever, it matched perfectly – in other words, the last strip to sow was a perfect-ish four-metre strip, with the right bout number. Normally, it's out of synch, or at a squiffy angle – but not this time.

As I drove the Massey and the empty seed trailer home in the dark, I couldn't help reflecting that it's these little victories that make farming fun.

November 8th

The weather forecast (and you know what's coming next) said early light showers would give way to a dry day – perfect to keep the drilling momentum going on a Sunday with nothing else to do. Sure enough, the opposite happened. It started dry, and then just as I was setting off in Tigger to refill the Deere, rain started.

It's Sunday, the lanes were heaving with walkers and cyclists, and Tigger had no functioning wipers. I abandoned refuelling, and set about putting the new eBay-sourced wiper linkage on. Either I'm getting better at car DIY, or Hyundai make their cars easy to work on. Either way, by lunchtime I had replaced the rods and ball joints, and the two wiper spindles, which were stiff as old boots. A lifetime of being parked outside is hard on a car.

The new ball joints didn't 'pop' on; they had to be forced with a lever, so they should stay on a bit better than the old ones. The wipers themselves were, upon inspection, utterly knackered, so I'll get a pair of those too.

Eleven o'clock came, so I paused for a couple of minutes, sitting in the back of Tigger, and had a little think about Great Uncle Leighton Flindt, who died of his wounds in October 1916, aged 18. On a murky grey November day, there were people walking, there were cyclists shouting, and even the odd strimmer dementedly working away. The Two Minute Silence isn't what it was, but that's just the way of the world.

The drizzle never came to much in the end, so after an early lunch I hauled the bowser out to Hurst Down and refuelled, and then cracked on with the bag and a bit I had in the drill. Hazel loaded the trailer with half a dozen more bags and arrived perfectly in the field just as I ran out. But by the time another couple of bags had been sown, the rain was back, and getting heavier, and the tractor was beginning to scrabble, even on the lovely soil up on the Top of Hurst Down. I called it a day. And by teatime, the rain was continuous and heavy. Oh well. I'll have a day off tomorrow. The forecast is suddenly fine for Tuesday onwards. How we laughed.

November 9th

What was that old saying? Oh yes: 'Do something once a month to baffle your neighbours.'

My big sister Helen forwarded an email to me from something called 'Itchenlist', another one of these community buy/sell web pages. There was someone there looking for used tractor tyres. Every farm in the country has a stock of old tyres – they were used on livestock farms for holding down the plastic sheeting on silage clamps. We'd tour the local garages taking away used tyres, and when a tractor needed a fresh set, the old ones were wheeled out of sight until the next silage-making season. One of the old boys was occasionally given the job of chainsawing the old tractor tyres in half (yes, really), and fixing the two halves into wooden frames to make round feed troughs for the cattle.

The practice of making an outdoor silage clamp stopped – not least because the Kidd 4' direct cut mower exploded one day (something to do with putting 110 hp from a Ford 7910 through a gearbox designed to be driven by a Super Dexta), and we switch to bagged round bale silage (not a huge success), then wrapped bales (much better). There was also the tiny issue of vast quantities of silage effluent being produced only a few hundred yards up the valley from the source of the Itchen. Maybe it was a good thing the gearbox disintegrated.

In the glory days of the suckler herd, the beautifully stacked heap of shiny round bales was a joy to behold. Of course, it was much more expensive than building the grass wedge out in Springshot, but there was next to no waste, the silage was like tobacco, and we needed no more tyres.

Getting rid of old tyres isn't easy. In more relaxed times, a bonfire or two was all you needed. November 5th was very popular. One of my very first jobs here in 1984 was a bit of fencing in the Hay Field. Some enthusiastic lopping had produced a heap of limbs and branches, and a fire was needed. A tyre was produced and set on fire – some generous helpings of diesel helped – and the freshly cut wood was soon gone.

Of course, back then, the footpath through the Hay Field was like all the footpaths in the countryside in the mid-1980s: unused. It was a genuine surprise to see someone walking it. Dad spent the whole of his farming career here completely unaware of the footpath across Roe Hill. No one ever used it. Now, there are hundreds of people using that Hay Field path every day. It has turned into the Wayfarers' Walk, as well as being part of one of the National Trust's walks around the estate. No chance of setting fire to a couple of tyres 50 yards from that path these days – and a good thing too. Anyway, the next day (in 1984) I went back out to the Hay Field to check the fire, to find huge dopey cattle nosing their way through the ash, and grinding their teeth contentedly on the steel plies that were left behind. I still can't understand how we didn't manage to kill one of them.

Three decades on, and all those old tyres are still here, stacked randomly round the farm. There are even some brand-new car tyres from the days of having an Amazone RPD drill – the 'latest' sowing miracle of the 1990s. It used old car tyres, reinforced with plastic rings, mounted on a beam to form a press just in front of the Suffolk coulters. Bloody brilliant set-up – although when the tyres disintegrated (as they did, being uninflated) it meant a monumental replacement job. You needed a good Stanley knife (to trim the inside off the replacement tyres), a half barrel of hot water kept warm by camping gas stoves (to soften the white plastic rings so that they'd 'fold' into the tyres), huge quantities of Fairy Liquid (to ease things into place), and – most crucially – the shoulder and arm strength of a prop forward. After a couple of days, the drill was reassembled and ready to go.

One year, I was up at Micheldever tyres, collecting another dozen part-used ones, when they suggested that buying 'new' would mean they'd last a lot longer, and I came home with a dozen shiny new and incredibly cheap Chinese tyres. Chinese products were still a novelty back then, kids – and not prone to kill half the world's population. But, for some reason, they never went on the Amazone drill. I think I got fed up with the two-day wrestling match. And my shoulders weren't what they were. The RPD concept fell out of fashion, and the next Amazone pack-top drill had a rather simpler set of hard rubber rings.

Those 'new' tyres have sat among all the old ones ever since. When my niece used the back barn for her wedding, there was a massive clear out of crap all around that yard. And dozens of old tyres resurfaced. The heap is considerable. I've looked once or twice into paying for proper collection and disposal, but procrastination always wins out. Neighbour Ashley took a few recently, to hold the sheets down on his straw stack, but the heap of old rubber didn't get much smaller. It sits, ugly and not unobtrusive, in the corner of the yard.

When word reaches you of someone looking to take a few away – and offering to pay – you jump at the chance. But when I rang the mobile number, he said he'd already had a flood of farmers offering their old tyres. He did ask how much I wanted for them, and I laughed. He could take them away from nothing.

It turned out that I was the only farmer who didn't want money, so an hour later I was lifting three old tractor tyres onto the back of a very smart Ranger double cab, being driven by an even smarter young man from Winchester College, off to their new home being used as fitness aids by fine young gentlemen. The tyres were strapped in safely, and off the Ranger went, passing neighbour John, who looked utterly baffled. Mission accomplished – for this month, anyway.

Meanwhile, the weather forecast changed – overnight – to a wet week, and the afternoon lived up to its promise. Hazel went off to the racing stables to do some accounts, and I did yet more of ours. Again. And sulked.

November 10th

Very wet again. I did more office work until I couldn't focus any more, then drove up to Gaskin's to get two new blades to complete the wiper overhaul on Tigger. It was so wet that I finished the accounts (again?), packed more copies of Book One, and Hazel spent all the money I'd made from selling books in Mole Valley Stores. Even an evening of beer, complete with porky scratchings, did little to lift the mood.

November 11th

Despite a stunning sunrise, it was probably rather optimistic for us to drive Tigger to the top of Dell Close, and then walk thought the trees to check how wet Hurst Down was, because the inevitable answer was 'very'. I drove home in yet another sulk. Hazel unloaded a shedload of dogs from the back and enjoyed a long walk home.

On the way back, I met the National Trust's building manager checking out the forlorn and empty cottages at New Pond. I asked how things were progressing with the promised work on our windows. Many of them are on the verge of falling out after years of less-than-tiptop maintenance. He assured me that they were in hand. I thought it best to keep things good natured and light – the Trust is in complete staff-related chaos at the moment, and every employee you come across has a haunted look. I wished him well and drove on.

I loaded up the Skoda with all the accountancy books, and set off for Havant. Halfway to the West Meon Hut, I felt a bit queasy, and decided I'd do a bit of a swift U-turn and head home – which was lucky: it was a big 'hello again' to last night's strange beer and pork scratchings mix, and an even bigger 'hello' to the sofa and a lit fire.

It isn't often I'm relieved to hear wind and rain sweep in again, but it at least meant I could curl up and enjoy a slightly bleary view of old episodes of *Friends* with a clear conscience. The 10pm squall line, almost a weekly thing at the moment, nearly shook the windows out of their panes; let's hope the Trust really do get on with repairing them. No drilling tomorrow.

November 12th

I haven't had my flu jab this year, and I'm one of the 'vulnerables' who should have one – not just because of the bronchiectasis, but also because I'm now about five-stone overweight. I rang the surgery just after eight, expecting a nightmare of questions and grumpiness, only to get the cheeriest receptionists imaginable. She looked me up, and did a mock, "Ooo, yes, you should have been called in!" I asked what the next step was. "Come in at 4.41pm today," she said. I laughed at the curiously specific time slot. She explained that they're doing 'one minute walk through' appointments. "See you then," I said.

Feeling much better than I did yesterday, I had another go at the drive to the accountant in Havant – this time with success. I did get some funny looks from the receptionists – probably because I wasn't wearing a mask, and you couldn't move for huge signs saying "PLEASE WEAR A MASK!". I dropped the big plastic box containing all the invoice and income files, bank statements, valuations and anything else we could think of on the table – next to another big sign saying 'PLEASE WEAR A MASK', and sped back home.

You wouldn't have any idea that there's another lockdown on from the traffic on the roads. The A3 north to Petersfield was perhaps slightly light, but the A272 was heaving, compete with Plod harvesting speeding fines. As usual, much flashing of headlights gave us lots of warning.

At the surgery, I'd expected a long queue of shuffling oldies, dutifully awaiting their flu jab. But when I got there, the car park was almost empty, and there were people going straight in as soon as they arrived – and popping straight back out. I was ten minutes early, but was ushered straight in for a quick painful stab, and then back out and home again. Have they mixed it with Bill Gates' digital 'inoculation'? If I start spouting inane eco-drivel, you'll know that they have.

November 13th

The gale had dried everything beautifully overnight, and I was raring to go just after breakfast. Luckily, yet another squall line swept through to stop any such daft ideas, so I got writing again. I was a day late with the next *Farmers Weekly* column – again – but managed to finish it while the rain hammered down. Trouble is, how do you write a rant about the utterly useless weather forecasters without repeating yourself? Today was supposed to be dry, after all. I managed to come up with something that wasn't too ranty, attached the screenshot of the lovely Louise Lear pointing at some bales in stubble and saying "this is a ploughed field", and sent it anyway. They seemed to like it.

Next job is to set the mouse traps in the attic – a job that normally starts when the clocks change, so they're late this year. Hazel complained that there was a great deal of mouse-based partying going on above her ceiling, so I clambered up there, cleared the dried-out bodies from the old traps, and reset them. A few years ago, I grew weary of having to use a ladder to access the old hatch over the bathroom loo, and then clamber and crawl round the huge chimney to get to where the action takes place, and called in Woollhead's the builder to put a proper loft hatch in the middle of the bedroom ceiling. It's now just a matter of unlatching the trapdoor with a long lever, unfolding a smart but scarily flimsy ladder, turning on the new light, and then getting to work. Let battle commence.

The forecast for the weekend was shocking, and the sun and wind had dried this morning's rain, so I decided that I had to try some drilling. Things are, once again, getting a bit desperate. The good soil on the Top of Hurst Down paid back my confidence and went surprisingly well. Once I'd done the landwork, I set off on the six turns of headland quite cheerful, but it didn't last. Going uphill on the south-east border was a bit of a mess. When I got to last year's headland tramline – which I'd loosened up by running through it with the seed 'off' – while marking out, I only just got through, and when I started over-sowing the landwork I did last weekend, it got very sticky. At one stage, I thought that I was going to get stuck, for the first time since 1987. And being stuck in the most remote and inaccessible part of the farm, on the inside of a sodden headland just as it was getting dark on a Friday night… I was very relieved to squelch my way out. Drop the revs, engage all the diff locks and 4WD and keep fingers crossed.

The last dregs of seed ran out with about 100 yards to go, which was good news. With the amount of wet weather they're promising over the weekend, the drill would be better left empty. I parked it up under the trees between Dell Close and Joan's Acre, walked back to pick up the Massey and the seed trailer, and called it a night. Progress, I suppose, of a sort.

A good start to the new-fangled Rugby Championship cheered me up enormously.

November 14th

Monumentally wet – buckets of rain for most of the day. Just for a laugh, I dug out the screenshot I'd done of the BBC weather predictions ten days ago. According to their forecast, a lovely dry spell should have been going for six or seven days. Clueless muppets.

Luckily, there was lots to do on a wet Saturday. *Farmers Weekly* had featured Book One in their 'Christmas Gifts Guide' and orders were arriving nice and steadily, so I was packing those.

Then there was the rugby, but only on something called 'Amazon Prime'. This is all a mystery to me, being a bit of an old git, but some Facebooking with assorted children revealed that signing up for the free trial that Amazon are offering, then plugging Hazel's laptop into our big TV would result in an afternoon of wonderful sport. They were right. Italy vs Scotland was a thriller, England vs Georgia somewhat less so.

Astonishingly, Sasha, Evie and I managed the Clump loop in between deluges.

November 15th

No rugby today – someone in either France or Fiji had tested positive – but luckily there was the last day of the British Touring Car Championships to enjoy. Real humans driving real cars round hair-raising tracks, three races in one day – one wet, one dry, one wet again – and each one a 'look away if you dare' race. Fantastic. You know it's good racing when a pile of cars goes round a corner, and the commentator is reduced to gibberish trying to describe the action.

In between races, Mr Amazon kept sending me notifications of copies of Book One being sold. He takes a few quid from each sale, but all I do is print off labels and pack books into envelopes. It's probably very unfashionable to say so, but I think Mr Amazon is doing a great job on my behalf.

It was only when we were locking up shop at the end of another day of hideous rain and squalls that I realised that I hadn't set foot outside all day. Bizarre.

November 16th

We had a bit of a drive round to check for damage after the weekend's wind and rain. No trees down, but evidence of some serious rain. The Joan's Acre road looks as though it had had a flood down it, with leaves, branches and general debris piled up in great heaps wherever the flow slowed briefly. It was a relief to see the Bottom of Hurst Down relatively unscathed. I didn't dare venture up to the top, which can pan after heavy rain.

Tod came round for an update – in other words, to compare notes of our (and everyone's) dismal progress. We agreed that we're still ahead of last year; in November 2019, I'd sown Chalks, BML's and half of Rick and Clump. And that was it. What made it worse was that only a couple of months before that, we'd driven up to Newcastle to drop a last child off at university, and driven back with a very odd feeling of satisfaction. Not just from a perspective of having got three children into three good courses at proper universities, but that we'd just finished the most bounteous and fall-over easy year of farming. Autumn 2018 had been the kindest ever, and the rest of the farming year followed suit. I particularly remember steering the Audi we were testing that week off the M40 onto the busy roundabout where you join the A34 north of Oxford, and thinking that life is good.

Life is still 'good' of course – it has just been a challenging year-and-a-bit. Give us a couple of dry weeks, and life would be even better, though.

November 17th

All a bit Groundhog Day at the moment. The sun hardly rose, everything was wet, Hazel did some shopping in Mole Valley Stores and Tesco, I packed books and caught mice. We had a distanced visit from a tractor salesman, seemingly unaware that I'm unlikely to buy anything from his company ever again, after having to send back a tractor he supplied us a few years ago. And we hadn't had to formally reject a machine on this farm since the SWB Land Rover that Dad sent back in the late 1970s.

November 18th

A fabulous start, nice and dry, and then rain swept in again. It was another day of packing books, resetting mousetraps, fighting off bored flatcoats who are convinced we should be out shooting, and then, before you knew it, it was dark again. The forecast, however, was more cheerful. Not that we believe them anymore.

November 19th

The forecasters are sticking to their guns: after an iffy day tomorrow, we are due a dry spell. After writing the next *Flindt on Friday*, I then decided to take them at their word and do some seed preparation. I took the Massey down to the Drier Yard and brought back the seed trailer, still with its single bag on it, and loaded all the remaining Crusoe. We've got five tonnes left for about 21 hectares, which makes for a nice heavy late-November seed-rate. Assuming that we do get it in in November, of course.

On the way to the Drier, I had a call from a mobile number, and pulled over to answer it – warily. My mobile number has somehow made its way out to the junk call fraternity, and I'm beginning to get calls about 'investment opportunities' and 'accidents that weren't your fault'. The buggers are now using landline and mobile numbers to fool you into answering, too. These days I approach an unknown number with caution.

It was as far from a dodgy call as you could get. It was the organiser of a farmers' club in Lincolnshire, and he was asking if I'd help out with the modern equivalent of an after-dinner speech – a Zoom conference. I thanked him for the invite, but said I didn't think it would work at all. I've only got one joke, and it would be a shame if our piss-poor internet connection meant the punchline got missed. I promised to be first on his list of guest speakers when common sense returns, and I can drive up to Lincolnshire, have a few beers, have a good meal, tell my joke, sell a few books, get roundly insulted for an hour or two, grab a bed in a new best friend's house, and drive back the next day.

The next test car arrived – a Skoda Octavia. And on the day that Mad Boris, prodded by Princess Nut Nuts, has announced the end of petrol and diesel cars by 2030. Heartbreaking.

November 20th

A stunning frosty start, and it all went downhill from there. Big sister Helen arrived with a friend and set off for a long yomp around the farm. Unfortunately, she set off using routes that would have been accessible living here in her youth, and spent a lot of the walk wandering round fields in circles, trying to find a way out. They arrived back at home safely after several hours, looking well exercised – and slightly soggy, thanks to yet another band of rain that had moved in during the morning. Not quite the 'drizzle followed by sunshine' that the weather forecasters had promised.

The next *Flindt on Friday* was sent and approved, and I'm using my one 'unpaid' column of the year (it's complicated) to give Book One yet another free plug, while giving the flood of 'green' farming books a bit of a kicking. I was feeling quite cheerful when *Farmers Weekly* said they were happy with it.

And then the accountant emailed details of our next tax bill. We've had a couple of good years on the farm, and for some reason paid little or no tax last January and December, but even so, I was genuinely shocked to see that we're going to have to find £33,000 in January 2021. That'll round off a monumentally shitty year in the most spectacularly shitty fashion. It's my fault, of course; I should be doing more buying and selling to maximise tax efficiency, I should have volunteered to pay more tax last year instead of deferring (which, if truth be told, I can't actually remember volunteering to do), I woulda coulda shoulda, etc.

And to think we only recently discussed a proper holiday in the spring – the first since 2011. No chance of that – unless Book One continues to fly off the shelves. Another 20 sold today, and I ordered another 500 from Dan at the publishers. A long way to go to pay that tax bill, but, as they say, every little helps.

Cain the cat threw up all over my bed, too, and that didn't help at all.

November 21st

Hazel was out early loading bales of straw for another very happy customer. Straw sales have been fantastic this year, helped by the poor harvest, and our worries a couple of years ago about having too many bales stacked in every corner of every barn have proved unfounded. We do wonder if we should be more ruthless and jack the price up to cash in on the situation – but we haven't.

I took Sasha out on a slug check, and found a few in Drier Field and Bottom of Hurst Down, but I'm hopeful that the wheat will get away from them. The ex-Editor's blue Jimny – fresh from an astonishing MOT pass – came skipping across Dell Close as Sasha and I returned to Tigger. He and his boy were headed for the Hurst Down dell for some pigeon shooting. I let them get on with it, drove home, lit an unnecessary fire and enjoyed some Saturday rugby.

And it didn't rain.

November 22nd

November gloom is really starting to kick in. The news is full of what Carrie might or might not let us do for Christmas, and – increasingly – voices saying the whole thing is a shambolic cock-up. The *Mail* and *The Sun* have broken conformist ranks over the weekend, both of them saying 'hold on a minute – this isn't making sense anymore!'. Welcome along, boys. I stood in Bungalow Field way back in March, chatting to the Eminent Surgeon who lives on its boundary, and said, "This is all a bit odd, isn't it?"

And then there's Brexit – remember that? If I were an old cynic, I'd say that everything is being carefully orchestrated to ensure yet more delays, or a monumental fudge, and a BRINO. The papers are full of Boris handing over massive sums of cash, and agreeing to let the French use British waters for fishing – but I suppose we must wait and see what the final details are. I rather miss the days when I didn't wake up angry.

The next lockdown details – or rather, the new 'tier' system which will kick in on December 2nd – will probably keep on affecting our little shoot, which is pissing us both off mightily. We're not party animals, we don't host grand dinners for 30 of our closest friends – but we do love having about a dozen chums round for an armed walkabout every fortnight or so over the dark and depressing winter months. It looks very much like that will be a non-starter for the rest of the season.

I'm pissed off about it, Hazel's pissed off about it, and there are huge heaps of flatcoats who can't understand why these short, short days aren't being regularly punctuated with rampaging around the farm picking up pheasants. Still (I thought to myself as I finally gave Tigger its first wash since before harvest), we're lucky. Children doing well in jobs and uni, and our lives pretty well untouched by it all. And lots of copies of Book One are selling, and the rugby (on the office computer via Amazon Prime) was fun to watch while I packed them.

And the days get longer in a month's time.

November 23rd

It was a nice dry Monday morning – perfect to finally get some farming done. I texted Tosdevine to see if he was available for some slug pelleting on Drier Field, and a whole bunch of stubble Roundup-ing. He was on the phone at once – and it was still dark. He could come in and do both today, if that suited. I said I'd double check on things like water supply, and ring him back.

Good thing I did check: the water tank in the yard was almost empty. One day I'll plumb in a proper ballcock to make sure it's always full. Until then I'll go on finding random degrees of tank fullness. Great band name. I rang him slightly sheepishly to point out the slight logistical issue. He asked if he could come in later, when the tank had filled. I pointed out that the pressure up here is so dismal it'll take the whole day to fill. We agreed he should come in tomorrow. I left the hose pipe trickling all day.

His slug pellet man arrived, having ATV-ed it across from East Meon. He looked a bit cold and frazzled as a result. I sent him off to Drier Field with a map and lots of bags of metaldehyde.

I had a long afternoon in JA/DC, drilling ground that was just about travelable. I did the landwork of Dell Close (not a lot), and the long work of Joan's Acre, before realising that I was dangerously low on fuel, which seemed to go well with the smell of diesel that had been wafting into the cab. Then an unforecast shower tipped things over the sticky edge. A quick engine bay check revealed a nasty leak from the braided hose that goes from the top of the diesel filter back to the tank. I'll check that tomorrow when I refuel.

Much of the late afternoon was taken up with a very happy panic about Book One. Sales after the 'Christmas Gift Guide' in *FW* have been so good that there's a real chance I'm going to run out just as the next huge plug appears in my column. Dan from Tricorn Books said that the reprint wouldn't get here for ages, and so I managed to persuade the *FW* team to push my column back a week – they agreed on the condition that I come up with something else suitable in the next 12 hours.

I went to bed humming with a dozen ideas, but none of them ready to be finished within that timescale. Mind you, a Book One buyer sent a message that her copy hadn't arrived. Odd – and a bit distracting.

November 24th

Mysteriously wet again, so I got up stupidly early (for me), had a go at about five different short-notice columns, and then admitted defeat. We've got several hundred copies of Book One still in the old playroom, and most of them will still be here on Friday, when the next book plug comes out. If they all sell in a few days, so be it. It'll be a fantastic problem to have. I emailed *FW* and told them to press on as originally planned.

Tosdevine's sprayerman arrived late morning, and set off to do most of Godwin's – where the winter beans will be going – and Blackhouse Road, where all the blackgrass is growing majestically.

After filling up the bowser – draining the main tank ready for a cheap-ish refill – I drove out to Dell Close and refuelled the Deere. Or rather, I did once I'd cleared an air lock from the pump. Last time I used it, I drained it a bit too thoroughly, and air got through the whole system. I stood there getting crosser and crosser, as the pump whined emptily, and all the tools to do some bleeding were locked in the tractor and the keys were still at home. I was just about to head all the way home in a monster sulk when I thought I'd try back-tipping the little bit of diesel that was in the delivery hose into the pulp, by lifting the nozzle and then the rest of the hose, up into the air. It worked – it was just enough to get the flow going. That saved a lot of tantrums. I played around with the leaking diesel pipe on the tractor for a bit, and thought 'sod it, it'll just have to drip for a bit'.

And the day didn't get any better. Part of a tooth disintegrated as I tucked into my post-salad chocolate bar. At that very moment, of course, I was unaware that a tooth had disintegrated; I just thought it odd that what I thought was a plain dark chocolate bar appeared to have large crunchy bits in it. It's only when the tip of the tongue finds a missing section of tooth that a slight panic sets in. Does it hurt? Luckily, no. Should I leave it – there's a lot of drilling to do, and the sun is actually shining? No – it could well get worse if ignored. Is there a dentist available under these lockdown circumstances? Amazingly, yes. I rang my new one, the one I'd only visited a few weeks ago, and explained my predicament.

"Two-forty-five this afternoon OK for you?" asked the receptionist. I grabbed it at once. Drilling can wait, although it seemed only fair to have a decent shower to try and get rid of some of the *Eau de Diesel* resulting from the morning's excitement.

By three o'clock, the hole in the tooth was patched up, and I was walking back to my test Skoda, feeling very relieved. Alresford was remarkably empty, and those who were out on the streets weren't bothering with masks. It was all rather pleasant.

Hazel was just setting off for some dog work when I got home, but I managed to persuade her to help out with getting a couple of hours of late drilling in. I headed down to Dell Close in the truck and got going. She brought the seed trailer out half an hour later, and took Tigger home. I plodded on through some fairly stickly headlands – and one or two bung-ups, but got them both finished shortly after dark. They won't win any seedbed prizes, but it's wheat in the ground in November.

Any evening cheerfulness was soon dispelled by another Amazon message saying their copy of Book One 'hadn't arrived', and I needed to send another. Bother.

November 25th

It was nice and dry for a bit, then a couple of bands of heavy showers came through. But it was an indication of the state of rural crime these days that we decided to bring the Deere and the drill back from Joan's Acre to the corner of the Folly. It made a bit of a mess of Drier Field's southern headland – which is just beginning to green up a bit – but it cleared the way for Hazel to pop out with the loader and put all the telegraph poles back across the gateways.

I needed some more AdBlue, and I thought a new diesel pipe might be needed for the Deere, and – most importantly – I needed to put some miles on the Octavia test car, so I drove to Hunt's at Chilbolton. They're still not 'open', and what I needed had to be told to a member of staff who, luckily, emerged with everything. He suggested a trim and a re-fit of the old pipe first, as they get porous near where they've been enlarged to go over the fitting on the diesel filter.

From Chilbolton I did a fantastic Three Maids' Hill–Winchester–Alresford bypass–Chawton–Froxfield–Petersfield and then home run. Very nice it was, too, although the fuel gauge failed to move even after all those miles.

There was a small crisis when I got home; neighbour John has been using Godwin's barn to store and sell his fine selection of Christmas trees, and they've been stacked around the two grain trailers which are full to the brim with spring beans, ready – eventually – for cleaning and bagging up. The rats have been delighted to find warm cosy trees that they can live in AND use as a way to get into the trailers and gorge on the beans. John had had a right panic when a tree destined for a primary school turned out to be full of rat droppings and bean husks. Never mind the virus – that's what you call a real health hazard.

Luckily, after some fairly nimble tractor work, we got both trailers out of that barn, and parked up in the main tractor barn. I left John opening up and re-netting some of his valuable trees. The forecast – dare I say it? – is so good, I could actually have left the trailers outside. Or maybe not.

November 26th

Once I'd got the next *FonF* column done, I did another run out in the Octavia, and then sat in it and made lots of notes. Hazel spent the afternoon up at the stables doing accounts, and I pretended to write up the Octavia while waiting for the pick-up team to arrive. I seem to remember going down a Google rabbit hole on the technicalities of naval gunnery. So not a totally wasted day.

November 27th

Time to get some more seed in the ground. After checking that Drier Field was moving on quite nicely after its slug pellets, I called into the Folly armed with all the kit to mend the diesel leak on the Deere: knife, new hose, hot water in a Thermos, some cleaned glasses and some long-nosed pliers to get to the spring clip. In the end, it was simple job; I cut an inch off the hose and refitted it. Sorted. A huge relief, especially as it was bloody cold out there, and my hands went numb in no time. Not really the conditions for some intricate pipe surgery.

Hazel brough the seed trailer up from the Drier Yard and popped one bag of Zulu on it – just in case my sums go wrong out in the Hangar, and I need to top up with something – anything. I took the drill across Springshot – having done the little zigzag needed to get across the raised road without grounding the tines, as I did last year in front of a small crowd – and marked out a headland. I then drilled what was left in the tank, just in time for Hazel to appear in Tigger and give me a lift home for lunch.

The Hangar drilled very nicely. I often swear about it for its remoteness and its popularity with the lost public, but to have a field that went in so well in these conditions at the tail end of November is very handy. I would have finished it much earlier, had it not been for assorted calls and visits from ex-editors looking for some shooting. Hazel sent him over to the L-plantation to get some rooks, which always

242

seem very keen on our sowings over at that end of the farm. I did wonder why there were so few volunteer beans in the Hangar. Was it that the combine driver (me) had done such a fine job in September, or that the rooks had hoovered them up in the months since then? The latter was far more likely. He shot one, anyway.

The *Flindt on Friday* piece pushing Book One had done its job. By bedtime, 50 orders had come in, and I was panicking about envelopes and labels, and, of course, stocks of the book itself. Great problem to have. Trouble is, the forecast is still fine, and I should be out in the tractor, not stuffing books into envelopes.

November 28th

Blimey – what a lot of books people are buying. A huge compliment. Most of the day was spent printing off labels, writing individual 'thank you' notes, and stuffing copies of Book One into a rapidly dwindling supply of envelopes.

We took a break at one stage to bring the tractor and drill back from the Hangar, and for Hazel to hang the ex-Editor's rook out in the middle of the field. I even put one bag of Zulu in the drill when I got home, ready for a mad rush tomorrow. And then went back to packing books.

November 29th

A most unusually early start for me, writing up the Skoda for the February issue of *The Field*. They like copy in nice and early this time of year, what with Christmas chaos coming up. Then it was books, books, and more books for an hour, and the orders poured in. I was rapidly running out of envelopes, ink for the printer – and books. If this goes on, some judicious rationing of the online inventories will be in order.

Luckily, farming called, and I thought I'd better make the most of this run of dry weather and crack on with the Zulu in Cheyney. I did a calibration in the yard (7,500 kg of seed for something like 33.5 hectares, and a thousand grain weight of 47 gives... er... I give up) and set off cheerfully.

I should have guessed it wasn't going to go well when I nearly got stuck marking out the southern headland, and after a turn and a half, I had to abandon. The heavy land was still a quagmire. I hitched the drill off up at the north end and came home in a huff.

With the tractor now free, I emailed the seed cleaning company to see if they fancied doing all the trailers of beans. "Tomorrow?" was the reply. Excellent. And a surly Amazon driver arrived late in the evening with 200 more envelopes.

November 30th

Thank God for the pick-up hitch. With the seed cleaning gang on the way, I had a heck of a lot of trailer shifting to do. First up, the huge bale trailer (still on loan from Mac via John, who is using our handy smaller one for his Christmas tree trade) which was loaded with seed from yesterday's aborted drilling. I took that down the Drier Yard and put the Zulu in the right-hand lean-to – where it will probably stay till next September – and then brought it back empty. It had a puncture. Bother. Convention states that something that happens while you're borrowing a bit of kit is your responsibility, so I rang Micheldever Tyres and invited them out when they had a moment.

With much huffing and puffing and leaning out of the back of the tractor, I picked up and moved all three grain trailers (two big green ones, and the small blue one) and got them all parked up and ready. As soon as I'd done that, the seed cleaning gang rang and said they weren't going to make it today after all. I probably sounded a bit grumpier than I should have done in replying – these things happen.

Such as the book which appears to have fallen out of its delivery envelope on its way up to Lincolnshire. I had a very apologetic phone call from a fellow farmer, saying I'd sent him an empty envelope. He said it looked as though the sticky flap had just come unstuck. I promised him another one. I know you're supposed to expect certain losses in this 'selling to the public' lark, but I wouldn't mind the envelopes keeping whatever you've stuffed into them in.

News that almost the complete stock of 250 books had gone within 72 hours cheered me up a bit, although I then got grumpy about not having got things organised better. Hazel spotted the mood I was in and volunteered to go and put all the trailers back in the barn for me. Bless her.

December 1st

Hurrah for online banking. We knew very early in the day that our vital Single Farm Payment had safely arrived, clearing the overdraft and giving us a precious few days of being in credit. And the sun shone beautifully on a reasonably sharp frost. Good start to the new month.

It's probably no coincidence that the money has arrived just when the last announcements are being made of the post-Brexit agricultural policy. Everything seems to be as we expected: direct payments phased out over seven years, some curiously undefined environmental schemes being phased in, and a single lump 'retirement' payment being more than just a possibility.

All the usual suspects were cluttering up the letters page of *The Times* with their eco-nonsense, and how this was the chance to effectively stop large areas of the UK from growing food. I dashed off a letter in reply, saying how much I was looking forward to it as it would make those of us still farming much more profitable, and pressed 'send'.

Then it was back to the bean cleaning – or would have been if they'd turned up at their allotted 11 o'clock slot. By midday, I was ringing to see where they were, and it was almost getting dark when they finally arrived in the yard. And it was nearly eight o'clock, with a stunning moon rising, when they left. True, we'd done 13 tons of spring beans and eight tons of winter beans, but I was cold, hungry and grumpy. We'd had troubles with augers not working, spare ones burning belts and having to operate at quarter speed, and fuel running short on the generator, so it was past my home time when the noise finally died down.

I think we're supposed to check the beans for this and that, and do a thousand grain weight test, and a germination test, but this year, there's no commercial seed available. You sow what you saved, and that's that. I've seen enough seed growing out in the fields to guess that the germination is fine.

December 2nd

Bella the flatcoat has a little problem, which started not long after she had the lovely litter of puppies. As soon as she gets the slightest idea that Hazel is on the move, she starts to bark. If she sees the top of the laptop being folded down, or even Hazel moving from a kitchen chair, she'll start an annoying wuffing.

It's a thousand times more annoying when it's at 3am. We cannot work out what's making her bark at that time. True, there's a lot of fox activity on at the moment, and the moon was incredibly bright last night, so the owls were really giving it some, and the mice above the kitchen ceiling are getting pretty noisy too – it could be any of those I suppose.

But when it kept going until six, I'd had enough. I got up and got dressed, went downstairs and suggested they shup up. Which they did for a bit, until there was another wuff. At which point I went a bit mental. By the time I'd finished, there were four dogs, not entirely sure what they'd done wrong, but knowing it was something, cowering in the hall. But at least they stopped wuffing, and Hazel could get some sleep.

When she got up, I sneaked back to bed for a couple of hours, and generally felt terrible for the whole day, as we did shoot preparations for tomorrow.

The Times printed my pro-chemical farming letter, just below Dyson's similar one.

December 3rd

'Rain before seven, dry by eleven' didn't really apply today. It was wet when we got up, wet while we finished getting the last details in place for the shoot, and wet for the rest of the day. I think there was a dry bit around eleven o'clock, but it didn't last.

We did the home 'S' (four drives in Chalks and Roe Hill) for a bag of 14, and most of them being surprisingly challenging. Our guests were pleasantly surprised. We rehashed the day's plans to a much-welcome cup of tomato soup in the Drier barn, abandoning the idea of yomping all the way to Pipeline and Long Field, deciding instead to take a short cut through the woods to Barracuda, and then Folly and Bob's Wood.

Barracuda turned out to be a stunning success. After the two long thick lines of cover and hedgerow were beaten towards the dell, we four guns took up the points of the compass around it, and the beating team went in. The result was one of the most enjoyable half hours we've had on our little rough shoot. A couple of dozen birds came out unpredictably, and about half a dozen came down. And the Folly proved to be more of the same, and when that drive had finished, I suggested to the assembled team that we call it a day. We were like nine drowned rats, all of us getting a bit cold, and the bag was good enough. Not surprisingly, everyone agreed that a hot meal was called for, and we all headed home.

It's a damn shame that a hot meal (where we all ate too much, drank plenty and generally reflected on a wet but thoroughly enjoyable day) would probably have been illegal, and therefore couldn't possibly have taken place.

December 4th

No one woke up with a streaming cold or pneumonia, which was a bit of a surprise after yesterday. Bella was worn out, Evie had a funny 'limber tail', hanging down uselessly. Not funny for her of course, as a flatcoat's *raison d'etre* is to wag its tail furiously. Sasha was limping, so only Tim felt 100% on the canine front. Luckily, today was a non-shooting day for them all.

For me, it was time for a rare awayday. The printers had done a high-speed job of knocking up another 500 copies of Book One, and I had agreed to drive up to their warehouse in Chippenham and get them. I could have waited for them to be delivered on Monday, but it seems wrong to have Amazon and eBay 'out of stock' for too long.

The first job was to get Tigger converted from 'shoot bus' to 'motorway haulage machine'. Out came all the sticks, feathers and empty cartridges. Tools got moved to the front seat, and the back seats were folded down, revealing a splendid cavern for 500 books. I checked over the engine bay, and Hazel, being the one less likely to put her back out, got all the tyres pumped up. It's amazing how squishy they go after six months of neglect.

I was on the cusp of setting off when the ex-Editor rang with a request to sit up in the Blackhouse woods and do some roost shooting. By the time we'd discussed that idea (of course he could) and done a brief debrief of yesterday's shoot, it was time for an early lunch.

Finally, just before midday, I was on the A34, hurtling north toward the M4 at Newbury, listening carefully for noises that suggested Tigger was about to blow up. I've no idea why I was so pessimistic; I suppose it was because all it had done for months is potter round the farm, a couple of miles at a time. But no; four freshly pumped and recently balanced tyres were as smooth as anything, the temperature gauge stayed steady, and we sat at a civilised 70 mph (ahem) all the way up to Chieveley, then east down the M4, coming off at junction 17 and heading south into Chippenham.

There's no satnav in Tigger, of course, but luckily I can memorise maps (sad git) so found the depot easily. The address 'Bumper's Farm' suggested a discreet barn conversion in the corner of a farmyard, but a bit of Googling revealed a massive industrial estate next to a massive housing development on what was, of course, once a farm. Trouble is, you then get stuck into 'old map dot com' or the excellent side-by-side (one old, one new) maps organised by the National Library of Scotland (nope, me neither), and get sucked into a melancholy rabbit hole of demolished farms, flattened country houses, and vanished historic features. All gone. Forever.

After 80 high-speed miles, Tigger and I were threading our way through Bumper's Farm industrial estate, past well-known names and some obscure ones, turning right just after the big Post Office depot and right again into the printers. There was no one about, so I pressed a couple of 'ring for attention' bells, but got none. I wandered round for a bit, found all my books ready to go, so it was tempting to just load up and be gone, but thought that would never do. More exploring found something that looked like reception, and more button pressing managed to reveal the inevitable charming Eastern European receptionist. She looked rather shocked at a farmer in full farming kit (even wellies) but promised to find someone to help load.

A couple of minutes later, and local lad with a local accent was firing up the gas-powered forklift and trying to squeeze the books, still on their little pallet, into the back of Tigger. He went back, forth, up, down and sideways until we decided it would be far simpler to fling them off by hand. So we did, all 32 boxes, in about a minute. I thanked him for his efforts, and set off for the motorway. Just before three, I was back home, and filling the old playroom with a lovely-smelling pile of books.

Luckily, I had no time to start clearing the backlog of orders, because the ex-Editor arrived for a cuppa with the wild look in his eyes that suggested he had had a good time up in the woods. He'd shot ten as they raced over the treetops, and was thrilled to bits. A good couple of days with the gun for him, then.

There was a late evening run of cars coming up the hill from Kilmeston, which suggested either a rally or hare coursers. A quick trip out in Tigger, now back doing farm pootling jobs, revealed a code on a small sign down at the Springshot gateway. It was definitely a rally, although, in the end, not more than a dozen cars went noisily past. Another hobby nobbled by Carrie.

The farming papers were full of the details of the farming subsidy changes that have now been finalised. Big cuts over the next seven years, and being replaced with something that no one seems to know about. We all knew that it was coming, of course, and some of us voted for Brexit in the full expectation that it would happen, in the full expectation of having to adapt or die.

Meanwhile, in the Brexit negotiations themselves, the word is that everything has ground to an acrimonious halt after the French threw some new demands on the table. I doubt anything we hear is actually true, and the whole thing is pure theatre, but it all adds to the melodramatic feel of late-night pizza-fuelled final negotiations. I suspect a massive sell-out is on the cards.

December 5th

The early morning radar showed a thick bar of heavy rain rotating anticlockwise, with Stockbridge at its centre. I had a long and arduous day indoors beckoning, but Hazel was off to Murph's for a day picking-up with Bella. I suggested she took plenty of coats, even if the forecast suggested that the rain was fragmenting somewhat.

She did, and it did, but the storms that replaced the continuous rain were pretty spectacular – with hail and a constant feeling of imminent thunder. A very good day to be indoors, drinking tea, eating leftover shoot cake, and packing dozens of books into envelopes while watching rugby on the surprisingly good Amazon Prime.

When Hazel and Nessa got back, they looked slightly washed away and rosy in the cheeks, but they too had spent the day doing what they really like, so everyone was happy.

December 6th

More of the same. Hazel set off with a flatcoat, this time with Tim, for a long training day up at Mullenscote, and I watched rugby, ate cake and packed books. It was dry, but very cold and grey, and I even had a short session chopping some firewood for the sleepy shoot team when they got back. All very dull, all very December.

December 7th

Grey, cold and damp. I walked Drier Field and Hurst Down, and was quite pleased with the wheat, slowly making its way up. The top of Hurst Down looks quite respectable, through the thick mat of beans.

Hazel dropped off a massive heap of books at the Alresford Post Office, and I continued to pack more of the weekend's sales. But then there was a very odd thing: messages started coming through about missing books. They were all part of the huge sales a week ago, and were all posted on the Monday and Tuesday. There were some very lively messages, and I can't blame them. The 'projected delivery date' was last Friday – and nothing had arrived.

Each one got a polite reply from me, and a request that they wait just a few more days; if nothing arrived by then, I'd happily post a replacement. One or two were so cross I packed up a replacement on the spot – with a note asking for the first one to be sent back if and when it arrived. Funny old game, this selling to the public. It was quite comforting when Neighbour Robert Jnr called in for a cuppa and told some tales of selling his legendary sparkling wine direct to the public. I ended up counting my blessings.

December 8th

The morning brought more grumpy messages and a hard frost – almost hard enough to pop out and try a bit of drilling. But not quite. In fact, I decided that today was the Pig day (as in the movie, not the Kubota – i.e. "that'll do!"), and it was time to go and bring the drill home from its forlorn station at the south end of Cheyney. Funnily enough, after last winter's late drilling successes, I'm quite relaxed about it. I reckon we've got another two months to get it in.

After another flurry of messages and replies, some truth began to emerge about the Book One problem. Someone very unkindly put a one-star review on my Amazon selling page, furiously pointing out that her book hadn't arrived. Mr Amazon was having none of that, and put a thick black line through the snide comment, and wrote underneath "the situation is beyond the seller's control". Intriguing. Was it a human hand that did it? Or an algorithm, or a bot?

I set off to the dentist to have a filling re-done in a state of slight puzzlement. Mind you, it gave me something to concentrate on while she numbed me up (successfully – which is unusual for a redhead), removed the old filling and refilled the tooth. The secret of that sort of job is to drift off a million mental miles away, and let them get on with it. I was very impressed with their handiwork. And so I should be for £260.

Back home, more of the 'missing book' mystery was falling into place. One buyer sent a message saying she appreciated that there was a postage delay, but did we know how long. I messaged her back, and asked how she knew there was a delay. She at once sent me a screenshot of a message she'd got from Royal Mail, saying her parcel was running late, and apologising. A huge relief; if everyone in that huge batch of books had got that message, then there should be a few less angry messages.

The trouble with Amazon is that it doesn't automatically give a tracking number when you buy postage through them. eBay however, does, and may explain why not a single eBay buyer was asking where their parcel was. I reduced the Amazon inventory to zero, and stocked up over on eBay. The rest of the afternoon and evening were free of rude messages, thank God. And no toothache.

December 9th

Another frantic day at the keyboard – good thing there's no farming to be done. Lots more orders for Book One were coming in, and almost as many angry messages from buyers whose copies had not arrived. Maybe not 'almost as many', but their grumpiness was quite startling. I replied to each as gracefully and as apologetically as I could – and most buyers (once they realised it was me selling from the kitchen table, not Mr Boo Hiss Megacorp Amazon) were understanding. One or two wanted replacement booms NOW, so I printed more labels and sent off freebies.

Then *Farmers Weekly* were on the line asking where the early Christmas articles were – I'd promised that I'd get them in ages ago, so they can get the magazines set up for the long Christmas break. Luckily, I had one nearly done in my head, so I bashed that off and sent it in.

Hazel, who obviously hasn't done enough standing round in the freezing open air, set off to Barrow Hill again with Bella, and came back thrilled with her picking-up. Barrow Hill is a good challenge for any dog, and Bella had done really well. And they'd stayed dry, which made a change.

It was fortunate for a neighbour that it was dry. He'd taken his beloved dogs for a yomp around Bramdean Common, and they'd vanished. He and his wife spent the whole day calling and whistling, but, as ever in those horrible circumstances, not knowing really where to start. Friends and neighbours plastered alerts all over social media, with picture of two angelic little buggers.

It was nine-thirty in the evening when they just happened to be calling and whistling up in the depths of Cheriton Wood – and one dog appeared out of the darkness. Some faint barking led them to the other, somehow stuck in a bit of garden behind a deserted house. Another one of those 'how lucky is that?' moments – like Hazel just catching sight of the 'found – one cat' sign in the local shop window that led her to a bruised and battered Cain five years ago.

Some late-night calls to him and her were in order to share the elation of finding much-loved pets. Everyone sounded shattered, and he's got a long day shooting tomorrow.

December 10th

Hazel was up absurdly early for a dog walk with a friend – in almost total darkness –but that's mid-December for you. Once it was light, she kindly delivered another couple of bags of sold books to the Alresford sorting office, and then headed off to the stables for an afternoon with the accountant. Anyone would think I'm not very good company at the moment.

Meanwhile, I packed more books, replied to angry emails, and went and chopped some wood to let off steam. Maybe Hazel's right.

December 11th

It was a relief to see Royal Mail's issues all over the papers and radio this morning, confirming what the posties have been saying. They have been taken totally by surprise by Christmas, home shopping and the virus. Can't blame them – it's not as if they had any warning, is it? I hope that everyone who ordered a copy of Book One and is on the edge of sending me another furious message, reads the newspapers.

In between dealing with a few more WISMOs ('Where is my order?'), sending out a few more sales (despite me covering the eBay page with 'UNLIKELY TO ARRIVE IN TIME FOR CHRISTMAS!!!'), and getting the New Year's Day *Farmers Weekly* column sorted, I managed to get a nice Drier loop walk in with Sasha.

She is daft, that dog. For some reason, she won't walk unless she can carry the mankiest of old tennis balls in her mouth. She carefully puts it down every so often to check for new smells and then has to go back and find it. Occasionally she'll drop it ahead of me, retreat a few yards and stare at it, daring me to kick it or pick it up and fling it, but then dives on it just before I can reach it.

This routine is all very well, until she comes across one of the badger holes in the Folly. She tiptoes a few feet down the huge entrance, and then carefully pokes her nose into the hole. Before you know it, she's let go of the precious tennis ball, which vanishes into the deep chalky depths. She then stands and looks at me as if I'm going to lie down and put my arm full length into a badger sett. I think not. She has to make do with no ball for the rest of the walk. I wonder if that counts as illegal disturbance of a sett?

December 12th

I thought a stomp across Hurst Down would cheer me up, and it did – in places. Some of the horrible heavy sideland ground has had a nasty outbreak of slugs, but I could hardly stand up on it, so I doubt an ATV would get anywhere. Then there were more books to send, more angry WISMOs; it's all getting repetitive.

We're approaching the deadline for getting all poultry indoors. There's another outbreak of Avian flu, totally eclipsed by the coronavirus, of course, but all our chickens have got to be kept in from Monday. Poor old Hazel had to set about the chicken shed, getting it tidied up and cleaned up for next week. Good old 2020; it never stops giving.

December 13th

Not a great day. Grey. Cold. Clammy. Wet. I had a long night of bad dreams – all the classic ones in sequence. The Am Dram one, from my days with the Cheriton Players. I know the script perfectly all the time I've got it in my hand. As soon as I put it down, the words vanish from my head. And it's a huge show. And it's tonight.

I'm on a skiing holiday, and all the snow is melting, and suddenly we're in Venice, clinging to the side of a building as waters rise. Our guide is telling us it's perfectly normal. Through a window of the building, we can see museum pieces, and there's an ancient chair that one sat in to get mystical predictions of tide times. It looks suspiciously like a golden loo, but there we go.

Finally, I'm in the Conder bins – the 500-ton storage/cleaning system put up by Dad in the 1970s. The rats have got in; there's shit everywhere, and I'm trying to clean up the crop before the lorries turn up. Corn is getting mixed up – there's wheat on barley, barley on wheat. Elevators are conking out, and huge heaps of corn are piling up… it was nice to wake up. I think it's safe to say that there's a bit of stress building – and I'm never one to admit to it. Brexit, virus, missing books, rain…

Hazel went off in the rain for another long day's gundog training at Mullenscote, and I packed books that were still selling on eBay. It's easier on eBay to track them, and send more personal messages that huge delays are ongoing, so I'm only selling there now.

Neighbour Robert chugged into the yard in his Land Rover, and we had a sombre cuppa in the kitchen. The Editor happened to be up in the orchard doing some late season scrumping, so he joined us. A fun-filled riot it wasn't. It's all very downbeat.

Mr and Mrs Editor turned up again at dusk for more tea, just after Hazel got back from dog training, and even that was a bit of a downer. Everyone's getting a bit fed up. Good news is in short supply – even if I had a day free of angry Amazon customers.

December 14th

At last, the routine of rain and grumpy messages was broken when Jonathan made it back from Newcastle Uni in the little white Hyundai i20, complete with a fellow student whose family live near here. Perfect for sharing the petrol bill.

It was very reassuring to hear stories of students getting on and making the best of an absurd situation. They seem to be having a perfectly good time of it, doing everything that students should do – and getting some studying in, too. Or so he said.

But he brought really good news of a philosophical kind. I've spent many weeks getting myself into a cyberstew about the virus going-on, and, specifically, something called the Great Reset, which is the World Economic Forum's master plan to change, well, everything. I've watched videos of how capitalism is dead, how by 2030 no one will own anything, everyone will be smiley and happy, not need a job…

Don't believe it anymore. Jonathan and his fellow economics students are rampant capitalists, with master plans to be earning six figures by the time they're 25. And I have to say he's off to a good start with placement interviews with the Bank of England and UBS. I thought the latter sold sofas. But apparently not.

We talked long and late, and it was well past 11 when we got to bed – just in time to hear a car slow down on the road just outside the house. As I drew the curtains, I saw someone walk round from the back of the car after slamming the boot, climb in, reverse back up the hill, turn round in our drive and speed off. It was very odd. Odd enough for me to pop downstairs, grab a torch and inspect the road. Within moments, I had both cats helping me – and if they're fine, that number one worry is out of the way. I went back to bed none the wiser.

There's always the relief that it wasn't the 'poachers' catapulting birds out of the trees just below the house. In fact (he says, tempting fate) it has been a quiet autumn in that department. A small bit of good news in a grim autumn.

December 15th

The accounts came back, and there was good news and bad news. The good news is that we've had one of our most successful years ever, and the bank manager will be very pleased. We must be doing something right. The bad news was that we've had one of our most successful years ever, and the tax man will be very pleased. He's already going to get a huge chunk out of us early next year from last year's accounts, and God knows what these accounts will mean. We must be doing something terribly wrong.

There were a few more angry messages about vanishing books, and a couple more cheerful messages to say that books had finally arrived, which cheered me up no end. A long walk round a sodden farm with Sasha soon put paid to that, though – and the late evening wrestle with Jonathan, with me trying to defend our vital food stocks in the fridge, may not have been a terribly good idea. He's a flipping gorilla.

December 16th

Sure enough, at some time in the night, there was a funny feeling in my neck, and something felt not right. Bloody painful, actually. Sleep wasn't brilliant after that. That'll teach me to try and wrestle with a gym bunny. I've had a very iffy neck for decades, probably a legacy of a mediocre rugby career as a prop, but it has been a long time since I've had it as painful as this. Jonathan was mortified, but it wasn't his fault. I spent the day packing a few books, answering yet more angry emails – and some 'it's arrived' emails, too. Hazel, bless her, did a huge heap of shoot preparation, cooking, cleaning, hoovering, washing the floor.

December 17th

The Good Lord decided to send us a fantastic day for shooting – probably as a much overdue apology for the deluge a fortnight ago. It was a stunning sunrise, although everything was drenched after more heavy overnight rain.

Plans for an early start to make the most of good light on what is nearly the shortest day were scuppered by the usual late arrivals – but no one really cares. That's the great thing about our little rough shoot: stuff that is considered a cardinal sin on a stuffy shoot is perfectly acceptable here. Chat on your phone between drives? No problem – we're working farmers. Bring a five-shot semi-auto? If your old side-by-side is knackered, you need something to shoot with, obviously – although please stick with two shots at a time. Stay for lunch? Please do, but no one's upset if you're happier going home under these mad virus-related circumstances.

It probably didn't help that we'd decided to try a new route round the farm, and start up at Pipeline, but we finally set off on the first drive at ten-fifteen. But no one minded. When a brown spaniel yo-yo-yo-ed its way into the cover, ignoring all requests to get back, nearly no one minded. It was bit of a shame to see the Pipeline Twelve (as they are known) making an early exit from the excellent cover.

Many of them headed across to Long Field, and we had more luck there. The thick green cover on David's fields next door had been grazed off by sheep, so the birds were much keener to sit in the shooting strip. And by the time we'd finished Barracuda, the bag was a perfect 16, and it was time to yomp back through the woods to the Drier Yard for elevenses.

Again, we do things slightly differently here. No alcohol or pretentious nibbles. It's sugar-heavy children's party stuff; Coca-Cola, lemonade, flapjack, lemon drizzle cake, chocolates, majestic sausages from the West Meon Hut shop, and piping hot tomato soup. I always like stepping back a bit and watching the feeding frenzy that eight or so grown-ups indulge in. And all while standing in remarkably warm December sunshine.

A short walk to the Folly was worth the effort, with Tom the Auctioneer doing particularly well, and we thought we'd end the day with the awkward equilateral triangle that is Bob's Wood. It worked its magic again, fooling everyone with silent pheasants and low pigeon – although we found ourselves getting caught up with Trust walkers, also out enjoying the sunshine. Good thing we had our cheep'n'cheerful walkie-talkies that (unbelievably) still work after six years. We could stop and start to make sure no one got upset by what we were doing.

The bag was our ideal 26, so it was time to pack up and go home. Some walked back to the farmhouse, some walked to the Drier Yard to pick up all the vehicles we'd left down there first thing.

It was a quiet evening. Boris had done what he was told by the Marxist scientists, and wrecked Christmas for countless millions of people, and talk is now of tiers and holiday meet-ups. It's just grim.

December 18th

More rain – we were lucky yesterday. More WISMOs – but only one or two – and more messages saying that the books had at last arrived. Sometimes the first and its emergency replacement arrived at the same time. I suggested to the lucky recipients of two books that they pop a tenner in the post and keep the second one.

December 19th

Not sure where to start today. It got off to a reasonable start, with only a few biblical hailstorms to upset Hazel and Nessa as they went picking-up at Murph's shoot. The book complaints died down a lot more, and the 'it's here!' messages got a lot more, too. Jonathan had his favourite female friend (NB not a girlfriend) over for a long walk with Tim, and I lit a fire and watched some rugby.

Things seemed to be calming down just enough to make you think that the foulest of years was finally coming to an end, and, yes, we could start to get our heads round Christmas.

Boris Gump and his hideous cabal of ecofascist advisors were having none of it, and in an onanistic frenzy of Cromwellian puritanism, have cancelled Christmas. The reason is that a mysterious super strain of the virus is 'ripping through' vast areas of the country, and at short notice, everything we thought was set in stone for Christmas has been smashed to pieces. A new 'tier' has been introduced for London and the south-east – which will trap Anthony in London – and what people in the other tiers can do has been severely curtailed, which we think will trap Diana in Cambridge.

It's horrific. If the hospitals were full, if excess deaths were higher than normal, if the virus were decimating people we knew, I'd be a lot less angry at these restrictions. But they aren't, so I'm seething. Last night, we had a humdinger of a row with Jonathan (a good-natured one, though) about the Great Reset agenda – which is the aim of Klaus Schwab and his henchmen at the World Economic Forum – and how Schwab's greatest fan just happens to be a certain Matt Hancock. I told Jonathan that his fantastically capitalistic ambitions are doomed, as life as we know it, with money, possessions, democracy and all that jazz will be gone in a generation.

I thought he'd taken it well, and in the right spirit, but I suspect I may have laid it on a bit too thick. Over tea, when we were trying to come up with some sort of alternative Christmas plans, he broke down in tears. A hulking great young man of 20 sobbing at the kitchen table. I hope Boris and his scientific advisors are content.

A summer thunderstorm in the small hours – two days before the winter solstice – rounded off as pretty black and surreal day.

December 20th

A late start after a broken night, and a day to start getting some sort of Christmas plans started. In may not be on the 25th, and it may not be with those we thought we'd be with, but it was time (now that we'd all calmed down a bit) to see what can be done under the circumstances.

Anthony is stuck in London under tier 4, and made it quite plain on an internet chat that he has no intention of coming down. For a start, he's working till late Christmas Eve, and working flat out with everyone suddenly booking cars to get away from London. He didn't reckon much of those who were hiring cars; he's following the government line very seriously, and he's firmly supportive of the official line that those doing a runner should unpack and stay where they are. His flatmate's parents jumped in their car and drove up to London to take him home for Christmas. He seemed more worried about the ethics of that than the fact that he'll be alone on Christmas Day.

Diana will at least have company in Cambridge, and seemed content to stay there. We discussed the idea of her getting to Oxford somehow, and we'd nip up the A34 and bring her home, but she seemed uneasy at that.

In the end the decision was to put everything back until January – possibly to Anthony's birthday on the 4th. I went for a long walk with Sasha, mulling over the stuff I'd been reading about on the web saying the authorities (i.e. the WEF) aren't planning to 'end' this until 2025.

Hazel transferred some chunky financial Christmas presents to Anthony and Diana to cheer them both up a bit. It's desperate that it has come to this, but at least we're not trying to handle aged and confused parents, or young and confused children. We're relatively well set up.

December 21st

The shortest day, and yet another bizarre one. Hazel was out for her morning yomp with four dogs, and rang me to say there was a tractor and log trailer making its way down across Godwin's to the graveyard. Now, I'd got wind that this might happen a few weeks ago, when the Parish Council rang to say a tree needed sorting out in the graveyard, and could they use our fields – which back onto it – for access. We agreed that it might have to wait for a spell of dry weather (God knows when that might be) and that the contractors – good local lads – must get in touch with me to discuss logistics – and to get my go-ahead.

You can imagine my surprise (as they say) to hear that they were messily squelching their way across hideously saturated ground, completely unannounced, and with a certain amount of bloody cheek. I jumped in Tigger and shot off to catch up with them – and the ground almost defeated Tigger. We had a fairly sharp exchange of views. I told them that they were supposed to have got in touch with me ("Oh, didn't the Parish Council tell you we were coming?" they protested, somewhat unconvincingly), and that they were not to even think of loading up the huge yellow forks of their log trailer and drive back across my fields. I took some pretty meaningless photos of the damage they'd caused already, and squelched my way back up the hill, probably making about as much mess as they had, but grateful that Tigger managed to get all the way to the top; I would have looked a right twit having to go and ask them for a tow out.

Not long after Hazel had set off to post yesterday's book orders, a message came through from Farm Marketplace to say that yet another buyer had lodged a WISMO. I looked up the order number: it had been emailed to me. But I could find no print-off copy, or even a record in the crucial Big Book of Postings. It was slightly worrying – it was the first one, in nearly 3,000, that has got through my ruthlessly efficient office system. I rang the buyer, thinking I could use my charm to calm her, but she was the first (again) to be grumpy and ungrateful for the call. I promised to put another in the post, and asked that she return the first when it arrives. Probably the best result, bearing in mind that I don't think I'd posted the first one in the first place.

In fact, I thought it wise to pull out the stops in this case, so, once I'd packed and labelled it, I drove to Alresford sorting office to get it away as quickly as possible. It was shut. Luckily, a postie was just finishing stuffing his van to the brim, and kindly took the book and vanished in the building with it; not before he'd asked if it was another copy of my diary. Nice little ego boost there.

Next stop (after lunch): the accountants in Havant to pick up all the records so that November's chunky VAT reclaim can be done. I rang them first, and found them all working as normal, despite being in tier 4. They promised to put the files and books out in the porch for me to pick up.

There was no sign of armed guards or checkpoints as I entered Havant. Just the usual drab concrete buildings looking even less attractive on a short, wet day. I was in and out of the foyer in five seconds, and back onto the A3(M) in moments. Traffic was pretty well as normal, with idiots in BMWs causing the usual mayhem. I got back in time to meet up with a local farmer who – unbelievably – hadn't bought a copy of Book One. He insisted on taking three, and giving me 40 quid for them. I haggled him down to 35 (odd – I was the seller), but then couldn't find a fiver as change, so I said I'd owe him. Gotta love dealing with fellow farmers.

Out in the real world, the new 'super-virus' continues to sweep through the UK, forcing the rest of the world to shut their borders, with lorry queues on the M20 and flights in chaos. The only folk happy these days are Remainers, especially with the Brexit negotiations dragging on and on. It's tempting to say that it's all a charade leading up to the inevitable sellout, but that might just add to the all-round grumpy mood.

Actually, that's not quite true. Replacement copies of Book One are reaching buyers almost at the same time as original copies, and I've had several messages to say that they'd like to keep both copies. I've suggested bank transfers and cheques, and that will nicely eliminate Mr Amazon and Mr eBay's cut on those copies. I still chuckle at being asked where people should send cheques, as if there aren't enough clues about where we live in a book called *Sweet Home Hinton Ampner*.

December 22nd

Everything felt a bit more cheerful today – surely not the lengthening days kicking in yet? I had a long walk over Hurst Down, finding wheat where there was once none. Sasha had a good session driving Murph's pheasants out of the dell, emerging with a big grin on her face as if to say, "is that what flatcoats do?" Mind you, when we met Murph's guinea fowl in Dell Close, she was stunned to a standstill. A dozen great fluffy balls all scolding away was quite a sight. It was good to see the wheat in Dell Close making an appearance, too.

Jonathan was all smiles when I got home. He'd been accepted on a placement at the Bank of England when his second year finishes. Not surprisingly, he was proud as punch. A year and a month beckons living in London and working in the City proper – not far from where his Uncle Ian works now, and where his great-grandfather Hamilton Flindt worked for the Westminster, a very long time ago. Hamilton was founder of the Westminster Bank Horticultural Society, but I doubt Jonathan will have the time or inclination for that sort of thing. He'd been rejected by UBS the other day, but I told him that that was for the best; no one wants to buy sofas these days.

December 23rd

There's a nice routine to the early mornings now. Pack a couple of very late-ordered books, drive into Alresford sorting office and hand them in to a chorus of good-natured abuse. "Is that all?" demanded the wonderful Jane, who used to deliver to us, but is now behind the desk at reception. "Which fool wants to buy your book?" scoffs the cheeky Polish postie with whom I've had numerous good-natured Brexit debates. I always drive home with a smile.

Unfortunately, some basic farming beckoned. It wasn't that the ground had suddenly dried up, but the forecast is saying it will indeed get dry, but proper cold at the same time. That's my cue to get the precious sprayer undercover. Over the years I've tried flushing it through with expensive anti-freeze or a hundred litres of liquid fertiliser (messy), but in the end getting it in a barn but still 'ready to go' is a much better solution. Trouble is, barns erected in the sixties aren't that handy for modern machines – which is why most of my kit lives outdoors.

The good old Deere started at first turn – I still remember Ford 6610s that couldn't handle a weekend off work, never mind standing idle for a fortnight. I took the front weight off to avoid collisions while shuffling round the yard and assorted barns, and, after much opening of barns doors and gates, got the sprayer parked up in the spotlessly clean Godwin's barn. Neighbour John has finished his annual Christmas tree trade in it, and it gets swept to within an inch of its life afterwards. I must let him and his team work their way round all the barns.

After an early afternoon shower, it was off to the dentist to have a session with the hygienist, which is something I'm not keen on. It's probably because all previous ones seem convinced that they're nursery school teachers. My new one today was remarkably matter-of-fact, and only spent half an hour scraping dramatically at the stuff on the teeth that no one knows how to pronounce. Ta-ta. Tartar. Taran-tarah. Tarantula. Tora-tora-tora! Whatever; it took a bit of shifting, although I'm always suspicious that they're just making holes for the dentist proper to work on next visit. I parted with another £79 (we're all in the wrong job) and joked with the whole reception room about what tier we'd all be in by the time of my next appointment in June. "23!" "45!" "Ten million!" and so on.

It was just getting dark, so I thought I'd nip up to the Horsch dealer in Micheldever and pick up the £200 part I'd ordered after the drill conked out in Chalks ages ago – the breakdown that cost £300 in labour while two men scratched their heads for three hours, and then a five-minute phone call to Horsch by me finally cured the problem. I confess I'm a bit sore about coughing up £500 under those circumstances.

While I was at the Horsch dealers, I asked the storeman if Claas still do small combines – Claas is another of their franchises up there. "Of course," he replied, and went rummaging for brochures, as well as a 2021 calendar. And I'd only been home five minutes when their salesman was on the phone, promising an early visit in the new year to talk about a replacement. I may be getting ahead of myself, but I think the time might be right to think about replacing our TC5070, so I agreed we'd talk later. I had a grumble about the £500 for the Horsch repair, and he joked about it being knocked off the bill for a new combine. We'll see.

Talking of grumpy, I had a late evening email from Amazon, telling me off for using their site to encourage people to buy via other channels – strictly against the Amazon rules. It took me a moment or two to work it out, but then it all made sense: I've been sending out freebie replacements for books that Royal Mail have lost, and recipients have been sending messages to say they'd like to keep both, and what's the best way for them to pay? I've been suggesting cheques, or transfers, and even sending my email address for one chap who wanted to use PayPal. I think it was this last one which has sent the Amazon algorithms into petulant meltdown. My account is in danger of being suspended. You'd never guess I've sent the best part of ten grand their way in the last 14 months. Bastards.

December 24th

The day was dominated by Brexit news. Boris Gump and the EU Ice Maiden have finally agreed a deal – or so we were told when we turned our radios on first thing. They just have to sort out some technicalities on herring (I do hope it's subsidies – or herring aid) and it will all be over. Trouble is, this was the message through all the morning bulletins, all through lunchtime, and well into the afternoon. At one stage, it seems that after all the fanfares, it was going to crash and burn.

But no. Finally, both sides held triumphant press conferences to announce what a great victory they had achieved. I have to say that Boris did seem the more convincing of the two. Initial reaction from the dreaded Twittersphere was – inevitably – mixed. Hard core Brexiteers were calling it a sellout for the fishermen and the curiously specific Scottish seed potato producers. Moderate Brexiteers were pointing out that the deal on fishing is long term, but still positive. And the hard core Remainers were in full meltdown. Taking that to be the best sign, I abandoned the computer and went for a long walk.

I had no dogs to take, because Evie is very much on heat, Tim (still a complete dog) is fairly frantic, and Hazel is splitting them into pairs and running shifts with each pair locked in the Skoda. It's a flipping nuisance, but it'll only be for a few days more. We don't need any more puppies at the moment.

In Clump, I was joined by a black spaniel which had been merrily hunting through the trees, driving deer and hares out in a panic. I met the owners, a jolly nuclear family walking up from New Pond, and suggested that letting a spaniel loose in the countryside isn't terribly responsible. They looked at me as if I was quite mad, and reluctantly put the beast on a lead. Nice to know that in an ever-changing world, spaniels will still be the most unsuitable pet dog in the world.

The poor old postie arrived well after dark, and dropped off a big pile of Book One-related post. There were cheques and cash from those who had agreed to keep – and pay for – the second freebie copies, and five 'return to sender' copies, which looked like they'd had a pretty hard life on their travels there and back. Some looked like the sorting offices had been using them as hockey pucks on the floors of their offices. I suppose I should be grateful that they're back here at all. And an Amazon message came through from another buyer saying that their book had arrived, but in an open envelope. I must buy more Sellotape.

By evening, the reaction to Boris' deal was beginning to crystallise: it seems to be acknowledged as a Good Thing. There's a lot to be scrutinised, it's being rushed through (not always a good sign) but many industries and talking heads seem content. Farming seems to have survived (unless you're a Scottish seed potato producer, of course). A Welsh farming spokesman seemed delighted early in the day, but luckily the BBC managed to persuade him to say some negative stuff by the evening. In an ever-changing world...

December 25th

An odd Christmas day – but I think we all expected that. For a start we had a good frost, although maybe not as hard as predicted. When you've gone to all the trouble of getting the sprayer under cover, you like to see minus five. The sunrise was stunning, though.

There are no toddlers to run round the house shrieking. Just Jonathan – and he was never going to get out of bed before late morning, so I had my porridge, lit a fire and sat down to enjoy ITV4's highlights of the British Touring Car Championships. The commentators have enough trouble keeping up with the actions during a typical live race, so the highlights were even more exciting; hard to know where to look when everything kicks off. How the boys with the microphones keep track of the mayhem is astonishing. And the post-race interviews still sound like normal people talking normally to each other in the pub. And we haven't done that ourselves for months.

Christmas dinner was unusual. Hazel did a fantastic joint of beef, and three of us sat round a narrow arc of the huge shoot table and tucked in. No crackers, no presents, but a lemon meringue pie that was delicious. I ate about a hundredweight of it, which probably wasn't wise.

We left Jonathan in charge of setting everyone up with a post-lunch Zoom call (Mr Zoom, I suspect, has had a good year), and despite the terrible internet we get out here, all five of us managed an hour chatting away and comparing notes. Everyone seemed to be ending the year on an upbeat note – new jobs, new flats, new placements – Anthony seemed the only one not 100% happy with his job, but seemed to agree that now is not the time to give it up. But it was a lovely hi-tech way to 'get together' for a bit on Christmas Day. Both Hazel and I felt our spirits lifted by it.

After a sunset that was almost as spectacular as the sunrise, we scrutinised the TV schedules for something to watch – and failed to find anything. Out came the old DVD player and the Coen Brothers box set, and having got the surround-sound speakers up and running again, we settled down to the joy of *Oh Brother, where art thou?* It was good enough to help me forget the feeling that I had definitely eaten too much lemon meringue pie, and was suffering a bit. I even went and got some Rennies that were a couple of years past their 'use by' date. They did the trick, though.

The only big mistake was to finish the TV viewing with some Victoria Wood highlights. We sat through it with stony faces. True, it was comedy from a simpler time (35 years ago, for goodness sake), but the BBC managed to find a whole new set of talking heads (most of whom Hazel and I had never heard of) who praised the late Ms Wood for her accurate comedic portrayal of evil 'right-wing people'. Good old BBC.

December 26th

The lovely sunshine of yesterday was gone, replaced by a cold, grey day with a biting northerly wind. It was all rather depressing, although the Boxing Day low that traditionally comes after the Christmas Day 'high' was somewhat smaller. I did the Clump loop, and could hardly stand up on the saturated ground.

We thought we'd do another 'movie night', and were just plucking a Tarantino from its case and firing up the old but still functioning surround-sound system when the phone rang. Unfortunately, it wasn't a nice long Christmas catch-up with someone – it was our tenant in the bungalow, in a right state because one of the radiators was spraying water everywhere. Not what anyone needs at 7.30pm on Boxing Day.

Tarantino was put on hold as urgent phone calls were made, all of them fruitlessly, but I got hold of James the Plumber on his Facebook page. He said he could come out now, or early tomorrow morning. I rang the bungalow back, and they said they'd turned the boiler off, and the spray was now a dribble, and, yes, they could put up with that overnight. Luckily, the impending arrival of Storm Bella meant that it was getting milder by the minute. I messaged James the Plumber, thanking him, and asking him to pop out in the morning. He said that would suit him, because he's still trying to get to the bottom of the ongoing problems in No. 1, and he'd look in there at the same time. It seemed to matter not to him that tomorrow is Christmas Sunday.

Mind you, his family are like that. His father ran a building company in Ropley for decades, and we used him for everything. No job was too small. The old tractor driver would ring in a panic from No. 2 with a leaking tap, and there would be someone there later in the day. And when the massive south-east chimney toppled into the house in the storm of January 1990, James' father was up there on the roof (or what was left of it), trying to cover the hole with a tarpaulin in winds that were still terrifying. Mum and Dad, who still lived here then, were white with shock at events, and couldn't believe his bravery.

With everything sorted (I hoped) we settled down in front of the roaring fire for *Once upon a time in Hollywood*. Perhaps I wasn't in the mood for 150 minutes of self-indulgent twaddle, but I didn't reckon much of it at all. And I normally love Tarantino.

Storm Bella arrived as we were going to bed and shook the house pretty hard. I drifted off, hoping that the chimney re-build had been thorough enough. I'd hate to have to summon James to repeat his father's heroic deeds – or to have to fish Jonathan out from under the rubble.

December 27th

The National Trust's loader tractor was out early, which is usually a sign of a tree down somewhere significant, and by the time I set off in Tigger for a bit of a farm inspection, it had already cleared fallen debris just below the farmhouse and up on Roe Hill. Everything did look a bit shell-shocked in the morning-after sunshine, and there had obviously been another deluge to accompany the high winds. The bottom of Roe Hill was flooded, and the pond at New Pond was overflowing onto the road. No drilling today. Although they promise a dry spell is on its way. How many times have we heard that this year?

Boris' Brexit deal is beginning to come under some scrutiny, and those who were somehow destined to be unhappy with it are, of course, unhappy. Some of the fine print has revealed stuff that seems to have been somewhat misquoted by those hailing a great victory. I've read numerous times that fishing will be totally under our control in five-and-a-half years' time, but other pundits are pointing out that such a claim is nonsense. Everyone shouting at once via electronic media makes it confusing as to who to believe. It's the way of the modern world.

December 28th

The dramatic pink sky over a hard frost was a bit ominous, and not long after breakfast the first snow arrived – great big slobby flakes mixed with sleet and rain, with no real chance of settling. Hazel and Jonathan set off for a long walk with all the dogs (now possible thanks to Evie finally going off heat) and came back quite chilled and damp.

They came back with reports of rooks in the Hangar, so I thought I'd do my daily constitutional that way for a change. The vast rookeries in and around Hinton Ampner Park can trash a field in no time – as I found with the spring wheat earlier in the year. If they've got their sights set on the Hangar, it could be a long winter trying to keep them off.

The problem is how to get there. Many years ago, I would have driven along Dark Lane – the track from the source of the Itchen to New Pond. These days it's overgrown and impassable to vehicles, although that's not a bad thing with the rise in off-roading as a hobby. Instead, I walked across the Top of Englands – now a quagmire with all the foot traffic and rain – and through the grounds of Hinton Ampner House. There were a few families enjoying a day out, but the House is a dull spectacle on the best of days; on a hideous December day it looks more like a repainted Portacabin. I kept walking, past the church where I was christened, and through the workshops at the west end of the grounds. Climbing over the fence, I reached what was once the cricket pitch, where the mighty Hinton Ampner XI took on other village teams.

I played for them once, when brother Ian and I were summoned to make up numbers. I think we got one run between us. The hilltop pitch was all very quaint, but you had to send someone down to third man to tell him the game was over. There was a tiny pavilion on a concrete pad, with no 'facilities' whatsoever; you walked back to the House's stable block for teas and loos.

The pavilion got commandeered by the big posh shoot that used to take place on the farm, who moved it to the beaters' yard at New Pond. It was then brought back by the Trust and restored to its concrete plinth. It sits rather sadly now, overlooking the vast spoil heaps dumped on the square when the Trust were building their 'green' woodchip plant. At midwicket (if the bowling is from the Cheriton end) one of the vast beech trees has blown over, and has been left, no doubt to provide a useful microenvironment for microscopic animals (or some such nonsense). There were small children playing in its shattered branches and trunk as I walked past, which is a much better use, even if the ghosts of the old boys in charge of the outfield might not approve. Of the tree that Mr Dutton planted next to the pavilion to mark the Silver Jubilee in 1977 there is no sign. It has probably fallen foul of time and neglect, rather than the Trust's woke, and therefore anti-Royal, agenda.

I exchanged a couple of cheery words with the parents of the playing children (they probably would not have been interested in a short history of Hinton Ampner CC) and kept walking toward the top corner of the Hangar. There was a time when the Hangar bank was open to our livestock, and you could walk the length of it. I used to do it regularly with my folding El Chimbo .410", shooting the odd rabbit. The fact that cattle walked over it and grazed it meant the grass was short, and it paid to hide behind a trunk and just wait. Somewhere in the trees was a wooden grave marker for a dog. Long gone now, I suspect. The whole bank is now an overgrown mess.

Once I'd negotiated a couple of fences and some creepers that I could have sworn had a mind of their own, it was nice to see the Hangar greening up nicely. As with all the winter-sown crops this year, it has had no herbicide, so it's pretty grubby, but the Crusoe is coming up well, and the rooks don't seem to be doing any damage. There's no sign of any uprooted seedlings anyway. It cheered me up enormously as I headed down towards the SE corner, where I got onto Dark Lane for a slippery and dangerous walk along the bottom of the valley, then left at the Springshot gateway, and up the hill home. It was so nice to get some grip on the road that I stuck to it, rather than cutting in at the cattle barn and coming up through the old tennis court.

Two Addams Family films and a warm sitting room fire were the perfect antidote to the misery of a cold, wet and utterly 'not right' Christmas break. In theory, it's back to normal tomorrow – although I can't see my daily regime changing much. They're promising more snow and rain, so the chances of jumping in a tractor are minimal.

December 29th

The ex-Editor rang, asking if it was OK for him to drop in for a cuppa. I've given up worrying about the rules and regulations about virus lockdowns, and told him to come on up. He seemed somewhat shaken, though, and explained that he has two friends in hospital with the virus. Suddenly, he's feeling much more anxious. It didn't help his mood that his heaving mantlepiece of shoot invitations for January has been shredded. We sat and discussed how we could put a rough shoot together here without breaking any rules. Could we 'meet up with one other person' and form a gun team, and Hazel does the same with another dog person? Does pheasant shooting fall under agricultural shooting – which is allowed? Hard to say. Sad that it has come to this.

Sasha and I went for a Drier loop walk to contemplate all this nonsense, and met a man wandering around the Drier Yard. I asked if he was lost – my usual opening line before starting on "you shouldn't be here".

"No, I'm not lost," he said. "I've got terrible gout, and can't manage the woods, so I'm waiting for the rest of my family – but have to keep moving!" And you can't get a fairer explanation that that. We chatted for a minute, and I accused him of Christmas overindulgence bringing the gout on. It was hard work getting Sasha away from him. She'd rushed up to greet him in a way that worried me for a moment or two, but she was just doing her spooky checking over of someone in slight distress, and proceeded to lean against him and generally sympathise with him in a way that meant they were new best friends. Very special dog, that one.

As I reached the top of the Folly, I paused to get my breath back, and saw a group of walkers striding confidently across the wheat in Drier Field. Was it worth heading back to have a word? Or rushing home to get Tigger? No. Chances are that they were our gouty friend's family, and it wasn't worth spoiling a beautiful friendship.

December 30th

Probably best not to mention that Jonathan jumped in his little Hyundai i20 and drove to Oxford to pick up Diana, who had caught the slow bus from Cambridge. He brought her home for a much needed few days of R&R. It was probably illegal.

Meanwhile, in Westminster, the Brexit deal made it through the House of Commons, then the Lords, and then received Royal Assent. All in about 20 minutes. It feels very odd. No doubt all the lights will go out at 11pm tomorrow.

December 31st

The cold weather stopped being an enjoyable novelty and started being a flipping nuisance. It crept into my office and the kitchen and refused to move. It doesn't help that all the windows are falling out – we were promised replacements by Christmas by the landlord – and the single-storey bit of the house has no roof insulation.

Still, it was good excuse to chop some more logs and get both the log burner in the hall and the sitting room fire lit.

Neighbour Robert Jnr called in for an update on hay availability, and might possibly have had a coffee – or not. His father-in-law rang just as he was leaving, and we had a bit of a catch-up, but it's just not the same as sitting at the bar in the Flowerpots.

Over tea, we had a bit of a review of the year, and decided that Team Flindt had actually had rather a good 2020. Hazel had successfully bred a fine litter of puppies, adding 'great dog breeder' to her CV just below the line about 'famous picker-up' and now 'dog trainer' up at Mullenscote. Diana has chased and got a fantastic new job – with money to match. Jonathan has managed to get his dream placement at the Bank of England in the summer, and Anthony has moved into his first flat, rather than a series of 'spareroom dot coms'. I look forward to hearing news about his job plans.

We've had a really unconventional but successful year on the farm, crashing our way through floods and droughts, disintegrating combines and conking-out machines. Perhaps my machinery replacement policy needs a tweak. Cash flow has benefited hugely from straw sales, Book One sales and really good final prices from last year's harvest. We have a full thousand tonnes of stuff sitting in the Trinity Grain long pool from this year's, with prices getting higher and higher by the week. Let's hope their selling team manage to catch the best selling points.

The year's events have clobbered pub trips, the shoot, and the band – and they are my three favourite things. But we've stayed well, kept relatively sane and kept smiling – most of the time.

We settled down in the sitting room (four dogs, Cain the cat, Diana, Hazel and I – Jonathan was busy upstairs) for the New Year's Eve television. We tried *Skyfall* for a bit, but knew it too well. *Hot Fuzz* was good until the 40-minute shootout at the end, and we didn't even bother with *Hootenanny* for fear of salty Remainer tears pouring out of the TV speakers. Eleven o'clock came (with the BBC reminding us right up until 22.59 and 30 seconds that we were all doomed), and I raised a bottle of Crabbie's ginger beer to Gina Miller, Bob Geldof, Steve Coogan, Lord Adonis (who the fuck's he anyway?) et al, and then we all went to bed. Curiously, the electricity supply stayed on.

January 1st 2021

Nice not to have a hangover this morning, but it would have been even nicer to have sore shoulders and fingers from playing my Roland piano until the small hours. But no, it was all very quiet and restrained for a new year. Very cold and grey, too, again, so both fires went all day, and today's films were *Stardust* which was fun (even at the tenth viewing – if we ignore Ms Dane's gurning) and *Murder on the Orient Express* (which was barking mad, once it got going.)

Sasha and I did the Clump loop, just to check that the ground is still too soggy for any farming.

January 2nd

Anthony had plans to come down from London and have a short weekend here at home. He rang mid-morning to say he'd bring a new Vauxhall down for me to 'test' for *The Field* – proper test cars from press offices have dried up again. There was one problem: he'd taken a COVID test, and the results hadn't got back yet. There was a great deal of debate about the merits of such a test, and the morals of coming down here if he didn't have a result. I have to confess it all got a bit heated, with me being in the minority (of one) that the whole thing is bollocks. I had a long walk to calm down.

It also cheered me up, as I found the Crusoe in both Joan's Acre and Drier Field had come on nicely. Still full of weeds and in need of a good roll, but a healthy plant population, nonetheless. And Anthony rang while I was out to say he was indeed negative, and would be home later. Good news.

We have four bedrooms in this old farmhouse, and five of us home means that Hazel and I have to share a bed again. There was a time – nearly forty years ago – when that was the most thrilling prospect possible, but practicality now overrides an unexpected outbreak of middle-age romance. And when I say 'practicality', I mean the lack of sleep that is inevitable when one bed partner snores. I'm certainly not going to point any fingers here.

Hazel and I agreed to give it a go, though, and the fates conspired to make it a long night. Yes, there was indeed snoring, but Mr Fox decided to circle the house baying for company. Just as I was contemplating that it would be a good idea to pop downstairs, find the gun cupboard keys, dig out the Anschutz .22, put batteries in the nightsights, tell the dogs to calm down and go back to bed, come upstairs again, tell the rest of the house to shut up and go back to bed again, the fox vanished into the distance. Just as I was dozing off again, smug that I had made the right decision, he arrived back, barking for Britain. Not a great night.

January 3rd

Not Christmas Day, but we pretended it was. Hazel did another huge lump of beef, and we had a fantastic family Sunday lunch. It was only slightly ruined by the National Trust's enormous wood-chipper roaring for most of the day over in the gardens, but the Trust, in its wokeness, despises old-fashioned concepts like family and Sunday, so does its best to trash family Sunday lunches. We're 500 yards away from the gardens and it's a horrible racket from here. I dread to think what it must be like for those living even nearer.

We opened presents after lunch, helped by Tim, enjoying his first Christmas. There were so many that the dogs eventually gave up helping, and collapsed in a line in front of the roaring log burner. At last, we could get on unhindered. There were lots of clothes and books, and a fantastic assortment of silly presents too. Somehow, we didn't get round to playing Monopoly, or racing demon, and we didn't even open the Quality Street. We obviously didn't pretend it was Christmas hard enough. I think Anthony – who normally wins Monopoly – was quite disappointed.

January 4th

Anthony 26th birthday, but after yesterday, we didn't really mark it. Diana and I got into the Grandland and I took her back to Oxford up the A34, and she caught the slow bus to Cambridge from there. The roads were still busy, and I was very proud to resist the MacDonald's magnet on the way past Winchester services when heading home.

I couldn't resist a drive down the A31 to Alresford from Winchester, to check out the Brexit/doomsday lorry park. The westbound carriageway has been commandeered as a customs area, and all traffic moved onto the eastbound side. I could see millions of cones, numerous Portaloos, dozens of officials, scores of Portacabins, arrays of floodlights – and one lorry. We're doomed, I tell you, doomed.

After a late lunch, I thought the Grandland need a few more miles, and on more minor roads, so went to Chilbolton to get a set of engine service stuff for the John Deere. It has probably only done about 400 hours since the last service, but I have a feeling we might get busy soon.

In the evening, we dutifully sat down and watched Boris Gump announce another lockdown. The first two hadn't worked, so imposing another one makes perfect sense – to someone somewhere.

January 5th

Anthony was planning to drive back to London in the Grandland later on today, so I grabbed a notebook and a pen, and sat in it for five minutes making notes for the write-up. I then headed indoors through the falling flakes of snow to get another coat; it was too cold for words (literally and metaphorically) in there. There was lots to jot down, which was good from the point of view of writing an article, but meant that I was freezing by the time I was done.

He set off in the late afternoon, in a slightly sombre mood. I think he's worried about setting off back to London while the virus is (apparently) rampaging through the city, but he needs the job and the money, and finds the farmhouse very dreary. He got back in double quick time, but got home to a leaking boiler – poor plumbing is definitely the theme of the Christmas holiday.

January 6th

It's hard to know how to react to the Trump-related riots, and the storming of the Capitol. Nothing is ever as it seems theses day, and no explanation is too absurd to be true. I've always rather liked Trump, based solely on the premise that anything that upsets the BBC/*Guardian* has to be a A Good Thing. But these days, it's just another reason to turn off the news with a shake of the head and a sigh.

Back in our world (the real world?) I got the Grandland written up, and thought I'd chase up future test cars. Fiat confirmed the Panda Cross, and Martin at BMW found me something extravagant for February, which is good news. Somehow it came as no surprise, as we exchange post-Christmas greetings and stories, to read that his boiler had blown up on Christmas Eve.

A late afternoon yomp around Hurst Down revealed some reasonable-looking Crusoe, and tracks from a scrambling bike that obviously got 'lost' at some time over Christmas. Bastards.

January 7th

It's not getting any warmer. I walked out to check on Godwins's to see if it was dry or frozen enough to maybe have a go with the CO3 and the winter beans. On the way, I saw the new neighbour in the garden of Godwin's Cottages having a much-needed clear up and fire, so stopped to introduce myself and have a chat.

The rumour mill (and the fact that a lovely collie had been spotted under perfect control) had already established that he was of farming stock, and had moved back to the UK after running a farm in France. He looked a bit worried when I asked him the No. 1 most vital question, compulsory for every new resident: did anyone in his family play an instrument? It tuned out that his daughter played guitar. This is good news on two levels: we might be able to recruit her for the band, and they are unlikely to be upset by the noise if and when we even get back into Shed 3b for rehearsal.

Even standing still for ten minutes was enough to chill the bones, and I didn't spend long in Middle Broom before deciding that drilling was still out of the question. I looped round the Chalks dell and headed back indoors.

Neighbour Robert arrived for a chat, but no coffee, pleased as punch to have negotiated the bureaucracy and got his virus jab – although calling in for coffee probably negated the health benefits. Tod was next on the doorstep, waving a wad of notes for the old welder that has been sitting in the barn for 20 years. I was very happy for him to take it away and get it going if he could. I was more worried about losing out on the deposit on the big gas cylinder that vanished, but that was just me being dog in the manger. Neighbour John finished a very welcome but probably illegal stream of visitors with a request to go out and gather some firewood. "Are the Trust still allowing fires?" was his half-joking query. Don't bet anything against it.

The result of all these very welcome comings and goings was that I didn't get the next *Flindt on Friday* in on time, and the kitchen didn't warm up once. Luckily, *FW* gave me another day, and the Trust's pet builder rang out of the blue to say they would be starting work on the rotten kitchen window first thing in the morning.

January 8th

An early start. I'd managed to get a day extra to come up with something for *Farmers Weekly*, and had had a few ideas overnight. The problem is that nothing has happened for a few weeks, and I have to say that I've rather enjoyed not having the weekly deadlines. Trouble is, when ideas and inspiration flow easily, it's good money for not much effort.

It helped that the new deadline had been set by the imminent arrival of the builders to do the kitchen window. I was writing before six, and finished by eight, just as the first van arrived. It sat in the yard for 40 minutes – as builders do – so I had time to polish the article a bit, and then send it off.

It wasn't really the best day to have a six-foot by three-foot hole in your kitchen; it was one of the coldest days I can remember. We shut the doors down to the hall, lit both fires and put the central heating on full blast. We had lunch in front of the sitting room fire – tomato soup and ham sandwiches – while watching the excellent *Bangers and Cash*.

The New Holland rep rang to ask details of the old combine. He'd been down to give it a checkover with a view to possibly doing a deal for a new TC5.80, and couldn't find the key. He'd looked in the 'usual place' (all combine drivers will know where I mean) and couldn't find it. That's because I gave up storing it there a couple of years ago after setting off in the combine (having for some reason used the spare keys) and managed to lose the main set somewhere in the Folly. Since then, I've always taken the key home.

The builder finally got the old windows out – I say 'old', but it's one of the plain ones put in by Dad when he moved in and blitzed the original kitchen in 1960 – and got the new one in. The kitchen became more habitable, even if it was a bit smelly with sealant. Sasha and I did the Drier loop, partly to clear our heads from the smell, partly to stretch our legs in the cold sunshine, but mainly to see if the roller shutter door had been wound down again after the New Holland man had checked the combine over. It had, of course. Still, I needed the walk.

January 9th

Hazel spotted new COVID-related shooting guidance over on the BASC website: rough shooting is now permitted again, as long as those taking part are local, and you only meet up with one other person. The authorities have apparently agreed that this constitutes your daily exercise.

There then followed a long day of trying to work out how to make this work. Not surprisingly, the ex-Editor was heavily involved in these high technical legal discussions. If he and I met, and walked the strips, and shot a couple of pheasants, that would be entirely legal. If Hazel met up with one of her picking-up gang, and went for a walk, that would be entirely legal.

The big question is how can we liaise the two groups of two without getting reported to the rozzers, and getting a full armed helicopter response? Could the two guns walk the strips (either side by side or end to end) and the dog team watch from a suitable distance and send the dogs when needed? Hazel pointed out that the dogs would miss out on their flushing work.

So the next plan was one gun with one dog (still legal) starts at one end of the strip, and one gun and one dog (still legal) start at the other. And the two pairs walk towards each other, and shoot any birds that get up. All the boxes ticked, from our point of view.

The big question is, of course, at what stage in the process of walking towards each other would two pairs become an illegal gathering of four? We could do all communicating with our faithful walkie-talkies, and stop 50 yards from each other (which is more separation than most walkers are doing round the estate at the moment). But would the fact that we're organising as a four get us into trouble. Who knows? Our problem is that the little shoot is so important to us that we'd be fools to do anything that might risk us losing it. We all agreed to think on it further.

I chopped wood and lit as many fires as possible against the freezing grey day. Hazel, obviously still in keeper mode, went out in Pig and topped up the pheasant feeders, and reported that plenty of big strong birds are out there.

January 10th

A typical freezing Sunday routine. Puzzles in the papers, chop logs, do the Drier loop, snooze on the sofa, curse that there's no sport on TV – all the usual stuff. Hazel had a more productive day, meeting up with Nessa for couple of hours of dog training in one of the pastures, and enjoying an online training seminar from Mullenscote in the evening.

In the evening, it suddenly got warmer. I had to have a check outside that it wasn't solely down to the new windows in the kitchen, and found that the wind had changed and the vicious cold had gone. Hurrah – although that probably means rain is imminent.

January 11th

I must have watched too many films on TV yesterday – either that or the cider and peanut mix from late last night was playing havoc with my sleep. I had the most vivid 'am dram' nightmare I've had for years. The details were crystal clear: it was a Wednesday, the day before the first proper performance. I had the copy of the script, well worn, with notes and stage directions filling the margins – in my handwriting. But I couldn't remember a single bloody word. Every time I opened the script, the words were complete strangers to me. I rang Richard the White Hunter cricket captain (and also a bit of an amateur thesp) for help. He seemed utterly confused. (Mind you, in real life, he's always confused.) He said we'd had two very successful dress rehearsals on the Monday and Tuesday. Why all the fuss? God, I was pleased to wake up from that dream.

It was now warm enough to step outside and do some physical work, so, after packing a healthy bunch of weekend Book One orders, I decided to set about reassembling the Horsch CO3. When the ST4 had conked out in Chalks, I'd gradually stripped parts off the CO4 until we found which bit had conked out. Instead of carefully refitting the parts to the CO3 when the job was done, I'd piled them all up in the farmhouse. The time had come to refit them all.

By teatime, I'd refitted tyres, assorted cables and 'radar adapters'. One of the tiny pins that locks the main control cables had gone missing in all the to-ing and fro-ing, which was annoying. A quick call to the Horsch dealer revealed that an 'overhaul kit' – including new pins – would be 50 quid. I'll keep looking for it; this breakdown has cost me quite enough already.

Neighbour Murph poked his head over the gate at the east end of the barn where the CO3 is parked up. He'd been out in the Back Meadow, checking his sheep who are still grazing here (he is 'between shepherds' at the moment), and probably heard my cursing and swearing at wheel bolts that won't line up. We had a chat, and both agreed that we could officially start to get grumpy now. Which cheered us both up enormously.

Meanwhile, the Trust's builders had been in again, and done a bit of repair and maintenance to the kitchen's north window. This one is not a simple 'rip out and replace' job, as it's hundreds of years old, so there's a lot of tinkering and patching in to be done. The main problem is a rotten sill, which came away to reveal some surprisingly sound wood underneath. A morning's hammering and fixing made the whole thing look slightly less of a mess. I don't think the kitchen has been that airtight in decades.

January 12th

Yes, it's milder – which means we can actually get outdoors and do stuff – but it has been replaced with wind and rain. No surprise there, of course. The windows rattled overnight, and the world was drenched by dawn. There goes any plan for some sneaky January drilling.

Not to worry. There has been an outbreak of livestock plans instead. We haven't had sheep or cattle of our own here for some time, and Hazel and I had a high-level farm policy meeting a few nights ago to discuss this – i.e. we interrupted a re-run of *The IT Crowd* while scoffing peanuts and drinking ginger beer on the sofa.

The back barn is lying empty (except for all the machinery being stored in it), and it's a really good livestock barn, having been put up especially for Hazel's fantastic suckler herd enterprise in 1994. March 21st, 1996 put paid to all that, of course. We've got a pile of good hay left, and some good straw, and – to put it frankly – Hazel is bored. There's no proper shooting or picking-up, and life has gone a bit quiet. Time to find some baby calves and spend a spring and summer feeding them up.

She'd already made a few calls to assorted calf suppliers, and her favourite has promised a dozen, so we decided to start clearing the barn out. The CO3, the little livestock trailer that goes on the back of Pig, the old fuel bowser, the mounted grass harrows and the little drum mower were all evicted, with most of them heading over to the big barn at Godwin's. All that's left is the little blue trailer full of bean tailings from the seed cleaning gang's work late last year. I'm not entirely sure what we do with those.

With immaculate timing, Murph emailed to ask if he could use the barn at the end of this week for a bit of sheep handing before his flock leaves us, so Hazel agreed to that. He also said that he'd already pencilled in the new neighbours to help with lambing this year, which was quick work on his part, and hugely convenient for everyone. Let's hope the arrangement works.

January 13th

A very odd feeling: we're having a shoot tomorrow, and there's no preparation to be done. Hazel didn't spend the day slaving over the Aga, making flapjack, sticky toffee pudding and chicken pie. Instead, she did a trip round Alresford picking up medicines for me and the dogs. She had to call in at the vets to gets the dogs weighed before they'd give out any more of whatever she'd gone for. Sasha – the vicious attack dog – strolled in happily with the nurse, but Tim, the lovely friendly flatcoat, refused to go in without Hazel – so she had to go in with him. Yet another rule broken, in a year of ten-thousand broken rules.

We'd all agreed to shoot in 'plain clothes' (to attract as little attention as possible) so there was no checking of long socks, ties (for necks and calves) and plus-fours. Only the walkie-talkies needed a quick check on their batteries, since the two teams of two would most certainly not be coming within speaking distance of each other. Well, that's the plan, anyway.

I walked Hurst Down again, for no other reason than to just stretch my legs, and it was saturated – again. As it got dark, we lit lots of fires – again – and settled down for a proper look at the freshly arrived draft set of accounts. They're very healthy – again – and the hunt is on to reduce the profits in some way. The accountant had spotted that the handing and processing costs of our grain now tucked away safely at Trinity Grain hadn't made their way into the expenses column. That was probably due to the fact that we sold nothing 'off the combine' this harvest; if we had, those costs would have been noted then. Something like that – I know as much about accounting as I do about 13th-century Abyssinian architecture. The accountant had actually pointed this oversight out, and we agreed that it was a chunk of expenditure that should be added. The good news was that the profits took a handy tumble as a result. Funny to think that 20 years ago we were desperate to boost profits to keep the bank's cold-eyed vultures at bay.

January 14th

Time for the Hinton Ampner Shoot, version 5.0. 1.0 was the posh, big bag driven version, dating from the dawn of time until 2010. 2.0 was the first walkabout days we did in '14/'15, after the Trust came knocking on our door and said we could, nay, should have a rough shoot, but with no strips and no birds put down for that first season. 3.0 was the era with strips and birds and varying numbers of beaters/ pickers-up. 4.0 was the start of this season, operating under the Rule of Six. And now we have 5.0, with two teams of two – one gun, one dog person – working our way round the 'home S'.

In truth, it wasn't just the 'home S' – Hazel walked down to the bottom of Middle Broom in the cold driving sleet, to meet the ex-Editor after he'd popped across the road, and the two of them came up the dog-leg hedge between Middle Broom and Child's Broom. There was a massive flock of birds down there – that land is some of the most undisturbed in the whole parish – but they were not in the mood to be flushed. They simply walked up the hill ahead of the dogs, and then did a big loop and walked back down again.

By the time Team Hazel radioed me from the far end of the Back Meadow, ready and waiting to work their way through the upper Chalks strip, they were wet through, and the ex-Editor's barrels were undirtied. I, however, was still in the kitchen waiting for picker-up Julie, who traditionally does a thousand things before breakfast, and as a result is always late. Just as Hazel agreed to ring her and see where she was, the battered Shogun Sport arrived in the yard, and Team Charlie was finally ready to go. We 'dogged in' a dozen from the back barn, and then headed off across the tennis court to start the first 'drive'.

Bizarrely, in a strip that was looking a bit knackered, and with just one person 'beating' from each end, there were loads of birds. We'll ignore the fact that Bella had a red mist moment, and rushed off to flush a huge group round the feeder far too early, and say that it went very well. In fact, all five strips (Chalks north, Chalks south, Clump, Big Field and the top of Roe Hill) that we did went very well. After only two hours, we had a dozen, the dogs were done, and everyone was drenched and cold – but very happy.

Nearly everyone. Unlucky Alf wasn't happy. He'd popped out into the Hampshire countryside to plunder some roadside logs, and rather fancied the large tree we use as a poacher barrier at the top of Roe Hill. He expected a nice hour filling his boot(s) with free logs, as no one would be out and about on a day like today. What he got was a monumental earful from Hazel as she emerged from the neighbouring shooting strip just as he was starting. Off he went with his tail between his legs. Poor chap. What are the chances of that happening? No wonder he was immediately christened Unlucky Alf.

But we did miss the big tea, and the pie, and the sticky toffee pudding and all the post-shoot 'banter' (hideous word), but we managed to get outside, and wield our huge weapons. And in these mad times, that's what counts. It all felt a bit odd to be snoozing on the sofa by early afternoon – just as the rain cleared for a lovely evening.

The day didn't get any less odd: there was a curious volley of fireworks in the early evening from a very nearby house. Nothing too dramatic, just a dozen or so very loud bangs, but enough to make you grateful that no cattle were nearby. And then, just as I was trying to sleep, there were two flashes that lit up the bedroom windows. Was it a car coming over Roe Hill? Someone flashing a torch at the house? Far off lightning? Or perhaps a fireball lighting up the clouds? Ten minutes standing at the window revealed nothing, although it did seem to settle the mind a bit, and I finally dozed off. A curious end to the day.

January 15th

Time for a farm finance day. Hazel and I had given the accounts a good checkover over the last couple of days, and didn't feel there was anything more worth querying, so just had an email exchange with the accountant rather than another Zoom meeting. They've ended up as a very healthy set of accounts, just slightly less successful than last year's.

The next job was to sort out the tax bill that has resulted from last year's accounts – and the complicated fact that we hadn't been paying any for a couple of years, and it has caught up with us. A five-figure lump is due at the end of the month.

Money is cheap at the moment, and we've been investigating how we'll raise funds to pay it. HMRC are doing a 'pay in instalments' scheme, at 2.5%. If we think the lump sum could come out of our overdraft (unlikely), it would be 2.6% – our interest rate is 2.5% over base, which at the moment is an absurd 0.1%. We could take a chunk out of the lump sitting in our account at Trinity Grain, but they charge 3% over base, so that would be 3.1% – and I've set myself a target of not touching the Trinity Grain fund until as late as possible.

I rang the bank manager to see what they could offer. A 'Small Business Loan' would come in at 6.1% – so that was right out. And then, as if by magic, I had the thought of the Government's 'Bounce Back Loan' scheme – a six-year loan, interest-free and repayment-free for the first year, and then 2.5% after that. "What a good idea!" said the bank manager. "You can apply through us." So I did. Twenty minutes of keyboard work later, and it was all done. I did worry about the 'has your business been affected by the virus?' question, when the answer is 'yes, all our prices have gone up', but I kept my conscience clear by thinking of all the book sales that I haven't been able to do because of the cancelled dinners I'd been booked to tell my joke at – and sell books. We discussed transferring a monthly amount to our reserve account (a dusty relic of the golden days of the early 1990s, when cashflow was so good we could keep a lump in it AND get fantastic interest every month – base was 10.38% when we took over the farm). I'm not keen on that idea, because we'd be paying extra interest on the money transferred across. I'll just have to remember to pay the whole lump off next January. Who knows how things will be by then?

Meanwhile, another day of frantic news on the wheat markets (the USDA report was very bullish) sent wheat to £210/tonne. How's that for timing?

January 16th

A lazy Saturday. I had a long and curiously slow walk round the farm, pondering life. I'm going to be 60 this year. Blimey. The farm looked rather special in the winter Saturday light, and I suddenly felt more fond of it than ever.

January 17th

A really lazy Sunday. Hazel went for a mid-morning walk and reported queues to get through the kissing gates. Probably best to stay indoors. *Shrek 2* and a warm fire beckoned.

January 18th

Jonathan's home-based uni exams started today, so what we needed was some peace and quiet. What we got was some unbelievably noisy – and cheery – painters and decorators. They'd come to finish off the new and repaired kitchen windows, and the first thing they noticed was that the woodwork repairs were incomplete. Some of the vertical sections of the frames were still rotten.

After several worried phone calls to the head man, it was decided that they'd do some cutting out and replacing of woodwork. So, instead of the gentle swish-swash of paint brushes, the house shuddered and shook to the dentist-like sounds of reciprocating drills and saws.

I checked with Jonathan how he was getting on, but he seemed quite relaxed, and just kept turning the music up in his headphones. Luckily, these exams are lockdown ones; the uni knows there's no point doing anything timed, or that relies on committing facts to memory. Instead, it's a series of essay-type questions, and he has a couple of days to do them. He didn't seem to mind the racket coming from the kitchen, which was lucky; I certainly did not want to ask the builders to go.

Sasha and I did the Drier loop, and added a diversion, crossing Drier Field, going through the woods and up into Broom Field to look at the waterlogged and mostly rotted Zulu. It looked a bit better than it did last time I tip-toed up there, but there's still an awful lot of acres bare. We did the diagonal across White Hill from the Barracuda Dell to Springshot gateway, all still unsown, but with a nice flush of blackgrass waiting for some glyphosate before we get out there with the drill. Sorry – *if* we get out there with the drill. The forecast for the next few days is shocking.

January 19th

The local Claas rep wanted to come out and talk new combines, so I popped down to the Drier Yard and opened up the roller shutter doors so he could cast an eye over the old New Holland TC5070. A drive from there up Joan's Acre road to check the Crusoe had to be abandoned when I met a fleet of scaffolding-loaded Transits, and had to back into the Literary Agent's drive. He happened to be in his garden, so we stopped for a chat (probably illegal). We decided that one good title for this second book would be *Ten Thousand Broken Rules*.

When I got back, there was an email from Mrs Lit Agent, who was in a right stew about the forthcoming rain, and was asking who should she chase up about digging out the roadside soakaways? I think she knows very well that it's my hobby – and probably the only hobby that's legal these days – and knows that I'll make it my job to get out there with a spade before the deluge.

The Claas rep arrived wearing a mask, of course, and seemed slightly uneasy about coming indoors. I told him to remove the mask just in case Sasha takes offence, and to come in and have a cup of tea. We adjourned to the dining room to sit on either side of the huge shoot table – not for any health reasons, but because the painter was once again in the kitchen, doing the insides of the windows while the rain hurtled down.

The hunt is on these days to find a small combine suitable for our 750–800 acres. My spec is very simple: five straw walkers, grain tank around 6,000 litres (so we get two fills in our ten-tonne grain trailers), header width around 17 ft (so the grain trailers have time to get to the yard and back), come with self-levelling sieves for our multitude of slopes, weigh around the ten-tonne mark, and have some sort of extra thrashing drum – and that's about it. The list is then very short: John Deere abandoned their link with Finland's niche producer Sampo Roselew a couple of years ago, the Breganze-built Laverda/Fendt/Massey Ferguson small models don't do self-levelling but are admirably simple. Deutz's small models have got too big, and the local Deutz dealers used to be the Massey dealers – if you've read Book One, you'll know why that is significant. CaseIH are all 'rotaries' (which tend to render straw unbaleable) with massive tanks – and that's the lot.

All that's left is the New Holland TC range (and even that's been culled down to just a couple of models) and the smallest Claas Tucanos: the 320 (which doesn't have a second drum) and the 420, which has a tank just verging on too big. We ran through all the options, and I sent him on his way to look at our New Holland. I should have washed it, but there we go.

Hazel spent the afternoon doing accountancy up at the stables, I chopped lots more logs, stared at the rain, and nipped out during a dry interlude to dig the damn ditches. Grandpa's Best Spade disintegrated on me just as I was getting going, so I had to do a lot with an old fork hoe and my heel. Meanwhile, the ex-Editor rang to ask if he could stand in the Blackhouse woods with his gun – conditions were perfect for some treetop pigeon shooting. He called late in the evening to say he'd shot nine with 11. His idea of heaven. Not as much fun as heeling out soakaways while trying not to fall over.

January 20th

Storm Christoph duly arrived, restricting the painter to indoor work only. Hazel and Jonathan did a long walk in the deluge with all the dogs, and I did one a bit later in the evening to check that my carefully hand-dug ditches were working. They were.

January 21st

I tried a thousand times to come up with the next *FonF* column – again. One day, we'll be up and running, and doing things on the farm, and something will happen that will blossom into an article. One day. All I had in mind was the bizarre 'net zero' webinar I'd joined in with a few months ago, and the nonsense that arose from that. Trouble is, it kept descending into an anti-green rant, and I've just done one of those – about 'regen' farming. Round and round I went, getting nowhere. It didn't help that our now very chirpy painter was chipping the last of the old putty off the window frames. Chip, chip, chip, thump, thump, thump… Poor old Jonathan was upstairs trying to do another uni exam, so it was even worse timing for him.

The next test car – a Fiat 500X Sport – arrived mid-morning. Luckily, the driver has a wingman in another car these days, so I haven't got to give anyone a lift to a station. It took him 20 minutes to give the insides the now-compulsory wipe down, which is odd; I thought it had been established that surface transmission of the virus was impossible, but hey ho.

The cheery painter finished taking out all the window frames and screwed a large piece of plywood over the window. "See you Monday!" he cried. I pointed out that today is Thursday. "Oh, I don't work Fridays," he explained. Our dark and cold kitchen is not going to get any less cold and dark with its main window covered all day – for three days.

January 22nd

We've certainly got the Claas salesman fired up. He produced with a fantastic quote, having removed a lot of extravagant gadgets and gizmos from the original specification. It was rapidly turning into a 'no-brainer deal'. I did think I'd found a. fatal flaw, though: there was no mention of a disawner in the leaflets, and we grow a lot of barley here. A disawner is vital. I emailed with this query, and a request to go and see one, and give its tyres a kicking, which, as we all know, is how you check out any vehicle.

I went for a walk across Hurst Down to ponder the idea of a new combine further. The ground was frozen hard, although the fantastic and amazingly warm January sunshine was threatening to turn it back to slush quite quickly. I took a few pictures of the dramatic sky, and having persuaded myself that the Crusoe had moved on from pathetic spindles of green to quite respectable looking plants, went home for lunch.

The Fiat 500X Sport needed a run out, and it wasn't nice. Odd, because from the outside, it's a cheeky mini-SUV full of quirky kooky cuteness, but it was horrible to drive: loud, skittish, uncomfortable and unsettling. I'll give it a few more drives over the next few days to see if I warm to it.

The Claas salesman emailed to say that the Tucano 320 did have a disawner of sorts, but the nearest machine we could go and look at was in Lanarkshire. I struggled in the Fiat doing 30 miles, so 400 is right out of the question

January 23rd

In a way, it was nice to have a completely calm and mundane Saturday, and one that could have been any Saturday from the last few weeks. Hazel did dog training out in the field with picker-up Nessa, I went for a long walk with Sasha, chopped some logs, looked in vain for some sport on the television, found *Shrek 2* – again – and fell asleep in the middle bit – again.

January 24th

Jonathan's 21st birthday was announced by a terrifying clap of thunder at 6.37am. Just the one, with no wind or rain; when it finally got light there was just a gloomy steel-grey bank of cloud coming in from the west. And you have to give the weather forecasters credit on this one. They'd said a band of snow would be here from about eight until midday, and they got it absolutely spot on. Sleety stuff turned to snowy stuff which started to come on pretty thick. It was quite a relief when Hazel got back from her early paper run in a spectacular blizzard.

The local Facebook pages were hilarious: all these self-appointed experts on nature and the countryside, full of anger and criticism of what we farmers get up to, and most of them asking what the big flash and the boom was. I wrote many a sarcastic reply, and luckily deleted every single one. The front passed by late morning, and for an hour or two it was Christmas card time, with stunning blue skies over surprisingly deep snow.

For months I've been meaning to replace the pull switch in the bathroom, which has been crackling and buzzing every time it's used. Luckily there was a spare one in the cupboard under the stairs, so with the brilliant white light off the snow illuminating every room (except the kitchen, which still has a massive bit of plywood over it) I grabbed the step ladder and a selection of tools and set to work. The first clue that the job might not be a total success was when I went to unwrap the new switch: the plastic wrapping was brittle with age. God knows when I bought it. I half expected the price sticker to be in guineas. And once connected, it struggled to work smoothly. I didn't reckon it was much safer than the one I'd replaced. I wound the cord up out of harm's way, and made a mental note to send Jonathan into Screwfix tomorrow for a brand new one.

For Jonathan's birthday lunch, Hazel did a splendid bit of lamb followed by a chocolate roulade, which vanished faster than you can say body mass index. A meal that would have caused me great pain a few years ago, but one that I can overindulge in confidently – even if I really shouldn't.

Everyone went out and walked – except me; I headed for the sofa, and this time fell asleep in front *Despicable Me*. Mind you, the lunch-related farts kept waking me up. They were enough to wake the dead.

Not much of a 21ˢᵗ birthday for Jonathan. Poor chap.

January 25ᵗʰ

You can't beat waking up too early on a cold dark January morning, rolling over under two warm duvets to turn on the radio, and getting some thrilling cricket. I'd probably get myself into all sorts of trouble by saying that some of the varying levels of consistency would have me (if I were i/c of the cricket corruption unit) checking out the betting markets, but some of the high drama does appear to come from nowhere.

It kept going through the morning to a great finish and a good win for England. It certainly makes great listening while trying to tidy up and approve the next *FonF* on a snowy and cold day – the painter was back to do the missing panes in the kitchen window, which didn't warm things up much.

Tod dropped in at lunchtime for a chat and some optimistic agronomy talk. We adjourned to the dining room, and sat on either side of the huge shoot table. Tod did look rather longingly at my hot tomato soup. I told him to bugger off and get his own.

I took the Fiat 500x for another spin, doing the Winchester/Three Maids' Hill/Stockbridge/Andover/Bullington Cross loop, and began to warm to it – a bit. It was still too noisy, and horrendously uncomfortable, but not as terrible as the first drive suggested. I must remember to make lots of notes while it's still fresh in the mind.

We hardly saw Jonathan all day – another of his remote 'exams' came through, which demanded a monumental multi-thousand-word essay. He even shut his bedroom door to keep distractions (i.e. bored cats) at bay. The quicker he gets back to his mates in Newcastle, the better.

January 26th

Only a few days to go in another diary, and nothing is happening. No farming – the farm is still saturated and frozen, with snow still lying (waiting for more, as Granny Flindt used to say). The tractor is still idle, two drills are parked up in the yard, and the sprayer is tucked away in the Godwin's barn. The daily virus briefings are best avoided – as is most TV and radio. We're lucky that there's three of us here, and we still have visits from a cheery painter. And four daft dogs.

And we are truly blessed not to have small children wondering what has happened to them and their school routines, and old people wondering why they can't see their beloved grandchildren. We're getting off lightly.

The New Holland dealer was on the phone quite early, asking if we'd had any thoughts about his quote. He sounded quite surprised when I said I was also mulling the one from the Claas dealer, and wanted to know which model I was interested in. I told him the Tucano 320 was the nearest like-for-like. I'm not sure if that will make him go and adjust his figures; I hope not. I always like the first quote to be the best possible, and not dependent on other factors, although he'll have to come down a long way to meet the Claas quote.

It's a mirror image of where we were in late 1995, buying our first combine since taking over the farm from Dad in 1991. We were trading in the old Dominator 96, and we'd had some demonstrations from Deutz and CaseIH (an early straw-mashing rotary) but ended up with quotes from Claas and New Holland for a TC56. The NH was by far the better quote, so we were pretty sure we'd plump for that.

At a ploughing match that autumn, we were collared by the Claas dealer of the time. He asked how we were getting on with quotes, and I told him that we were going to go for the NH, not least because it was far cheaper. He vanished into his briefcase and immediately lopped several grand off his quote. Somehow it made me less likely to accept his deal; if there was that much slack in the original quote, I felt I was being ripped off. We did go for the TC56. Great combine it was, too.

I took the Fiat for a final spin, over to Petersfield, up to Bordon and over to Farnham, and back via Alresford and Winchester. I couldn't believe what has happened to Bordon since I last drove that road – it now has a brand-new by-pass and ten billion little box houses jammed on top of each other. I suppose everyone's got to go somewhere. I still remember Bordon and Longmoor from my CCF days at school, when it was mystical woodland and occasional firing ranges, with tumuli popping up unexpectedly. I wonder if they stay untouched when the bulldozers arrive?

The three-mile Brexit emergency lorry park that used to be the A31 between Alresford and the Percy Hobbs roundabout was empty. Last time I drove past it, I saw one lorry. So things have obviously quietened down. The Fiat was still not quite right – but at least there will be plenty to say about it.

Tod rang to finalise the latest cropping plan for this year, which is a hopeful sign, and we decided how much seed to order. Crop Advisors (who handle the orders and put them out to electronic 'tender') were on the phone shortly after that to check that I still didn't want to order from one famous seed company (true; their clever 'rounding up' technique always results in you buying more tonnes than you wanted, ruling out the apparent savings per tonne), so Bartholomew's would get the order. Let's hope they're not in a hurry to get it out here – the barns are still full of unsown seed.

January 27th

Mild and wet – again. The Fiat was due to go today, so I grabbed a pen and a pad, and sat in it for half an hour, making as many notes as possible. It's always a good idea to pop the bonnet open, just in case there's something of note in the engine bay. I always find it sad when car manufacturers block in the engine bay with a huge cover – as if to stop anyone doing any DIY. The Fiat's little buzzy engine was on full display, but there was another problem: the bonnet wouldn't shut.

Once upon a time, you slammed the bonnet down as hard as you could, or put both hands flat on it and gave it good shove down, but the metalwork these days is pathetically flimsy. The last thing I needed was to send it back with two huge dents in the front of the bonnet. I must have spent another half an hour trying to work out why the latch wouldn't catch – had I dropped something in the engine bay? Had the snow and ice the other day somehow twisted the cigarette-paper thin bodywork? In the end, I slammed it with a bit more enthusiasm, and it shut. A great relief, especially as the Fiat pick-up team arrived at that very moment.

I did my Drier loop walk late in the afternoon (the ground was like a sponge after the thawing snow), and then settled down after tea for a webinar organised by the Tenant Farmers' Association. Now that I've resigned from the NFU, I'll be having to rely a lot more on their work on behalf of farmers. It was an update on the Agriculture Act and was meant to give us all a few more clues as to what to expect over the next few years – especially when it comes to assorted environmental schemes.

It was interesting that when the Q&A session started, our host said he'd had a flood of enquiries about the 'lump sum' subsidy payout concept; we're obviously not the only farmers (tenants or otherwise) keen to know how this idea might suit them. The high-powered DEFRA wonk, kindly giving up his evening time to join us, confirmed what recent rumours have been suggesting: the 'lump sum' will only be for those retiring from the industry.

His reasoning was quite simple. The Treasury is under a certain amount of strain at the moment (to put it mildly), and probably will be for some years, and, more ominously, how will DEFRA/RPA have leverage over badly behaving farmers in years to come if they've got all their subsidy money safely stashed away in the bank? All slightly creepy and reeking of authoritarianism. So much for any sort of 'freedom to farm', post Brexit. Food for thought, though.

January 28th

Our last shoot of the season, and another one that we were going to have to run sticking to the new regulations. Hazel set off to meet the ex-Editor, and they became a pair for the day. I greeted Nessa, and we became the other pair. We made our way to Pipeline using strictly separate means, and started at that end of the farm, planning to work away home from there.

Once again, it was a great success, with the ex-Editor and I having lots of shots and lots of birds flushed by just two 'beaters' and just two dogs. After Pipeline we did Long Field, and then Barracuda – after which there was a bizarre flapjack session, with the two teams making sure we didn't get too close while scoffing.

We kept the separation theme going after nibbles; Hazel and the ex-Editor went through Rough Field, through the narrow strip of woods into the corner of Drier Field, straight through Bob's Wood into BOMS, and finally up to the east end of the Roe Hill strip. Nessa and I headed north through White Hill, crossed Dark Lane, and headed into the Folly trees. A couple of cock birds ran out the top and flew over to Roe Hill – perfect – and one hen got up and flew over me just after I'd unloaded. I just had time to put one Purdey paper case in and was very pleased to hit it. Nessa's gorgeous yellow lab did a super retrieve, too.

We had to wait for cyclists and a walker before we could cross the road into Roe Hill, and I suddenly realised there was a flaw in the plan to shoot this end of the farm last: Trust visitors were piling into the estate on what was turning into a very pleasant January day. We did Roe Hill, Clump and the top of Chalks with eyes in the back of our heads, making sure that we kept very far apart from each other. A white van parked in the gateway of the Folly looked a bit odd, and it's a sign of the madness of these days that we all genuinely worried that it was snooping on us.

I felt sorry for the ex-Editor, who took up position for the Chalks drive in the rough ground below the old tennis court while Hazel and Bella flushed out the birds round the feeder in the old estate yard. He had to stand patiently while twenty or thirty birds flew over him, curling over the road. I was very relieved that he's gun-wise enough to only choose one to shoot – all the others had 'trouble' written all over them as they flew low over where many walkers park their cars.

All offers of cups of tea and cake were, of course, refused, and the ex-Editor and Nessa made their way home, and Hazel and I went back indoors. The poor painter – now just finishing – looked a bit startled as we arrived in the kitchen fully armed and knackered. He even turned down my kind offer of a brace of birds as he left for the last time. The final tally was 13, which for such a small team was brilliant.

We'd left nine birds carefully stacked in the Barracuda drive earlier in the day, so Hazel jumped in Pig to go and get them. She took Sasha and Evie for the ride, and me to go and fetch Tigger from the Drier Yard, where it had been parked first thing this morning. Finally, the day – and the season – was done.

We've shot six days, losing only one to the pandemic. The strips have been the best ever, but I'm damned if I know what I did differently. Proper fertiliser application may have helped, and much of the greenery working its magic at holding birds seems to be last year's sowings doing a second year. God knows. We've been amazed by the numbers of birds out there, too; we bought more ex-layers in the spring ("Ex-layers? That'll never work!" said all the experts five years ago) but one of the big shoots next door has scaled down big time this season (OK – we confess: we inherit birds from our neighbours).

The great sadness has been having to scale back the number of people involved. For five years we've run shoot days with four guns and around six dogs, which makes for lots of silliness and a good noisy meal afterwards round the huge shooting table. We pushed the 'rule of six' to its limits (and not beyond, oh no) and have had two days with just four people and no tea. And when the seven shooting days constitute much of your social life, that's a bit of a shame. Let's hope that by next October, things will be back to normal. I don't hold out much hope, myself.

We did have a good meal today, though. One of Hazel's chums had recommended a burger van that's doing the rounds, and she'd booked three burgers'n'chips for a five o'clock pick-up in Kilmeston. They were expensive – £12 each – but magnificent. We decided that for at least one of next season's shoots, we'd book the van to turn up in the farmyard and deliver a dozen piping hot cardboard boxes, full of artisan burgers and top-notch chips. I'm salivating just thinking about it.

January 29th

It isn't often you give thanks for the weather being foul – which it was. Hazel came back from her morning yomp with all the dogs somewhat earlier than normal, and with a concerned look on her face. There was a deer stuck in the sheep netting in the Back Meadow. It had tried to jump the fence, got a leg through the netting on the way over, and had spent the night on its back struggling. Utterly grim.

I rang the ex-vet to check on what's legal and not legal under these circumstances. He said that a close shot with the 12-bore, or even the .22, would be humane and legal. Trying to free it and let it go would be too dangerous for everyone involved. Even so, I was very relieved when Mark the Deerman answered his phone and said he'd could be out within 40 minutes – he'd definitely have the right kit for a swift and clean despatch.

Within the hour, the poor beast was released from its earthly bonds – literally and metaphorically – and, thanks to the driving rain and sodden ground, not a soul had walked past it on the footpath. I dread to think what would have happened if one of the Trust's visitors had been out early and seen it. We'd have had the police, the Trust themselves, or – God help us all and save us from such terrors – the RSPCA. Thank goodness we managed to avoid that scenario.

Slightly coincidentally, there was a moderately cross email waiting for me after I'd been out to see Mark out of the Back Meadow and locked the gates. It was from the Trust's agent asking if we'd been out shooting yesterday. There had been 'questions' raised at the House's 'visitor centre', asking about the shots heard on the estate. Could we ensure, the email said, that we tell the Trust of our shoot dates, so that Trust staff know?

I wrote – and rapidly deleted – a reply saying that the reason Trust tenants try to avoid telling Trust staff when any field sports are taking place on their farms is that it's a sure-fire way of guaranteeing you'll get two minibuses full of sabs charging across your fields. Instead, I wrote an apologetic email saying that we were so busy working round rules, regulations and chaotic lockdowns that we'd forgotten our contractual obligations. She seemed happy with that.

It was wet and horrible for the rest of the day, which gave me the chance to finish the already-late *FonF* column, inspired by the TFA Zoom meeting the other night – which *FW* seemed happy with – and then have a weapons-grade post-shoot snooze in front of a warm fire.

Meanwhile, out in the real world, all hell has broken loose over the supply of virus vaccines, with everyone at each other's throats, and the EU Commission shutting the Northern Irish Border. Ursula van de Leyen has united Nigel Farage, the DUP and Sinn Fein in condemnation. For this, she should be winning the Nobel Peace Prize, to add to her 'Foxiest Politician on the Planet' award. I should get out more.

January 30ᵗʰ

It's rather apt that a farm diary, started with the intent of chronicling the effects of the first year of Brexit, but which has spent 364 days hardly mentioning it, should now return to the topic. The EU Commission did a hasty backtrack on installing a hard border round Northern Ireland, and have shot themselves in both feet with their actions over the last 48 hours. We Brexiteers don't like to gloat, so we just think very loudly "we told you so – these are the sort of people we don't want to be ruled by!" The hardcore Remainers are, of course, sticking to their diametrically opposed view that the Commission can do no wrong, and the whole thing would never have happened if we'd voted the 'right' way. But when even the loathsome BBC seem to be siding with the UK (which it hates with every fibre of its billion-pound being), then you know the EU has cocked up. Happy days.

The rest of the last Saturday in January was just like the last few Saturdays. It was wet, I did a long walk, lit a fire, watched *Stardust* and *Despicable Me* (at the same time) again. I suppose one day it will dry out and we'll get some farming done. One day.

January 31ˢᵗ

Not a good night's sleep. Something woke me just after midnight, then again at around two and then about ten-to-five. In the distance I could head a low rumbling, like a Chinook, but miles away. It was loud enough – and of such low frequency – that it was unmissable, and penetrated straight through the background noise of Classic FM. Very odd. I even stood at the window for a bit and tried to hear where it was coming from. There was no sign of anything in the bright moonlight – which was a relief; I'd half expected to see a car or a lorry parked and idling, and up to no good.

It was also a relief to hear Hazel had had exactly the same bad night in the West Wing, so there had certainly been something going on. This old farmhouse is such an acoustic trap that stuff can be going on miles away, and we'll hear it. We mulled over all the options, and the best that we could come up with was night-time road works going on somewhere. I even got as far as the council's schedule of roadworks, but lost interest.

As a result, I had a very dozy morning, but managed to clear my head a bit after lunch with yet another walk round the Clump loop with Sasha. It was one of the coldest days of the winter so far, with sleet coming from the north-east, and I was glad that we didn't set off on anything more ambitious. The forecast is suggesting another week – at least – of wet. Then, as normal, it was time to light the fire and hit the sofa.

Tomorrow's weather is to be better – which should suit Jonathan, who packed up his little i20 with stuff, ready for a long drive back to Newcastle. He has decided to head back to uni to get some company and change of scene. You can't blame him; it's been fantastic having him home for the last few months – a bit of a bonus in these mad times – but he'd be much better off up there. It'll be a repeat of September 2019, when we first dropped him off, and had our first 'empty nest' crisis. We might have to breed/buy even more dogs. That would be fun – and take us straight back to where we were 12 months ago.

Funny old world.

FHA POST-SCRIPT

June 23rd 2021.

Five years ago today, the nation voted to leave the European Union. The arguing, the accusations, the rage and the fallouts from the vote continue to this day, although I've managed to keep friends with all but one of the Remainers with whom I've had lively arguments.

The establishment's predictions for the UK in general post-Brexit – 'Project Fear'- have failed to materialise. Farming's equivalent – Project Agrifear, which was peddled with ferocious venom by the Europhile NFU – has also failed to come down on us like a ton(ne) of bricks. In fact, it could be said that the UK has done very well in the last five years, and farming has enjoyed a rather special half-decade. The pound crashed on the referendum result, and all output prices – and, please note, subsidies – soared as a direct consequence. And the poor harvest of 2020 pushed grain prices even higher. No wonder both the new combine and the new tractor, ordered a few weeks ago, come with monumental delivery times.

Yes, subsidy payments are due to be phased out over the next seven years, but only the economically blinkered think that all other inputs and outputs will stay constant. And it is often missed that farmers still under the benevolent, generous and caring wing of the EU seem to be rioting. They, too, are suffering subsidy cuts and 'green' tripwires.

Meanwhile, Hazel and I approach three-score years, but have no successor leaping up and down to take the 'third tenant' option available on our AHA Tenancy. This might be the time, as bones start to creak, to contemplate another way of farming. Share farming? Employ contractors? Wall-to-wall butterfly mix? Wind turbines? Who knows?

Whatever we choose, there might be a diary to be written.